CWI Tracts

Managing Editors

K.R. Apt (CWI, Amsterdam)
M. Hazewinkel (CWI, Amsterdam)
J.K. Lenstra (Eindhoven University of Technology)

Editorial Board

W. Albers (Enschede)
P.C. Baayen (Amsterdam)
R.C. Backhouse (Eindhoven)
E.M. de Jager (Amsterdam)
M.A. Kaashoek (Amsterdam)
M.S. Keane (Delft)
H. Kwakernaak (Enschede)
J. van Leeuwen (Utrecht)
P.W.H. Lemmens (Utrecht)
M. van der Put (Groningen)
M. Rem (Eindhoven)
H.J. Sips (Delft)
M.N. Spijker (Leiden)
H.C. Tijms (Amsterdam)

CWI
P.O. Box 94079, 1090 GB Amsterdam, The Netherlands
Telephone 31 - 20 592 9333, telex 12571 (mactr nl),
telefax 31 - 20 592 4199

CWI is the nationally funded Dutch institute for research in Mathematics and Computer Science.

Parallelism in the numerical integration of initial value problems

B.P. Sommeijer

Seplae
Math

ISBN 90 6196 431 8
NUGI-code: 811

SD
1/24/94
DA

Preface

Algorithms for the numerical integration of ordinary differential equations (ODEs) have been studied for many years, if not for centuries. Although the most popular methods of today, i.e., the linear multistep methods and the Runge-Kutta methods, originate from the last century, the great break-through in their development was initiated by the introduction of the electronic computer in the 1950s. Since then, many efficient methods have been constructed and analyzed. This research has resulted in a couple of robust and reliable codes for the automatic integration of ODEs. Approximately at the time that questions arose like 'Is There Anything Left To Do ?' [Gear, SIAM Review 23, 1981], the appearance of the vector and parallel computers was a second impulse for the development of numerical methods. Initially, the field of numerical linear algebra was (and still is) (re)considered to exploit the facilities offered by the new architectures. Gradually, also researchers in the ODE-field got interested in these machines since 'almost anything in nature is described by differential equations'. The well established algorithms were re-examined in order to take advantage of these 'supercomputers'.

This research is certainly indispensable, since many problems in the technical sciences – such as real time applications, computational fluid dynamics, and all kinds of partial differential equations, in general – are still waiting for a treatment that is sufficiently efficient to cope with the demands.

At CWI, the study of parallel methods for ODEs started in the fall of 1988; some of the resulting papers are collected in this monograph. It consists of six papers (chapters), preceded by an introduction. All papers have appeared in scientific journals and are reprinted here with granted permission of the publishers.

The first two papers deal with parallel numerical methods for *nonstiff* ODEs and are joined into Part I. These papers are:

1. *Parallel iteration of high-order Runge-Kutta methods with stepsize control,*
   P.J. van der Houwen and B.P. Sommeijer,
   published in: J. Comput. Appl. Math. **29** (1990), 111-127.

2. *Block Runge-Kutta methods on parallel computers,*
   P.J. van der Houwen and B.P. Sommeijer,
   published in: Z. Angew. Math. Mech. **72** (1) (1992), 3-18.

The topic of Part II, containing the remaining four papers, is the construction and analysis of algorithms for the efficient parallel integration of *stiff* ODEs. Its contents reads:

3. *A-stable parallel block methods for ordinary and integro-differential equations*,
   B.P. Sommeijer, W. Couzy and P.J. van der Houwen,
   published in: Appl. Numer. Math. **9** (1992), 267-281.

4. *Embedded diagonally implicit Runge-Kutta algorithms on parallel computers*,
   P.J. van der Houwen, B.P. Sommeijer and W. Couzy,
   published in: Math. Comp. **58** (1992), 135-159.

5. *Iterated Runge-Kutta methods on parallel computers*,
   P.J. van der Houwen and B.P. Sommeijer,
   published in: SIAM J. Sci. Stat. Comput. **12** (1991), 1000-1028.

6. *Analysis of parallel diagonally implicit iteration of Runge-Kutta methods*,
   P.J. van der Houwen and B.P. Sommeijer,
   published in: Appl. Numer. Math. **11** (1993), 169-188.

The introductory chapter has been written with the aim to acquaint the reader with the concepts discussed in the papers. It has the intention to provide an entrance for the unspecialized reader. It discusses in less technical terms the ideas underlying the technical papers and comprises an example in which a problem from circuit analysis is integrated on a parallel computer by means of an automatic code based on one of the methods described in Chapter VI. Its performance is compared with the best sequential codes currently available.

Contents

PART I

PARALLEL NUMERICAL METHODS FOR NONSTIFF ODES

PART II

PARALLEL NUMERICAL METHODS FOR STIFF ODES

Introduction

1. MOTIVATION AND GENERAL SCOPE

Due to the never-ending demand for more speed in scientific computation, the available computerpower of new architectures has tremendously increased during the last decades. This is mainly obtained by new hardware design and by a prodigious progress in micro-electronics. However, this *hardware advancement* is not sufficient to meet the requirements as they occur in large-scale problems. The main problem in effectively exploiting this huge potential of computerpower is the fact that there is very *little software* available for these machines. In order to be efficient, this software should be based on algorithms that are well tuned to the new architectures.

Since many numerical algorithms were designed for the traditional sequential computers, the existing methods are not necessarily the best. This is particularly true in the field of numerical methods for ordinary differential equations. Therefore, it is highly desirable to (re)consider these algorithms and, eventually, replace them with more suitable candidates.

Herewith, we arrive at the major aim of this monograph: *the construction and analysis of new algorithms*, specifically designed for a wide class of new architectures, thus making an attempt to decrease the arrears of software with respect to hardware.

We will concentrate on numerical methods for the initial value problem (IVP) for the ordinary differential equation (ODE), written in the autonomous form

$$(1.1) \qquad y'(t) = f(y(t)), \qquad 0 \le t \le T, \quad y \in \mathbb{R}^N, \ f : \mathbb{R}^N \to \mathbb{R}^N.$$

Although parallel computers are available now for quite a few years, it is remarkable that the construction of parallel methods for (1.1) received only marginal attention and in fact is still in its infancy. A possible explanation may be that the integration of an IVP by a step-by-step process is sequentially in nature and thus offers little scope to exploit parallelism.

Nevertheless, there are some avenues: at first, there is the rather obvious way to distribute the various components of the system of ODEs amongst the available processors. This is especially effective in *explicit* methods, since they frequently need the evaluation of the right-hand side function f for a given vector y, so that the components of f can be evaluated independently of one another. Following the terminology of Gear [13], this is called *parallelism across the problem*. A more interesting approach, called *parallelism across the method*, is to employ the parallelism inherently available within the method. Concurrent evaluations of the entire function f for various values of its argument and the simultaneous solution of various (nonlinear) systems of equations are examples of parallelism across the method. Remark that this form of parallelism is also effective in case of a scalar ODE (i.e., $N=1$ in (1.1)), whereas parallelism across the problem aims at large N-values. Also notice that both approaches can be combined because they are more or less 'orthogonal'. Still another approach, which could be termed *parallelism across the time*, is followed by Bellen et al. [2]. Contrary to the step-by-step idea, they perform a number of steps simultaneously, thus calculating numerical approximations in many points on the t-axis in parallel. In fact, these methods belong to the class of *waveform relaxation* methods. Experiments have shown (cf. [2]) that a significant speedup can be obtained by this approach provided that the number of steps is (very) large. In this monograph we will confine ourselves to parallelism across the method.

Unfortunately, many existing algorithms that perform well on a sequential computer can take hardly profit from a parallel configuration. This feature necessitates us to construct *new* methods, specifically designed for parallel execution. In doing so, it was in many cases unavoidable to introduce some redundancy in the total volume of computational arithmetic. Hence, compared with a good sequential solver, it is overambitious to expect a speedup in the solution time with a factor s, if s processors are available.

In many of the methods considered in this monograph, a *small* number (typically in the range from 2 to 6) of concurrent subtasks of *considerable* computational complexity can be distinguished. Consequently, (i) these methods are aiming at so-called 'coarse-grain' parallelism and (ii) communication and synchronization overhead will be small compared with CPU time. In the following sections we will explain several approaches leading to parallel integration methods.

2. PARALLEL RUNGE-KUTTA METHODS

The general Runge-Kutta (RK) method to proceed the numerical solution of (1.1) from t_n over a step h is given by

$$(2.1a) \qquad y_{n+1} = y_n + h \sum_{i=1}^{s} b_i \, f(Y_i),$$

$$(2.1b) \qquad Y_i = y_n + h \sum_{j=1}^{s} a_{ij} \, f(Y_j), \qquad i = 1,\dots,s.$$

Here, $y_n \approx y(t_n)$, a_{ij}, b_i are the coefficients defining the RK method and s is called the number of stages. The quantities Y_i, the stage values, can be considered as intermediate approximations to the solution y. An RK method is said to be explicit if $a_{ij}=0$, $j \geq i$. Otherwise, it is called an implicit RK (IRK) method. For the algorithms described in this Introduction, our starting point will always be an IRK method.

A nice feature of IRK methods is that a high order of accuracy can be combined with excellent stability properties [6]. Well-known examples of such IRKs are the Gauss-Legendre methods (order $2s$ and A-stable) and the Radau IIA methods (order $2s-1$ and L-stable). A serious disadvantage however, is the high cost of solving the algebraic equations defining the stage values Y_i. Since the Y_i are coupled in general, this is a system of dimension $s \cdot N$, thus involving $O((s \cdot N)^3)$ arithmetic operations. This is the main reason that IRK methods have not received great popularity to serve as the basis for efficient, production oriented software. In the literature, several remedies have been proposed to reduce the amount of linear algebra per step. Examples of these are the Diagonally Implicit RK (DIRK) methods [23, 9, 1, 8] and the Singly Implicit RK (SIRK) methods [3, 5]. However, both approaches have their own disadvantages (cf. e.g. [15]). Another possibility to realize the excellent prospects that IRK methods offer, is the use of *parallel processors*.

Motivated by our starting point that parallelism across the method should also be effective for scalar ODEs, we will assume throughout that (1.1) is a *scalar* equation. This has the notational advantage that we can avoid tensor products in our formulation. However, the extension to systems of ODEs, and therefore to nonautonomous equations, is straightforward.

In describing the parallel methods, it will be convenient to use a compact notation for the RK method (2.1). Introducing $A=(a_{ij})$, $b=(b_i)$, $Y=(Y_i)$ and $e=(1,\ldots,1)^T$, all of dimension s, a succinct notation of the RK method reads

(2.2a) $y_{n+1} = y_n + h\, b^T f(Y)$,

(2.2b) $Y = y_n\, e + h\, A\, f(Y)$,

where $f(v):=(f(v_j))$, for a given vector $v=(v_j)$.

The main problem in the application of an IRK is the solution of (2.2b) for the stage vector Y; once this vector has been obtained, (2.2a) is straightforward. A direct treatment to solve (2.2b) (i.e., applying some form of modified Newton iteration) offers little scope to exploit parallelism, except for the linear algebra part, but this aspect is not discussed here. To solve Y from (2.2b), we propose the iteration process

(2.3a) $\quad Y^{(j)} - h\,D\,f(Y^{(j)}) = y_n\,e + h\,[A - D]\,f(Y^{(j-1)}), \qquad j=1,\ldots,m.$

Here, D is a *diagonal* matrix. This is crucial, since now, given an iterate $Y^{(j-1)}$, each individual component $Y_i^{(j)}$ of the unknown iterate $Y^{(j)}$ has to be solved from an implicit relation of the form

(2.3b) $\quad Y_i^{(j)} - h\,d_i\,f(Y_i^{(j)}) - \Sigma_i = 0, \qquad i=1,\ldots,s,$

where Σ_i is the ith component of the right-hand side vector in (2.3a) and d_i is the ith diagonal entry of the matrix D. Clearly, all Σ_i depend on $Y^{(j-1)}$, but can be computed straightforwardly (even in parallel). The bulk of the computational effort involves the solution of the s equations for the components $Y_i^{(j)}$, $i=1,\ldots,s$. However, given the Σ_i, the equations (2.3b) are *uncoupled* and can be solved in parallel. Hence, assuming that we have s processors available, each iteration in (2.3a) requires *effectively* the solution of only one implicit relation of the form (2.3b). This is especially advantageous in case of (large) systems of ODEs, because then each iteration in (2.3a) requires effectively the solution of a system of dimension N, the ODE dimension. As a consequence, the total iteration process has the effect that the solution of one system of dimension $s{\cdot}N$ has been transformed into the solution of a sequence of m systems, all of dimension N. Moreover, since D is the same in all iterations, the (parallel) LU-decompositions of the matrices $I - h\,d_i\,\partial f/\partial y$ can be restricted to the first iteration. Summing up, the total computational complexity of the iteration process is $O(N^3 + mN^2)$, whereas a direct treatment requires $O(s^3N^3 + Ms^2N^2)$, with M the number of (modified) Newton iterations required. Since typical s-values range from 2 to 6 and because the required number of iterations m is quite modest (see the Chapters IV, V and VI), we now arrive at a manageable level of arithmetic. Notice that this approach is quite similar to that of a DIRK method, where also only one LU-decomposition of a matrix of dimension N is required per step.

To start the iteration (2.3a), we need the initial approximation $Y^{(0)}$. One of the possibilities to choose this vector is given by

(2.3c) $\quad Y^{(0)} - h\,B\,f(Y^{(0)}) = y_n\,e + h\,C\,f(y_n\,e).$

Here, the matrix B will be chosen either zero or of diagonal form in order to exploit parallelism (in the same way as described for (2.3a)); C is an arbitrary full matrix. In the sequel, the initial approximation $Y^{(0)}$ will be referred to as the *predictor*.

If m iterations have been performed with (2.3a), then the new approximation at t_{n+1} is defined by (cf. (2.2a))

(2.4a) $y_{n+1} := y_n + h\, b^T f(Y^{(m)})$.

Once an underlying IRK has been selected (henceforth called the *corrector*), the freedom left in the iteration process (2.3) consists of the matrices B, C and D, and the number of iterations m.

With respect to the matrix D, we have considered several possibilities: first of all, there is the simplest choice, which sets D equal to the zero-matrix. Methods of this type are analyzed in Chapter I. Notice that the choice $D=O$ leads to an *explicit* iteration process and, consequently, the resulting scheme is only suitable for *nonstiff* equations. This approach has received relatively much attention in the literature (see [24, 21, 18, 4, 19]). Choosing the 'trivial' predictor $Y^{(0)} = y_n e$, the order behaviour of the resulting algorithm can be formulated as (see also [18, 19, 20])

Theorem 2.1. The method $\{(2.3a)$ with $D=O$, $(2.3c)$ with $B=C=O$, $(2.4a)\}$ is of order $\min\{p^*, m+1\}$, where p^* is the order of the corrector (2.2).   []

Notice that this method is itself an explicit RK methods with $s\cdot m+1$ stages. However, on a parallel machine, the *effective* number of stages equals only $m+1$ (provided that s processors are available). This means that if the number of iterations $m \leq p^*-1$, then we obtain an explicit RK method where the number of effective stages equals the order. This is an optimal result [18] and compares favourably with the situation for classical (uniprocessor) explicit RK methods, where the number of stages increases faster than linearly if we want a high order.

Next we consider the case of *stiff* problems, leading us to *implicit* methods, i.e., to $D \neq O$. Before specifying particular choices of D, we first want to discuss an aspect of the corrector which is relevant with respect to stiffness. In integrating stiff ODEs, a favourable property of the method is that it is 'stiffly accurate'. This notion has been introduced by Prothero and Robinson [25] and means that the RK method satisfies $b^T = e_s^T A$, with e_s the sth unitvector. Hence, b^T equals the last row of A, or equivalently, the last component of the stage vector Y is an approximation to the solution at the new steppoint t_{n+1}. Therefore, in case of a stiffly accurate corrector, (2.4a) will be replaced by

(2.4b) $y_{n+1} := e_s^T Y^{(m)}$.

Now, we return to the discussion of the matrix D; we distinguish two cases:
(i) D is such that after a *prescribed* number of iterations the resulting method has good stability properties. This approach is discussed in Chapter IV.

(ii)   Another option is to *solve* the corrector and to choose D in such a way that we obtain fast convergence in the iteration process (2.3a). This strategy is the subject of the Chapters V and VI.

In the following two subsections these cases will be briefly discussed; henceforth, the above Parallel Diagonally-Iterated RK methods will be denoted by PDIRK methods.

2.1. Diagonal iteration with a prescribed number of iterations

In Chapter IV, we will consider methods for which the number of iterations m is fixed. As we shall see, this number is dictated by the orders of the corrector and of the predictor. This strategy is motivated by the following theorem:

Theorem 2.2. Let p^* be the order of the underlying corrector (2.2). Then the order p of the resulting PDIRK method {(2.3), (2.4a), (2.4b)} is given by

$$\min \{p^*, m+r\} \qquad \text{for all matrices } B, C \text{ and } D,$$
$$\min \{p^*, m+1+r\} \qquad \text{if } (C+B)e = Ae,$$
$$\min \{p^*, m+2+r\} \qquad \text{if, in addition, } BAe = A^2e,$$

where r takes the value 1 if y_{n+1} is defined by (2.4a) (i.e., the nonstiffly accurate case) and $r=0$ if y_{n+1} is defined by (2.4b) (the stiffly accurate case).

Furthermore, if the corrector is stiffly accurate, then the corresponding PDIRK method has the same property.   []

Based on this theorem, we stop iterating as soon as the order has reached the order of the corrector, since a continuation of the iteration process would not increase the order of the PDIRK method (see also [4]).

With respect to the choice of the predictor, we restrict our considerations to the case $C=O$. For the matrix B we remark that $B=O$ or $B=D$ are obvious choices. Although B and D may be different diagonal matrices, the choice $B=D$ has the computational advantage that the LU-decompositions of $I - d_i h \, \partial f/\partial y$, which are needed during the iteration of (2.3a), can also be used in solving (2.3c) for $Y^{(0)}$.

The diagonal matrix D is still free and can be used to give the resulting PDIRK method optimal stability characteristics. In Chapter IV we distinguish two approaches: matrices D with constant and with varying diagonal entries. In the first case, i.e., D is of the form $d \cdot I$, it is possible to perform a rather thorough stability analysis. It turns out that unconditionally stable PDIRK methods can be constructed. A few of these methods are listed in Table 2.1. The relevant d-values can be found in Chapter IV.

Table 2.1. Unconditionally stable PDIRK methods with $D=d\cdot I$

corrector	matrices B and D	attainable order p	# effective stages	stability
Gauss	$B = O, D = d\cdot I$	$p \le 4, p = 6$	$p-1$	A-stable
Gauss	$B = D = d\cdot I$	$p \le 6, p = 8$	p	L-stable
Radau IIA	$B = O, D = d\cdot I$	$p \le 6, p = 8$	p	L-stable
Radau IIA	$B = D = d\cdot I$	$p \le 8, p = 10$	$p+1$	L-stable

If we allow the matrix D to have *nonconstant* entries, then it is possible to save one iteration without reducing the order, simply by setting $B=D=\text{diag}(Ae)$ (cf. Theorem 2.2). Some of the resulting PDIRK methods turn out to be only $A(\alpha)$-stable, however with α close to 90°. In Table 2.2, we collect a few methods with good stability properties.

Table 2.2. PDIRK methods with a nonconstant D-matrix

corrector	attainable order p	# effective stages	stability
Gauss/Radau IIA	$p \le 5$	$p-1$	strongly A-stable
Gauss/Radau IIA	$p = 6, 7$	$p-1$	$A(\alpha)$-stable, $\alpha > 83°$
Radau IIA	$p = 3, 5, 7$	p	$L(\alpha)$-stable, $\alpha > 89°$

2.2. Diagonal iteration until convergence

PDIRK methods with a fixed number of iterations, as considered in the previous subsection, are in fact special DIRK methods. It is well known [10] that DIRK methods possess a so-called *stage order* equal to 1 which, in general, drastically reduces the accuracy. As a matter of fact, in many stiff problems the actually observed order equals the stage order (or, sometimes the stage order + 1). As a consequence of this so-called *order-reduction* phenomenon, the relevance of methods with a high algebraic (i.e., classical) order and a low stage order is questionable. Therefore, apart from the 'fixed-m-strategy' we also consider the approach where the corrector is iterated *until convergence*. This implies that we can rely on all the characteristics of the corrector, like stability and accuracy behaviour and, in particular, the stage order. For example, s-stage IRK methods of Gauss and Radau type both have stage order s. In addition, they have a very high algebraic order (superconvergence) but, as observed above, this property seems to be of minor importance in many stiff problems. Therefore, in the Chapters V and VI, we also consider (A-stable) Newton-Cotes and Lagrange type IRKs; in these (collocation) methods the superconvergence is exchanged for an increase by one of the stage order. This is obtained by adding one explicit stage to the s implicit stages. The time needed for this extra explicit stage is quite negligible compared with the time involved in solving the implicit stages. Thus, we arrive at correctors with algebraic order = stage order = $s+1$, which are suitable for parallel iteration on an s-processor machine.

Having decided to *solve* the corrector, we can now consider (2.3a) as an *iteration* process, where 'iteration' has the classical meaning. This leads us automatically to a criterion for choosing the matrix D: this matrix should be such that we have *fast convergence* in (2.3a).

It is easy to show that the iteration error $Y - Y^{(j)}$, in first approximation, satisfies the recursion

$$(2.5a) \qquad Y - Y^{(j)} = Z(z) \, [Y - Y^{(j-1)}], \qquad j=1,\ldots,m, \qquad z := h \, \lambda,$$

where the iteration matrix Z is defined by

$$(2.5b) \qquad Z(z) := zD[I - zD]^{-1}[D^{-1}A - I].$$

Here, λ denotes an approximation to the derivative $\partial f/\partial y$ and should be understood to run through the spectrum of the Jacobian matrix in case of systems of ODEs. The convergence behaviour of (2.3a) is completely determined by the iteration matrix Z and we have the matrix D at our disposal to obtain fast convergence.

The main difficulty in choosing D is that Z depends on z, i.e., on the problem. Therefore, we cannot expect to find a uniformly 'best' D-matrix. Since we are aiming at the integration of stiff equations, we consider the influence of Z on the eigenvectors of $\partial f/\partial y$ corresponding to eigenvalues of large modulus. For $|z| \to \infty$, Z behaves as $I - D^{-1}A$. Thus a strong damping of these eigenvectors leads us to the minimization of the spectral radius of $I - D^{-1}A$. Observe, that the 'nonstiff' eigenvectors (corresponding to small values of $|z|$) are already damped since Z behaves as $z[A - D]$ for $|z| \to 0$. With this approach we obtain fast convergence. However, we do not claim that this choice of D is the best possible. For example, a more sophisticated strategy might be the minimization of (some norm of) $Z(z)$ over the whole, or the 'stiff part' of the left halfplane.

Another possibility could be to minimize the principal stiff error constants in the resulting PDIRK method; this option is studied in Chapter VI. Several other options to choose D are discussed in Chapter V and many of these have been used in numerical tests, but it turns out that the behaviour of the strategy based on the minimization of the spectral radius ρ of $I - D^{-1}A$ could not be improved.

Based on this approach, we have constructed methods for $s = 2, 3$ and 4. Only for $s = 2$ it is possible to determine D analytically such that $\rho(I - D^{-1}A) = 0$. For the larger values of s, the D-matrices have to be calculated numerically. The ρ-values increase with s and are (for the several correctors) in the range $(0.004, 0.01)$ if $s = 3$ and in the range $(0.02, 0.1)$ for $s = 4$.

2.3. A numerical example

To obtain insight in the actual performance of these parallel Runge-Kutta methods, we have tested a parallel implementation of a PDIRK method based on the 'minimal-spectral-radius-strategy'. For the corrector, we selected the 4-stage Radau IIA method. Since this IRK is of collocation type, the collocation polynomial passing through the stage values is easily computed in each step. The predictor $Y^{(0)}$ is obtained by extrapolating the collocation polynomial calculated in the preceding step. Since this prediction is rather accurate, it is to be expected that this will result in fewer iterations compared with the 'trivial' predictor $Y^{(0)} = y_n e$. We equipped this method with a provisional strategy for error control and stepsize selection (details concerning the implementation strategy can be found in [27]). The resulting code is termed PSODE.

We have implemented PSODE on the ALLIANT FX/4 computer (four parallel processors and shared memory) and applied it to several test problems. The goal of these tests is twofold: (i) we want to investigate to what extent the theoretical parallelization can be realized in practice; in other words, how close we can approach the ideal speedup factor 4 on this four-processor machine and (ii) we want to compare the performance of the code PSODE with that of a good sequential solver. To that purpose we select the recent (sequential) code RADAU5 of Hairer & Wanner [15]. This choice is motivated by the observation that it solves a Radau IIA method (viz., the 3-point 5th-order one); this starting point is quite similar to that of PSODE, although the approach to obtain the Radau-solution is completely different. Furthermore, we included in our tests the code LSODE of Hindmarsh [16]. This BDF-based code has formulas up to order 5 available, from which only those of first and second order are A-stable. Hence, LSODE is less robust as a *general* stiff solver, but, on the other hand, it is generally accepted as a good sequential solver and enjoys considerable usage over a long period.

In comparing the parallel code PSODE with the two sequential codes, we do *not* take into account effects originating from a possible 'parallelization over the loops'. By this we mean that a long loop is cut into s smaller parts which are then assigned to the s processors. In Section 1, this effect is termed 'parallelism across the problem' and can in fact be used by any ODE solver. Here we merely want to test *intrinsic* parallelism (called 'parallelism across the method'). In order to exclude the effects of 'parallelism across the problem', LSODE and RADAU5 are run on a single processor. In fact, the amount of intrinsic parallelism offered by LSODE and RADAU5 is very modest (see also the remark at the end of this section).

Of course, if one is interested in 'parallelism across the problem', then the sequential codes could be implemented on an s-processor machine. However, in that case a fair comparison would require assigning $4s$ processors to PSODE, since in each of the 4 concurrent subtasks of PSODE, the 'parallelism across the problem' can equally well be exploited (cf. Section 1, where we have mentioned that both parallelization techniques are 'orthogonal').

Summarizing, we may say that PSODE needs 4 times the number of processors given to a sequential code, simply because it possesses a 4-fold amount of intrinsic parallelism. The large number of processors utilized by PSODE reflects the current tendency in parallel computing, since modern architectures – and certainly those entering the market in the coming years – have an 'almost unlimited' number of processors (*massive parallelism*).

Another aspect which is of utmost importance for the performance of a stiff code, is the amount of linear algebra per step, which in turn strongly depends on the dimension of the ODE. Prior to the specification of our test problem, we will briefly discuss the characteristics of the various codes with respect to this aspect:

A common feature of the three codes is that they need from time to time an LU-decomposition of the matrix involved in their respective iteration processes to solve the nonlinear relations. Since the factorization of a general N-dimensional matrix requires approximately $2N^3/3$ arithmetic operations, this will dominate the total costs of the integration for *large-scale problems*. Here we may think of complicated problems from circuit analysis or semi-discretized (higher-dimensional) partial differential equations. In such applications, systems of ODEs with several thousands of equations are quite usual. In this connection we remark that both LSODE and PSODE deal with matrices of dimension N. Hence, it is to be expected that their mutual comparison is only marginally influenced if N increases and all other aspects are left unchanged.

Matters are different for the code RADAU5, since it has to deal with matrices of dimension $3N$. By exploiting the special structures in these matrices, Hairer and Wanner are able to reduce the total work of the LU-decomposition to $10N^3/3$ operations [15], thus gaining a factor 5 compared with a direct treatment, which would have required $2(3N)^3/3$ operations. However, this number $10N^3/3$ compares unfavourably with the number $2N^3/3$ (associated with LSODE and PSODE), and causes a serious drawback for RADAU5 when applied to large-scale problems.

To get a first indication of the performances of the codes, we have applied them to a small test problem originating from circuit analysis. It was first described by Horneber [17] and extensively discussed in [14, p.112] and [11]. This (stiff) system describes a ring modulator, which mixes a low frequency and a high frequency signal.

The modulated signal is then used as input for an amplifier. The resulting system of 15 ODEs is defined by

$$y_1' = C^{-1} \left[y_8 - 0.5\, y_{10} + 0.5\, y_{11} + y_{14} - y_1/R \right]$$
$$y_2' = C^{-1} \left[y_9 - 0.5\, y_{12} + 0.5\, y_{13} + y_{15} - y_2/R \right]$$
$$y_3' = C_s^{-1} \left[y_{10} - g(z_1) + g(z_4) \right]$$
$$y_4' = C_s^{-1} \left[-y_{11} + g(z_2) - g(z_3) \right]$$
$$y_5' = C_s^{-1} \left[y_{12} + g(z_1) - g(z_3) \right]$$
$$y_6' = C_s^{-1} \left[-y_{13} - g(z_2) + g(z_4) \right]$$
$$y_7' = C_p^{-1} \left[-y_7/R_i + g(z_1) + g(z_2) - g(z_3) - g(z_4) \right]$$
$$y_8' = -L_h^{-1}\, y_1$$
$$y_9' = -L_h^{-1}\, y_2$$
$$y_{10}' = L_s^{-1} \left[0.5\, y_1 - y_3 - 17.3\, y_{10} \right]$$
$$y_{11}' = L_s^{-1} \left[-0.5\, y_1 + y_4 - 17.3\, y_{11} \right]$$
$$y_{12}' = L_s^{-1} \left[0.5\, y_2 - y_5 - 17.3\, y_{12} \right]$$
$$y_{13}' = L_s^{-1} \left[-0.5\, y_2 + y_6 - 17.3\, y_{13} \right]$$
$$y_{14}' = L_t^{-1} \left[-y_1 + e_1(t) - 86.3\, y_{14} \right]$$
$$y_{15}' = L_t^{-1} \left[-y_2 - 636.3\, y_{15} \right],$$

where

$$z_1 := y_3 - y_5 - y_7 - e_2(t), \quad z_2 := -y_4 + y_6 - y_7 - e_2(t),$$
$$z_3 := y_4 + y_5 + y_7 + e_2(t), \quad z_4 := -y_3 - y_6 + y_7 + e_2(t),$$

and the function g, which models the characteristics of the diodes, is defined by

$$g(z) := 40.67286402 \cdot 10^{-9} \left[\exp\left(17.7493332 \cdot z\right) - 1 \right].$$

The signals e_1 and e_2 are defined by

$$e_1(t) := 0.5 \sin\left(2\,10^3\, \pi\, t\right), \qquad e_2(t) := 2 \sin\left(2\,10^4\, \pi\, t\right).$$

The technical parameters have been given the values $C=16 \cdot 10^{-9}$, $R=25000$, $C_p=10^{-8}$, $R_i=50$, $L_h=4.45$, $L_s=0.0005$ and $L_t=0.002$, resulting in a heavily oscillating solution. Not yet fixed is the value of the capacity C_s. In our test, we give it the value 10^{-9}, which seems technically meaningful. It is reported [14] that small C_s-values cause serious difficulties. In the limit, i.e. on setting $C_s \equiv 0$, we end up with a differential-algebraic system. The integration interval in our test is $[0, 10^{-3}]$; the initial values are given by $y_i(0)=0$, $i=1,...,15$. For several values of TOL (the local error bound) the results obtained by the codes RADAU5, LSODE and PSODE are collected in Table 2.3. Here, T_1 and T_4 denote the CPU time (in seconds) when the program is run on 1 and 4 processors, respectively. Recall, that we restrict the timings for the sequential codes to T_1. The accuracy is measured by means of Δ, which is defined by writing the maximum norm of the global (relative) error in the endpoint in the form $10^{-\Delta}$. Furthermore, $Nsteps$ denotes the number of (successful) integration steps and $\bar{m}$ stands for the average number of (effective) f-evaluations per step.

Table 2.3. Performance of the codes RADAU5, LSODE and PSODE for the circuit problem

Method	TOL	$Nsteps$	$\bar{m}$	Δ	T_1	T_4
RADAU5	10^{-2}	1275	9.0	1.1	33.1	
	10^{-3}	2277	7.6	2.6	48.6	
	10^{-4}	3922	6.7	3.8	72.4	
	10^{-5}	6761	6.1	4.9	110.9	
LSODE	10^{-3}	7054	1.5	1.4	33.6	
	10^{-4}	9772	1.4	2.8	44.1	
	10^{-5}	13266	1.4	2.9	57.7	
	10^{-6}	17887	1.3	3.8	74.7	
	10^{-7}	23310	1.3	4.5	93.1	
	10^{-8}	30253	1.2	4.9	114.3	
PSODE	10^{-2}	1185	7.3	1.4	80.0	21.4
	10^{-3}	1561	7.3	3.1	104.5	27.8
	10^{-4}	2272	7.1	4.1	146.4	39.6
	10^{-5}	3437	6.9	5.2	212.1	57.7

These results give rise to the following conclusions:

(i) with respect to our first goal, we see that the speedup factor for PSODE (obviously defined by T_1/T_4) is approximately 3.7, which is pretty close to the 'ideal' factor 4 on this machine. This factor rapidly converges to 4 if the dimension of the problem increases.

(ii) concerning our second goal, we observe a remarkable similarity between RADAU5 and PSODE: both codes need approximately 7 f-evaluations per step; moreover, to produce the same accuracy, the required number of steps is of the same order of magnitude (for the more stringent values of TOL, the difference in the number of steps increases, which is probably due to the higher order of PSODE).

There is however a striking difference between the two Radau-based codes and LSODE; this code is very cheap per step, but needs much more integration steps to produce the same accuracy. For example, to obtain a relative accuracy of about 5 digits, PSODE needs $\approx$ 3400 steps, RADAU5 twice as many, whereas for LSODE this number is 9 times as large. Taking into account the computational effort per step of the various codes, the comparison with PSODE yields a double amount of time both for LSODE and RADAU5. Approximately the same ratios are observed in the low-accuracy range (say, $\Delta=3$).

As mentioned before, this example is only a model problem describing a small (part of an) electrical circuit, and is still far away from a real-life application. However, even for this small system of ODEs, the performance of (this provisional version of) PSODE is already superior by a factor 2 to that of the (well-established) codes LSODE and RADAU5.

Summarizing, we can say that
- the PSODE-approach is much more promising to serve as the basis for an efficient, 'all-purpose' stiff solver than the LSODE-approach. This is due to the improved mathematical qualities, viz. the high order in combination with A-stability.

- In comparison with RADAU5, PSODE has the advantage that in large-scale problems, the (dominating) LU-factorizations require a factor 5 less computational effort. In this connection we remark that a few preliminary experiments with a problem of dimension 75 reveal that the overall gain of PSODE is already more than a factor 4.

For really large-scale problems we expect that the speedup factor will be in the range 6 - 8, depending on the required accuracy. This number is composed of the asymptotic factor 5 coming from the algebra part and the remaining factor 1.2 - 1.6 originating from the higher order of PSODE.

Remark: it should be mentioned that RADAU5 offers a possibility to exploit a small amount of intrinsic parallelism. In using two processors, the total number of arithmetic operations to perform the LU-decomposition can be reduced from $10N^3/3$ to $8N^3/3$. We refrained from adapting the code RADAU5 in order to exploit this feature.

3. PARALLEL BLOCK METHODS

Another technique to construct parallel methods for ODEs is based on *block methods* [26, 12, 28, 29]. For the construction of this type of methods, it is convenient to introduce the so-called *block vector*

$$(3.1) \qquad Y_{n+1} := (y_{n,c_1}, y_{n,c_2}, \dots, y_{n,c_s})^T, \qquad c_s = 1,$$

where y_{n,c_i} denotes an approximation to the exact solution $y(t)$ at $t = t_n + c_i h$. Similar to the preceding section, the methods will be presented for a *scalar* ODE; however, also for block methods, the extension to systems of ODEs is straightforward. Again using the convention that $f(v) = (f(v_j))$, a (one-step) block method is defined by

$$(3.2) \qquad Y_{n+1} = A\, Y_n + h\, B\, f(Y_n) + h\, C\, f(Y_{n+1}), \qquad n = 0, 1, 2, \dots,$$

where A, B and C are matrices of dimension s. Notice that (3.2) is a direct generalization of the (one-step) linear multistep (LM) method

$$(3.2') \qquad y_{n+1} = a\, y_n + h\, b\, f(y_n) + h\, c\, f(y_{n+1}),$$

with a, b and c scalar variables.

Initially, the block methods were introduced to circumvent the restrictions that apply to LM methods: the limitation on the order because of zero-stability (known as the 'first Dahlquist barrier') and the order-restriction with respect to A-stability (which is usually called 'Dahlquist's second barrier'). As we shall see, both restrictions can be avoided by changing from the LM methods to the block methods. Moreover, parallelism can be achieved in a very natural way.

However, it should be observed that – in contrast to the Runge-Kutta type of methods considered in Section 2 – the block methods are *not self-starting*. Clearly, the recursion (3.2) needs the vector Y_0, which requires as many starting values as there are distinct values c_i.

In the next two subsections, we will consider parallel block methods for nonstiff and stiff ODEs, respectively.

3.1. Parallel block methods for nonstiff equations

Within the class of LM methods, *nonstiff* ODEs are usually solved by the so-called *predictor-corrector* (PC) approach. We will consider a similar technique in the case of block methods. To be more specific, let us call the (implicit) block method

(3.2) the *corrector*. Solving implicit relations is avoided by defining an *explicit predictor* of the form

$$(3.3) \qquad Y^{\text{pred}} = E\, Y_n + h\, F\, f(Y_n),$$

with E and F matrices of dimension s. Substitution of Y^{pred} into the right-hand side of (3.2) yields the *block predictor-corrector* (BPC) method

$$(3.4) \qquad Y_{n+1} = A\, Y_n + h\, B\, f(Y_n) + h\, C\, f(E\, Y_n + h\, F\, f(Y_n)).$$

In accordance with the terminology used in the LM case, this application is called the PECE mode. Of course, one can continue this process by substituting the result of (3.4) into the right-hand side of (3.2), etc.; in this way we arrive at the $P(EC)^m E$ mode.

The parallelism in this type of methods is obvious: the s components in $f(Y_n)$ (and in $f(Y^{\text{pred}})$) can be computed concurrently, so that (3.4) requires *effectively* only two right-hand side evaluations per step (provided of course, that sufficiently many processors are available).

In the literature, several parallel BPC methods have been proposed. We mention the work of Miranker and Liniger [22], of Shampine and Watts (cf. Worland [30]) and the multistep block methods of Chu and Hamilton [7]. In Chapter II of this monograph, methods of the form (3.4) are analyzed and new BPC methods are derived for the cases $s = 2, 3$ and 4. Contrary to the methods given in the literature, the BPC methods in Chapter II exploit the feature that the components of the block vector represent approximations to the exact solution at *not necessarily equidistant* points.

Using this property, it is possible to obtain (zero-)stable BPC methods with as high an order as $2s$. This is obtained by first constructing a predictor of the form (3.3) of order $2s-1$. Notice that, similar to the LM situation, this predictor itself does not necessarily be zero-stable.

A next question might be: 'how many processors are needed for the parallel implementation of these BPC methods ?' For the schemes presented in Chapter II, we have the uniform answer: 'two'. This is achieved by requiring the first $s-2$ rows of the matrices B, C and F to contain zero elements. This implies that we do not need to assign a processor to the first $s-2$ components of the block vector, since their values and derivatives can be adopted from the preceding step. However, assuming that there is no restriction on the number of available processors, this property is not of a great practical value.

Summarizing: for $s = 2, 3$ and 4, it is possible to construct BPC methods with a nonempty stability region including the origin, which

  (i)   are of order $2s$,
  (ii) need (at most) s starting values,
  (iii) require, on a two-processor machine, effectively two right-hand side evaluations per step.

We remark that the methods proposed by Donelson and Hansen [12] share the properties (i) and (ii). However, their stability regions are not available and moreover, if they are implemented on a parallel machine, they would need s processors. In this connection, we remark that Donelson and Hansen did not have in mind to apply their methods in a parallel context; they merely wanted to circumvent the first Dahlquist barrier.

Finally, we remark that the methods proposed by Chu and Hamilton [7] share the aforementioned properties (ii) and (iii), but have an order not exceeding four. On the other hand, the stability regions of their BPC methods are larger than those of the methods derived in Chapter II.

3.2. Parallel block methods for stiff equations

For the numerical integration of stiff ODEs, a method should preferably

  (i)   be A-stable, and
  (ii) have a high order of accuracy.

However, it is well known that these are conflicting demands for linear multistep methods (this is the so-called 'second Dahlquist barrier'). One possible way to achieve the goals (i) and (ii) is to consider implicit block methods. In the literature, several methods of this type have been proposed. For example, in [28] Watts and Shampine construct block methods based upon quadrature formulas of the Newton-Cotes type and show that these schemes are A-stable for orders ≤ 8 (see also [29]). These methods fit into the class (3.2), however, they have a *full* C-matrix. As a consequence, the s components of the block vector have to be solved simultaneously, a situation similar to the one encountered in implicit Runge-Kutta methods (observe the resemblance between (3.2) and (2.2b)). Hence, these implicit block methods are not suitable for parallel execution.

In Chapter III we discuss what can be achieved within the class of *parallel* implicit block (PIB) methods, subject to the aforementioned requirements with respect to order and stability. To that end, the matrix C in (3.2) is replaced by a *diagonal* matrix D:

$$(3.2\,'')\qquad Y_{n+1} = A\,Y_n + h\,B\,f(Y_n) + h\,D\,f(Y_{n+1}), \qquad n = 0, 1, 2, \dots \;.$$

As a result of this 'simplification', we sacrifice a lot of free parameters originally occurring in the matrix C but, on the other hand, we now arrive at a scheme in which the various components of Y_{n+1} are uncoupled as far as implicitness is concerned (cf. (2.3b) for a similar situation in the Runge-Kutta context). Hence, having s processors available, scheme (3.2") requires *effectively* the solution of one implicit relation, the dimension of which equals that of the system of ODEs. This means that the computational effort per step is quite similar to that of the celebrated backward differentiation formulas (BDFs).

The next step is, of course, to raise the order of the PIB method beyond 2. To that end we perform a numerical search in the space of free parameters. For example, for $s=2$ we have the A-stable PIB method

$$
(3.5) \qquad Y_{n+1} = \begin{pmatrix} 0 & 1 \\ 0 & 1 \end{pmatrix} Y_n + h \begin{pmatrix} \dfrac{147}{220} & \dfrac{161}{220} \\[2mm] -\dfrac{50}{33} & \dfrac{23}{66} \end{pmatrix} f(Y_n) + h \begin{pmatrix} \dfrac{7}{10} & 0 \\[2mm] 0 & \dfrac{13}{6} \end{pmatrix} f(Y_{n+1}),
$$

with $c_1=21/10$ and $c_2=1$. In this PIB method, the second component of Y_{n+1} (i.e., y_{n+1}) yields a third-order approximation to the exact solution.

Continuation of the numerical search process for $s=3$, yields several fourth-order A-stable parallel block methods. For the same value of s it is even possible to raise the order to five, however, then we loose the property of A-stability. It turns out that an extremely small lobe in the nonpositive halfplane does not belong to the stability region of these methods. An adequate characterization of the stability region of these methods (and of the BDFs, as well) is obtained by extending the well-known concept of $A(\alpha)$-stability:

Definition 3.1.: A block method of the form (3.2) is said to be $A(\alpha, \beta, \gamma)$-*stable* if:
(i)   its region of stability contains the infinite wedge $\{z \mid -\alpha < \pi - \arg(z) < \alpha\}$, with $0 < \alpha \le \pi/2$, and all points in the nonpositive halfplane with $|z| > \beta$,
(ii) γ is the maximum value of the spectral radius of the amplification matrix $[I - zC]^{-1} [A + zB]$ for all z with $\mathrm{Re}(z) \le 0$ lying in the instability region. []

Using this definition, the stability characteristics of the methods derived in Chapter III and of the BDFs are summarized in Table 3.1 (notice that BDFs are straightforwardly fitted in the formulation (3.2)). In this table, the vector c contains the abscissae defining the block vector, i.e., $c := (c_1, c_2, ..., c_s)^T$, and an '*' means that the corresponding value is not relevant.

18

Table 3.1. Values of α (in degrees), β and γ for the BDFs and some PIB methods

Method	c^{T}	Order	α	β	γ
BDF3	(−1, 0, 1)	3	88.4°	1.94	1.046
PIB3	(21/10, 1)	3	90°	0	*
BDF4	(−2, −1, 0, 1)	4	73.2°	4.72	1.191
PIB4$_{\mathrm{I}}$	(5, 13/4, 1)	4	90°	0	*
PIB4$_{\mathrm{II}}$	(3, 5, 1)	4	90°	0	*
BDF5	(−3, −2, −1, 0, 1)	5	51.8°	9.94	1.379
PIB5$_{\mathrm{I}}$	(−2.747, −2.122, 1)	5	>89.98°	0.16	1.0000026
PIB5$_{\mathrm{II}}$	(1.6153, 4.7871, 1)	5	>89.98°	0.30	1.000069

4. CONCLUSIONS AND FUTURE RESEARCH

We have shown that iterating a *fully implicit RK* method leads in a natural way to parallel integration methods. This approach can be used both for stiff and nonstiff ODEs. Although it is conceptually not necessary to start with a fully implicit RK method, such IRKs are an excellent choice to serve as a method, underlying the iteration process.

In the *nonstiff* case, the Gauss methods are recommended because of their highly accurate behaviour. Moreover, the optimal order of these IRKs with respect to the number of stages, minimizes the number of required processors. Observe however, that this aspect is only of marginal interest. Following this approach, it is possible to construct explicit RK methods for which the (effective) number of stages equals the order. This property holds for an arbitrarily high order and is principally impossible within the class of sequential explicit RK methods.

For *stiff* equations, a stiffly accurate IRK is a good choice; in particular, Radau IIA methods are suitable candidates. In the stiff case, the parallel, diagonally-implicit iteration leads to methods with nice features, both from a computational and a mathematical point of view. The property that only one matrix of the ODE dimension has to be factorized per step, reduces the amount of linear algebra to an acceptable level. We have seen that performing a fixed number of iterations results in L-stable methods with a high algebraic order, but with a (at least, formally) low stage order. Alternatively, iterating until convergence yields a high algebraic order as well as a high stage order. Moreover, already after a modest number of iterations, these methods are unconditionally stable .

A different approach to obtain parallel ODE solvers is provided by the class of *block methods*. Contrary to the RK-based methods, they are, in general, not self-starting.

The results for *nonstiff* equations seems to be even more promising than for the RK-based methods: using s starting values, it is possible to obtain order $2s$ (thus far, only for $s \leq 4$) with 2 f-evaluations. Moreover, the number of processors can be restricted to 2, but again, this is not a significant advantage. However, the stability regions of the resulting block methods are much smaller than those of the RK-based methods and, moreover, we expect the block methods to have much larger error constants.

In the *stiff* case, A-stable block methods of orders ≤ 4 can be constructed as well as an 'almost A-stable' method of order 5. This result is less favourable than for the RK-based methods, where very high orders can be combined with unconditional stability. On the other hand, the block methods require only one implicit relation to be solved per step (and per processor), whereas the RK-based methods have to solve a sequence of implicit relations.

In the future, we plan to perform an extensive comparison between the parallel RK methods and the parallel block methods on the basis of a broad collection of test problems.

Apart from that, the code PSODE (cf. Section 2.3) is still in a research phase and needs a better tuning of its strategy parameters, since the performance of any code critically depends on such a tuning. In particular, these parameters have to be chosen in such a way that the number of LU-factorizations is minimized. Furthermore, we plan to extent the code with the facility to treat ODEs of the form $M y'(t) = f(y(t))$, where M is a matrix which may be singular, resulting in a differential-algebraic system.

To exploit the abundance of the available processors, one can reserve a number of processors − apart from those performing the integration method − which continuously update the Jacobian matrix and calculate LU-factorizations, corresponding to various stepsizes that are realistic for the present part of the integration interval (this would of course require an adaptation of the stepsize selection strategy).

Another, more theoretical, aspect that needs attention in the future, is the construction of A-stable block methods of orders exceeding 4. This might be obtained by exploiting more free parameters in the matrices A, B and D (see (3.2")).

REFERENCES

[1]   **Alexander, R.** (1977): *Diagonally implicit Runge-Kutta methods for stiff ODEs*, SIAM J. Numer. Anal. **14**, pp. 1006-1021.

[2]   **Bellen, A. , Vermiglio, R.** & **Zennaro, M.** (1990): *Parallel ODE-solvers with stepsize control*, J. Comput. Appl. Math. **31**, pp. 277-293.

[3]   **Burrage, K.** (1978): *A special family of Runge-Kutta methods for solving stiff differential equations*, BIT **18**, pp. 22-41.

[4]   **Burrage, K.** (1991): *The error behaviour of a general class of predictor-corrector methods*, Appl. Numer. Math. **8**, pp. 201-216.

[5]   **Butcher, J.C.** (1979): *A transformed implicit Runge-Kutta method*, J. Assoc. Comput. Mach. **26**, pp. 731-738.

[6]   **Butcher, J.C.** (1987): *The numerical analysis of ordinary differential equations, Runge-Kutta and general linear methods*, Wiley, New York.

[7]   **Chu, M.T.** & **Hamilton, H.** (1987): *Parallel solution of ODE's by multiblock methods*, SIAM J. Sci. Stat. Comput. **8**, pp. 342-353.

[8]   **Cooper, G.J.** & **Sayfy, A.** (1979): *Semiexplicit A-stable Runge-Kutta methods*, Math. Comp. **33**, pp. 541-556.

[9]   **Crouzeix, M.** (1975): *Sur l'approximation des équations différentielles opérationelles linéaires par des méthodes de Runge-Kutta*, Ph. D. Thesis, Université de Paris.

[10]   **Dekker, K.** & **Verwer, J.G.** (1984): *Stability of Runge-Kutta methods for stiff nonlinear differential equations*, North-Holland, Amsterdam.

[11]   **Denk, G.** & **Rentrop, P.** (1989): *Mathematical models in electric circuit simulation and their numerical treatment*, in: Numerical Treatment of Differential Equations, K. Strehmel (ed.), Teubner-Texte zur Mathematik **121**, pp. 305-316.

[12]   **Donelson, J.** & **Hansen, E.** (1971): *Cyclic composite multistep predictor-corrector methods*, SIAM J. Numer. Anal. **8**, pp. 137-157.

[13]   **Gear, C.W.** (1988): *Parallel methods for ordinary differential equations*, Calcolo **25**, pp. 1-20.

[14]   **Hairer, E., Lubich, C.** & **Roche, M.** (1989): *The numerical solution of differential-algebraic systems by Runge-Kutta methods*, Lecture Notes in Mathematics, vol. **1409**, Springer-Verlag, Berlin.

[15]   **Hairer, E.** & **Wanner, G.** (1991): *Solving ordinary differential equations, II: Stiff and differential-algebraic problems*, Springer Series in Comp. Math., vol. **14**, Springer-Verlag, Berlin.

[16]   **Hindmarsh, A.C.** (1980): *LSODE and LSODI, two new initial value ordinary differential equation solvers*, ACM/SIGNUM Newsletter **15** (4), pp. 10-11.

[17]   **Horneber, E.H.** (1976): *Analyse nichtlinearer RLCÜ-Netzwerke mit hilfe der gemischten Potentialfunction mit einer systematischen Darstellung der Analyse nichtlinearer dynamische Netzwerke*, FB: Elektrotechnik, Universität Kaiserslautern, Dissertation.

[18]   **Iserles, A. & Nørsett, S.P.** (1990): *On the theory of parallel Runge-Kutta methods*, IMA J. Numer. Anal. **10**, pp. 463-488.

[19]   **Jackson, K.R. & Nørsett, S.P.** (1990): *The potential for parallelism in Runge-Kutta methods, Part I: RK formulas in standard form*, Technical Report No. 239/90, Dept. of Computer Science, University of Toronto.

[20]   **Jackson, K.R. & Nørsett, S.P.**: *The potential for parallelism in Runge-Kutta methods, Part II: RK predictor-corrector formulas*, in preparation.

[21]   **Lie, I.** (1987): *Some aspects of parallel Runge-Kutta methods*, Report No. 3/87, Dept. of Mathematics, University of Trondheim.

[22]   **Miranker, W.L. & Liniger, W.** (1967): *Parallel methods for the numerical integration of ordinary differential equations*, Math. Comp. **21**, pp. 303-320.

[23]   **Nørsett, S.P.** (1974): *Semi-explicit Runge-Kutta methods*, Report Mathematics and Computation No. 6/74, Dept. of Mathematics, University of Trondheim.

[24]   **Nørsett, S.P. & Simonsen, H.H.** (1989): *Aspects of parallel Runge-Kutta methods*, in: Numerical methods for ordinary differential equations, A. Bellen, C.W. Gear & E. Russo (eds.), Proceedings of the L'Aquila conference, 1987, Lecture Notes in Mathematics, vol. **1386**, Springer-Verlag, Berlin, pp. 103-117.

[25]   **Prothero, A. & Robinson, A.** (1974): *On the stability and accuracy of one-step methods for solving stiff systems of ordinary differential equations*, Math. Comp. **28**, pp. 145-162.

[26]   **Shampine, L.F. & Watts, H.A.** (1969): *Block implicit one-step methods*, Math. Comp. **23**, pp. 731-740.

[27]   **Sommeijer, B.P.** (1993): *Parallel-iterated Runge-Kutta methods for stiff ordinary differential equations*, J. Comput. Appl. Math. **45**, pp. 151-168.

[28]   **Watts, H. A. & Shampine, L.F.** (1972): *A-stable block implicit one-step methods*, BIT **12**, pp. 252-266.

[29]   **Williams, J. & Hoog, F. de** (1974): *A class of A-stable advanced multistep methods*, Math. Comp. **28**, pp. 163-177.

[30]   **Worland, P.B.** (1976): *Parallel methods for the numerical solution of ordinary differential equations*, IEEE Trans. Computers **C-25**, pp. 1045-1048.

PART I

Parallel numerical methods for nonstiff ODEs

CHAPTER I

Parallel iteration of high-order Runge-Kutta methods with stepsize control

Reprinted from

J. Comput. Appl. Math. **29** (1990), 111-127

with granted permission from ELSEVIER SCIENCE PUBLISHERS B.V.

Parallel Iteration of High-Order Runge-Kutta Methods with Stepsize Control

P.J. van der Houwen and B.P. Sommeijer

Centre for Mathematics and Computer Science
P.O. Box 94079, 1090 GB Amsterdam, The Netherlands

Abstract. This paper investigates iterated Runge-Kutta methods of high order designed in such a way that the right-hand side evaluations can be computed in parallel. Using stepsize control based on embedded formulas a highly efficient code is developed. On parallel computers, the 8th-order mode of this code is more efficient than the DOPRI8 implementation of the formulas of Prince and Dormand. The 10th-order mode is about twice as cheap for comparable accuracies.

1991 Mathematics Subject Classification: 65L06
1991 C.R. Classification: G.1.7
Key Words: numerical analysis, Runge-Kutta methods, parallelism.

1. INTRODUCTION

Implicit Runge-Kutta (RK) methods for solving the initial value problem for the system of ordinary differential equations (ODEs)

$$(1.1) \qquad \frac{dy(t)}{dt} = f(y(t))$$

are seldom used in predictor-corrector (PC) iteration, because RK correctors are much more expensive than linear multistep (LM) correctors. This is due to the increased number of coupled nonlinear algebraic equations. Although RK correctors of order p usually possess smaller error constants than LM correctors of comparable order, an accuracy-computational effort graph will be in favour of PC methods based on LM methods. However, matters are different when parallel computers are used. It is well known that PC iteration, being a form of functional iteration (or Jacobi iteration), allows a high degree of parallelism, because, by partitioning the system of equations into subsystems of equal computational complexity, we can assign to each processor such a subsystem and perform the iteration steps in parallel. The problem is of course the partitioning in subsystems of equal computational complexity. In the case of iterating s-stage RK methods, there is a natural partitioning based on the s subsystems corresponding to the s stages of the RK method. In this way, the computation time involved in applying RK correctors can be reduced a great deal on parallel computers. We shall call these 'parallel, iterated' RK methods *PIRK methods*. The idea of iterating an implicit RK method to exploit parallelism goes back to Jackson and Nørsett [10] and also in [9], [11], and [12] such methods have been debated. Before continuing our discussion on PC iteration, we emphasize that the choice of an implicit RK corrector has nothing to do with the excellent stability characteristics such methods usually possess, since this property is not preserved when the PC approach is followed. Their choice is solely determined by the fact that a *high order of accuracy* is easily obtained and, particularly, because of the potential *parallelism* exhibited by these methods. Hence, in the sequel we will assume that the class of ODEs (1.1) is nonstiff and has to be solved with high accuracy demands.

If the predictor is itself an (explicit) RK method, then the PIRK method also belongs to the class of explicit RK methods. In Iserles and Nørsett [9] it was proved that explicit RK methods of order p necessarily require at least p *effective* stages, and in Nørsett and Simonsen [12] the question was posed whether it is always possible to find explicit RK methods of order p using not more than p effective stages, assuming that sufficiently many processors are available (an explicit RK method is said to have p *effective* stages if the computation time required for evaluating all right-hand sides in one step is p times the computation time required by one right-hand side evaluation). This question motivated us to look in the class of PIRK methods for explicit RK methods, the order of which equals the number of effective stages; such methods will be called *optimal* RK methods. We will show that PIRK methods generated by any (not necessarily implicit) s-stage RK corrector of order p do not require more than p effective stages provided that s processors are available. The next question is the least number of processors needed to implement an optimal explicit RK method. For example, in [12] a 5th-order, 6-stage RK method of Butcher which can be implemented on two processors requiring only 5 effective stages is mentioned. This method is clearly an example of an optimal 'minimal processor' RK method. So far, we did not succeed in answering the question of least number of necessary processors. Therefore, we have looked for RK methods of which the number of stages is small with respect to their order. It is well known that, within the class of RK methods, those of Gauss-Legendre type require least number of stages to obtain a given order; to be more precise, s-stage Gauss-Legendre methods have order $p=2s$. Hence, for an 'optimal' implementation of these methods, we need only s processors. Furthermore, the stability regions can directly be derived from known results for truncated Taylor series, they allow an extremely simple implementation, and we obtain automatically a sequence of embedded methods of varying order which can be used for stepsize control. PIRK codes of order 8 and 10 using automatic stepsize control are compared with the code DOPRI8 of Hairer, Nørsett and Wanner [5] which is a variable step implementation of the 8th-order explicit RK formula with 7th-order embedded formula of Prince and Dormand [13]. All codes use the same stepsize strategy. By a number of experiments, the performance of the PIRK codes is demonstrated. Both codes are considerably cheaper than DOPRI8 for comparable accuracies. In the Appendix to this paper, we provide a FORTRAN implementation of the PIRK methods. This implementation has the feature that the user can introduce arbitrary RK correctors by means of their Butcher arrays.

Instead of using (one-step explicit) RK predictors one may use LM predictors reducing the number of effective stages. First results based on LM predictors are reported by Lie [11], using a fourth-order, two-stage Gauss-Legendre corrector and a third-order Hermite extrapolation predictor. With this PC pair, one iteration suffices to obtain a fourth-order PIRK scheme. We shall briefly discuss the use of multistep predictors, in particular for RK correctors of general (nonquadrature) type. Various predictor methods are compared showing that the efficiency of PIRK methods using multistep predictors is higher, but the price to be paid for the increased efficiency is more storage and a less easy implementation.

Finally, the methods proposed in the following sections will be described for *scalar* differential equations of the form (1.1). Their application, however, is straightforwardly extended to systems of ODEs.

2. OPTIMAL RK METHODS

Our starting point is the s-stage, implicit, one-step RK method of the form

$$(2.1a) \qquad y_{n+1} = y_n + h b^T r_{n+1},$$

where r_{n+1} is implicitly defined by

$$(2.1b) \qquad r_{n+1} := f(y_n e + h A r_{n+1}).$$

Here, h is the integration step, e is a column vector of dimension s with unit entries, b is an s-dimensional vector and A is an s-by-s matrix. Furthermore, we use the convention that for any given vector $v=(v_j)$, $f(v)$ denotes the vector with entries $f(v_j)$. By iterating the equation for r_{n+1} m times by simple functional iteration and using the mth iterate as an approximation to r_{n+1}, we obtain the method

$$(2.2) \qquad r^{(j)} = f(y_n e + h A r^{(j-1)}), \quad j = 1, \dots, m; \quad y_{n+1} = y_n + h b^T r^{(m)}.$$

Since the s components of the vectors $r^{(j)}$ can be computed in parallel, provided that s processors are available, the computational time needed for one iteration of (2.2) is equivalent to the time required to evaluate one right-hand side function on a sequential computer. Hence, the total costs of (2.2) per integration step comprise the calculation of the initial approximation $r^{(0)}$ plus m right-hand side evaluations. In the following, we always assume that we have s processors at our disposal and, speaking about 'computational effort per step', we mean the computational time required per step if s processors are available. If the computational effort per step equals the computation time for performing M right-hand side evaluations, then we shall say that the method requires M *effective stages*. Here, and in the sequel, we have assumed that the costs per step are predominated by the time needed to evaluate the derivative function. If this happens to be not the case for a particular ODE, then the overhead, which is sequential in essence, will take a relative large portion of the total costs per step and, consequently, the parallel evaluation of the s (cheap) right-hand side functions will not result in an overall speedup with a factor s.

We shall call the method providing $r^{(0)}$ the *predictor method* and (2.1) the *corrector method* and the resulting parallel, iterated RK method will be briefly called *PIRK method*. It should be observed that in the present case of RK correctors, the predictor and corrector methods do not directly generate approximations to y_{n+1} as is the case in PC methods based on LM methods. However, at any stage of the iteration process we can compute the current approximation to y_{n+1} by means of the formula

$$(2.3) \qquad y^{(j)} := y_n + h\boldsymbol{b}^{\mathrm{T}} r^{(j)}, \quad j = 0, 1, \dots .$$

Let $r^{(0)}$ be an approximation to r_{n+1} satisfying the condition

$$(2.4) \qquad r^{(0)} = r_{n+1} + O(h^q),$$

resulting in $y^{(0)} = y_{n+1} + O(h^{q+1})$. Predictor methods satisfying (2.4) will be called predictor methods of order q.

Suppose that A and $\boldsymbol{b}^{\mathrm{T}}$ are such that the corrector (2.1) is of order p and let the predictor method be of order $q-1$. Then, it has been proved in Jackson and Nørsett [10] that the (global) order of y_{n+1} as defined by (2.2) equals $p^*:= \min\{p, q+m\}$. By using the simple predictor method $r^{(0)} := f(y_n)e = r_{n+1} + O(h)$, i.e., $q=1$, we immediately have as a corollary of this result the next theorem.

Theorem 2.1. Let $\{A, \boldsymbol{b}^{\mathrm{T}}\}$ define an s-stage RK method (which need not be implicit) of order p. Then the PIRK method defined by

$$(2.5) \qquad \begin{aligned} r^{(0)} &= f(y_n)e, \\ r^{(j)} &= f(y_n e + hAr^{(j-1)}), \quad j = 1, \dots, m, \\ y_{n+1} &= y_n + h\boldsymbol{b}^{\mathrm{T}} r^{(m)} \end{aligned}$$

represents an $(m+1)s$-stage explicit RK method of order $p^*:=\min\{p,m+1\}$ requiring $m+1$ effective stages. []

Method (2.5) can also be represented by its Butcher array. Defining the s-dimensional vector $\mathbf{0}$ and the s-by-s matrix O both with zero entries, we obtain

$$
\begin{array}{c|ccccccc}
O \\
A & O \\
O & A & O \\
\cdot & & \cdot & \cdot \\
\cdot & & & \cdot & \cdot \\
\cdot & & & & \cdot & \cdot \\
O & \cdot & \cdot & \cdot & O & A & O \\
\hline
\mathbf{0}^{\mathrm{T}} & \cdot & \cdot & \cdot & \mathbf{0}^{\mathrm{T}} & \mathbf{0}^{\mathrm{T}} & b^{\mathrm{T}}
\end{array}
$$

We remark that this Butcher tableau represents a direct translation of (2.5), resulting in $(m+1)s$ stages. However, written in this form, the O-matrix in the first row could be replaced by a scalar zero, since the prediction $r^{(0)}$ has equal components and, consequently, can be produced by one processor. This would lead to an explicit RK method possessing $ms+1$ stages.

Setting $m=p-1$, it follows from this theorem that the question posed by Nørsett and Simonsen [12] can be answered in the affirmative: any pth-order RK method $\{A,b^{\mathrm{T}}\}$ generates an explicit RK method of the form (2.5) of order p requiring only p effective stages. Such explicit RK methods will be called *optimal RK methods*. Of course, within the class (2.5) the number of processors needed for the implementation is dictated by the number of stages s of the generating corrector. For example, the 10th-order, 17-stage RK method of Hairer [4] generates an explicit RK method of the form (2.5) which is also of order 10 if we set $m=9$ and which is optimal in the above sense. However, the implementation of this method requires 17 processors. This suggests the problem of constructing RK methods of order p which are optimal and require least number of processors. The 5th-order, 6-stage RK method of Butcher mentioned in [12] is an example of such a method: it can be implemented on two processors requiring only 5 effective stages. From the theory of RK methods based on high-order quadrature methods, such as Gauss-Legendre and Radau methods [5], we can immediately deduce a lower bound for the number of processors needed to implement optimal RK methods of the form (2.5):

Theorem 2.2. RK methods of the form (2.5) are optimal if $m \le p-1$. For even p the least number of required processors equals $p/2$ and the generating RK corrector is the

pth-order Gauss-Legendre method; for odd p the least number of processors is $(p+1)/2$ and the generating RK corrector is the pth-order Radau method. □

Thus, optimal RK methods requiring less than $\lfloor (p+1)/2 \rfloor$ processors cannot be found among the methods of the form (2.5). Since (2.5) allows an extremely simple implementation and provides automatically a sequence of embedded formulas which can be used for error estimation (see Section 5) and order variation, we have not looked for methods requiring less than $\lfloor (p+1)/2 \rfloor$ processors.

In order to illustrate the significance of Theorem 2.2, we make a comparison with explicit RK methods devised for one-processor computers (sequential methods). In Table 2.1 the minimal number of stages s_{min} (and therefore the minimal number of right-hand side evaluations) needed to generate such methods of order p are listed. In addition, we list the number of stages S for which these RK methods have actually been constructed (cf. [5, Section 11.6]), and the numbers of effective stages S_{eff} and processors S_{pr} needed by the optimal RK methods of Theorem 2.2.

Table 2.1. Comparison of sequential RK methods and optimal RK methods of the form (2.5)

	p	≤ 4	5	6	7	8	9	10
Sequential	s_{min}	p	6	7	9	11	≥ 12	≥ 13
RK	S	p	6	7	9	11	–	17
Optimal	S_{eff}	p	5	6	7	8	9	10
RK	S_{pr}	–	3	3	4	4	5	5

Finally, we remark that if the RK corrector is based on quadrature (or collocation) methods, then the initial approximation $r^{(0)}$ can be interpreted as the derivative $f(Y^{(0)})$, where $Y^{(0)}$ is an approximation to $y(t_n e + hAe)$. Suppose that the components of $Y^{(0)}$ are computed (in parallel) by using an explicit $(q-1)$-stage RK method of order $q-1$ with stepsizes hAe. Then the resulting PIRK method is still an explicit RK method itself and it is optimal if $m \leq p-q$ corrections are performed.

3. MULTISTEP PREDICTOR METHODS

Evidently, we can save computing time by using multistep predictor methods. As observed above, such predictors should provide approximations to the derivative values $f(y(t_n e + hAe))$ in the case where the generating RK method $\{A, b^T\}$ is derived from quadrature formulas. Any set of linear multistep methods providing approximations to the components of $y(t_n e + hAe)$ serves this purpose.

In this paper we briefly discuss the case of arbitrary RK correctors where we cannot give an easy interpretation for the initial approximation $r^{(0)}$. In such cases, it is possible to construct multistep predictor methods by performing the auxiliary vector recursion

(3.1a) $\qquad f_{n+1} := f(y_n e + h\delta(E)E^{-k+1}f_n),$

where E denotes the forward shift operator, i.e., $Ef_n = f_{n+1}$. The predictor method is now simply defined by

(3.1b) $\qquad r^{(0)} := f_{n+1}.$

Here $\delta(\zeta)$ is a polynomial of degree $k-1$ whose coefficients are matrices of appropriate dimension (cf. [7]). The method defined by (2.2) and (3.1) gives rise to a k-step PC method requiring $m+1$ right-hand side evaluations per step. For $m=0$, this method fits into the class of methods investigated in [7].

By Taylor expansion of f_{n+1} (or, $Y^{(0)}$), conditions for the satisfaction of $r_{n+1} - f_{n+1} = O(h^q)$ can be derived in terms of A and $\delta(\zeta)$. For instance we have the following theorem.

Theorem 3.1. Let the corrector defined by $\{A, b^T\}$ be of order p, then the k-step PC method

$$
\begin{aligned}
f_{n+1} &= f(y_n e + h\delta(E)E^{-k+1}f_n), \\
(3.2) \qquad r^{(0)} &= f_{n+1}, \qquad r^{(j)} = f(y_n e + hAr^{(j-1)}), \quad j = 1, \ldots, m, \\
y_{n+1} &= y_n + hb^T r^{(m)}
\end{aligned}
$$

is of order $p^* := \min\{p, q+m\}$, where

$$
\begin{aligned}
q = 2 \quad &\text{if} &\qquad Ae - \delta(1)e &= 0. \\
q = 3 \quad &\text{if, in addition,} &\qquad A^2 e - \delta^2(1)e + k\delta(1)e - \delta'(1)e &= 0, \\
& & \tfrac{1}{2}A^2 e - \tfrac{1}{2}\delta^2(1)e + k\delta(1)e - \delta'(1)e &= 0. \quad []
\end{aligned}
$$

Example 3.1. The most simple example is the case where $k=1$ and $\delta(\zeta)=0$, so that $r^{(0)}=f(y_n)e$ and $q=1$. This case has been already considered in the preceding section. Next we choose $k=1$ and $\delta(\zeta)=A$. It is readily verified that the order conditions for the predictor are satisfied for $q=2$. The algorithm (3.2) assumes the one-step form

$$
\begin{aligned}
f_{n+1} &= f(y_n e + hAf_n), \\
(3.3) \qquad r^{(0)} &= f_{n+1}, \qquad r^{(j)} = f(y_n e + hAr^{(j-1)}), \quad j = 1, \ldots, m, \\
y_{n+1} &= y_n + hb^T r^{(m)}.
\end{aligned}
$$

If the RK corrector has order p, then by performing $m=p-2$ corrections this method is also of order p and requires $p-1$ right-hand side evaluations per step. Formally, the method no longer belongs to the class of one-step RK methods. However, in actual applications, the method is self-starting if we take $f_0=f(y_0)e$.

Finally, we choose $k=2$ and $\delta(\zeta)=2A\zeta-A$ which satisfy the order conditions for $q=3$. The algorithm (3.2) assumes the two-step form

$$
(3.4) \quad
\begin{aligned}
f_{n+1} &= f(y_n e + 2hAf_n - hAf_{n-1}), \\
r^{(0)} &= f_{n+1}, \quad r^{(j)} = f(y_n e + hAr^{(j-1)}), \quad j = 1, \dots, m, \\
y_{n+1} &= y_n + hb^T r^{(m)}.
\end{aligned}
$$

If the RK corrector has order p, then by performing $m=p-3$ corrections this method is also of order p and requires $p-2$ right-hand side evaluations per step. []

4. STABILITY

We consider linear stability with respect to the test equation

$$(4.1) \qquad y'(t) = \lambda y(t).$$

It is easily verified that application of (2.5) yields the recursion

$$(4.2) \qquad y_{n+1} = [1 + zb^T e + z^2 b^T Ae + z^3 b^T A^2 e + \dots + z^{m+1} b^T A^m e]y_n,$$

where we have written $z=\lambda h$. The stability polynomial is given by

$$(4.3) \qquad P_{m+1}(z) = 1 + zb^T e + z^2 b^T Ae + z^3 b^T A^2 e + \dots + z^{m+1} b^T A^m e.$$

In the particular case where we choose $m=p-1$, p being the order of the corrector, we obtain a stability polynomial of degree p. According to Theorem 2.1, this PIRK method is of order p so that the stability polynomial is consistent of order p, i.e., it approximates $\exp(z)$ with pth-order accuracy. Thus, we have proved the next theorem.

Theorem 4.1. Let the corrector be of order p. If $m=p-1$, then the method (2.5) becomes an (explicit) RK method with the stability polynomial

$$P_p(z) = 1 + z + \frac{1}{2!}z^2 + \frac{1}{3!}z^3 + \dots + \frac{1}{p!}z^p. \quad []$$

Using a result on truncated Taylor series (cf. [6, p.236]), we have the next corollary of this theorem.

Corollary 4.1. The method of Theorem 4.1 is stable in the interval $[-\beta_{real}, 0]$, where

(4.4) $\beta_{real} \approx 0.368\,(p+1)\,[19(p+1)]^{1/(2(p+1))}$. []

Defining $[-i\,\beta_{imag},\,i\,\beta_{imag}]$ to be the interval on the imaginary axis where the method of Theorem 4.1 is stable, we list in Table 4.1 the values of β_{real} (and its approximation provided by (4.4)) and of β_{imag} for orders $p=1,2,...,10$.

Table 4.1. β_{real} and β_{imag} for the method of Theorem 4.1

	$p=1$	$p=2$	$p=3$	$p=4$	$p=5$	$p=6$	$p=7$	$p=8$	$p=9$	$p=10$
True value of β_{real}	2.00	2.00	2.52	2.78	3.22	3.55	3.95	4.31	4.70	5.07
Value according to (4.4)	1.83	2.17	2.53	2.90	3.28	3.65	4.03	4.41	4.78	5.16
True value of β_{imag}	0.00	0.00	1.73	2.82	0.00	0.00	1.76	3.39	0.00	0.00

5. STEPSIZE CONTROL

In this section we will describe a simple strategy to implement the afore-mentioned methods with a variable stepsize in order to control the local truncation error. This strategy is the same as the one employed by Hairer, Nørsett and Wanner [5, p.167] in their code DOPRI8, in which they have implemented the 13-stage, 8th-order explicit RK method with the embedded method of order 7 of Prince and Dormand.

This strategy is based on the observation that when iterating the equation (2.1b) for r_{n+1} we obtain approximations $r^{(j)}$ of successively increasing order, i.e.,

$$r^{(j)} - r_{n+1} = O(h^{\min\{p,\,q+j\}}), \qquad j=1, 2,..., m.$$

Thus, apart from our final approximation $y_{n+1}:=y_n+h b^T r^{(m)}$, we can easily construct a reference solution (cf. (2.3))

(5.1) $y^{(k)} := y_n + h b^T r^{(k)}$,

for some $k < m$. Since $r^{(k)}$ has already been computed, this does not require additional right-hand side evaluations. This reference solution $y^{(k)}$ can be considered as an 'embedded' solution [5].

Now, as an estimate for the local error ε in the step from t_n to $t_{n+1}=t_n+h$, we take

(5.2) $\varepsilon := \|y_{n+1} - y^{(k)}\|$,

for some norm ‖·‖. Usually, one uses reference solutions $y^{(k)}$ such that the orders of y_{n+1} and $y^{(k)}$ differ by 1. Here we follow this approach and choose $k=m-1$.

First, we will discuss the case where we restrict our stepsize strategy to methods in which the number of iterations m is fixed in each step and is given by $m=p-q$. Hence, $r^{(m)}-r_{n+1}$ and $r^{(m-1)}-r_{n+1}$ behave as $O(h^p)$ and $O(h^{p-1})$, respectively, and, consequently,

$$\varepsilon = \|y_{n+1} - y^{(m-1)}\| = \|y_n + hb^Tr^{(m)} - y_n - hb^Tr^{(m-1)}\| = O(h^p).$$

Then ε is compared with some prescribed tolerance TOL and the step is accepted if $\varepsilon \leq$ TOL, and rejected otherwise. Furthermore, the value of ε allows us to make an estimate for the asymptotically optimal stepsize:

$$h \sqrt[p]{\frac{\text{TOL}}{\varepsilon}},$$

which will be taken in the next step (or to recompute the current step in case of rejection). However, to give the code some robustness, we actually implemented (cf. [5, p.167])

$$(5.3) \qquad h_{\text{new}} = h \cdot \min\{6, \max\{\tfrac{1}{3}, \ 0.9 \ \sqrt[p]{\frac{\text{TOL}}{\varepsilon}}\}\}.$$

The constants 6 and $\tfrac{1}{3}$ in this expression serve to prevent an abrupt change in the stepsize and the safety factor 0.9 is added to increase the probability that the next step will be accepted.

Apart from the variable stepsize implementation mentioned above, the PIRK methods allow for a simple extension of the control strategy by which also the *order* of the method may vary from step to step. This can be achieved by abandoning the approach of a fixed number of iterations. Referring to the description above, we can construct a *sequence* of reference solutions, i.e., after each iteration the 'embedded' solution

$$y^{(j)} := y_n + hb^Tr^{(j)}$$

is computed. Then, we use the difference of two successive reference solutions as an estimate for the local error, i.e.,

$$\varepsilon^{(j)} := \| y^{(j)} - y^{(j-1)} \|.$$

If, during the iteration, the tolerance criterion $\varepsilon^{(j)} \leq$ TOL is satisfied for some $j=j_0 < m$, then there is no need to proceed with the iteration process and we accept

$y^{(j_0)}$ as the numerical solution y_{n+1}. This suggests to try the next step with the value of m defined by $m=j_0$. Since

$$\varepsilon^{(j_0)} = O(h^{p*}), \qquad p* = \min\{p+1, q+j_0\},$$

a prediction for the next stepsize can be made according to (5.3), where p is replaced by $p*$ and ε by $\varepsilon^{(j_0)}$.

It may happen that the tolerance condition is *not* satisfied for $j=j_0 \leq m$. In such cases, the values of m and h predicted in the preceding step were not reliable. One may then decide to reject the current value of m and to continue the iteration process. This is particularly recommendable if the value of the current $p*$ is less than p. If the continuation of the iteration process does not help to satisfy the tolerance condition $\varepsilon^{(j)} \leq$ TOL for $j \leq M$, where M is some prescribed upper bound for the number of iterations per step, then the (relatively costly) alternative is rejection of the current value of h, to redefine h according to (5.3) using the most recent information on the error, and to perform the present step once again. In this way a variable order variable stepsize RK method can be constructed.

6. NUMERICAL EXPERIMENTS

We present a few examples illustrating the efficiency of PIRK methods on parallel computers. The calculations are performed using 14-digits arithmetic. The methods tested were all applied in $P(EC)^m E$ mode.

6.1. Comparison of various predictor methods

In order to examine the effect of various predictor methods on the efficiency of the PIRK algorithm we performed a few tests by integrating the equation of motion for a rigid body without external forces (cf. [8, Problem B5]):

$$
(6.1) \quad
\begin{aligned}
y_1' &= y_2 y_3, & y_1(0) &= 0, \\
y_2' &= -y_1 y_3, & y_2(0) &= 1, \quad 0 \leq t \leq T. \\
y_3' &= -.51 y_1 y_2, & y_3(0) &= 1,
\end{aligned}
$$

In these tests we used the 10th-order Gauss-Legendre corrector and the following predictor methods:

Predictor I:	$r^{(0)} = f(y_n)e$ (cf. (2.5))	$q=1$	$p=\min\{m+1,10\}$
Predictor II:	$r^{(0)}$ defined by the standard 4th-order RK	$q=5$	$p=\min\{m+5,10\}$
Predictor III:	$r^{(0)} = f(y_n e + hAf_n)$ (cf. (3.3))	$q=2$	$p=\min\{m+2,10\}$
Predictor IV:	$r^{(0)} = f(y_n e + 2hAf_n - hAf_{n-1})$ (cf. (3.4))	$q=3$	$p=\min\{m+3,10\}$

In the Tables 6.1a and 6.1b we have listed the values $D\backslash N$, where D denotes the number of correct decimal digits at the endpoint, i.e., we write the maximum norm of the error at $t=T$ in the form 10^{-D}, and where N denotes the total number of effective right-hand side evaluations performed during the integration process. Furthermore, we indicated the effective order p_{eff}, that is the order of accuracy which is shown numerically.

Table 6.1a. Values $D\backslash N$ for problem (6.1) with $T=20$.

| h^{-1} | Predictor I | | | Predictor II | | |
	$m=8$	$m=9$	$m=10$	$m=4$	$m=5$	$m=6$
1	5.6\180	6.5\200	6.9\220	5.3\180	7.0\200	6.8\220
2	8.0\360	9.7\400	9.8\440	7.8\360	10.2\400	9.7\440
4	10.6\720	13.0\800	12.3\880	10.5\720	13.3\800	12.2\880
$p_{eff} \approx$	9	10	10	9	10	10

Table 6.1b. Values $D\backslash N$ for problem (6.1) with $T=20$.

| h^{-1} | Predictor III | | | Predictor IV | |
	$m=7$	$m=8$	$m=9$	$m=7$	$m=8$
1	4.8\160	5.5\180	7.5\200	4.6\160	5.7\180
2	7.2\320	8.5\360	9.6\400	7.2\320	8.8\360
4	9.7\640	11.6\720	12.1\800	10.4\640	12.4\720
$p_{eff} \approx$	9	10	10	10	10

Comparing experiments with equal N (notice that these tables contain for each h and each predictor an experiment with $N=180h^{-1}$), we conclude that in most experiments the third-order predictor IV and the second-order predictor III yield the most accurate values. However, the price we pay is more storage and a more complicated implementation because of the auxiliary recursion for f_n. The predictors I and II produce comparable accuracies. As the added storage for the predictors III and IV is not offset by comparable reduction in the volume of computation, we recommend predictor I in actual computations. The resulting PIRK method is a true one-step RK method of an extremely simple structure, and consequently allowing for an easy and straightforward implementation. A FORTRAN code based on this PIRK method can be found in the Appendix to this paper.

6.2. Comparison with the 10th-order methods of Curtis and Hairer

Curtis [2] and Hairer [4] used the test problem (6.1) for testing and comparing their 10th-order RK methods. In Table 6.2 the results of the experiments performed by Curtis and Hairer are reproduced together with results obtained by the PC pairs consisting of the predictors I, II and III, and the 10th-order Gauss-Legendre corrector. Again we see that the simple predictor I can compete favourably with the predictors II and III.

Table 6.2. Values $D\backslash\!\!N$ for problem (6.1) with $T=60$.

Method	p	$60/h$	D	N
Runge-Kutta	4	12000	9.6	48000
Adams-Moulton-Bashforth	4	6000	8.1	12000
Runge-Kutta-Curtis	10	240	9.9	4320
Runge-Kutta-Hairer	10	240	10.1	4080
(2.2) with predictor I and $m=9$	10	156	10.0	1560
(2.2) with predictor I and $m=10$	10	150	10.0	1650
(2.2) with predictor II and $m=5$	10	150	10.1	1500
(2.2) with predictor II and $m=6$	10	156	10.1	1716
(2.2) with predictor III and $m=8$	10	210	10.0	1891
(2.2) with predictor III and $m=9$	10	168	10.0	1681

6.3. Comparison with the 8(7)-method of Prince and Dormand

The 8(7)-method of Prince and Dormand [13] is nowadays generally considered as one of the most efficient methods with automatic stepsize control for TOL-values approximately in the range 10^{-7} to 10^{-13}. In this subsection we compare the DOPRI8 code, as given by Hairer, Nørsett and Wanner [5], with the PIRK method based on predictor I and the Gauss-Legendre correctors of orders 8 and 10. To let the comparison of the DOPRI8 code and the PIRK codes not be influenced by a different stepsize strategy, we equipped the PIRK codes with the same strategy (see Section 5). These codes are respectively denoted by PIRK8 and PIRK10.

6.3.1. Fehlberg problem

As a first test problem we take an example from Fehlberg [3]:

$$
(6.2) \quad
\begin{aligned}
y_1' &= 2\,t\,y_1 \log(\max\{y_2, 10^{-3}\}), & y_1(0) &= 1, \\
y_2' &= -2\,t\,y_2 \log(\max\{y_1, 10^{-3}\}), & y_2(0) &= e,
\end{aligned}
\qquad 0 \le t \le 5,
$$

with exact solution $y_1(t)=\exp(\sin(t^2))$, $y_2(t)=\exp(\cos(t^2))$. For tolerances TOL running from 10^{-5} up to 10^{-12} we computed the D and corresponding N-values. Instead of presenting the polygon graph for these values as was done in [5], we preferred to present the DW lying on this polygon for a number of *integer* values of D. In Table 6.3 these values are listed.

Table 6.3. Values of N for problem (6.2).

Method	$D=5$	$D=6$	$D=7$	$D=8$	$D=9$	$D=10$	$D=11$
DOPRI8	595	759	963	1227	1574	1990	2503
PIRK8	379	495	623	786	978	1383	1874
PIRK10	327	388	490	704	884	977	1078

6.3.2. Euler equations

Next, we apply the codes to Euler's equation for a rigid body (cf. (6.1)). The performance of the code is presented in Table 6.4.

Table 6.4. Values of N for problem (6.1) with $T=60$.

Method	$D=6$	$D=7$	$D=8$	$D=9$	$D=10$	$D=11$	$D=12$
DOPRI8	415	576	728	898	1133	1422	1817
PIRK8	294	381	534	728	961	1172	1746
PIRK10	252	297	357	426	580	730	920

6.3.3. Orbit equations

Finally, we apply the codes to the orbit equations (cf. [8, Problem D2])

$$
\begin{aligned}
&y_1' = y_3, && y_1(0) = 1-\varepsilon, \\
&y_2' = y_4, && y_2(0) = 0, \\
(6.3) \quad &y_3' = \frac{-y_1}{(y_1^2 + y_2^2)^{3/2}}, && y_3(0) = 0, && 0 \leq t \leq 20. \\
&y_4' = \frac{-y_2}{(y_1^2 + y_2^2)^{3/2}}, && y_4(0) = \sqrt{\frac{1+\varepsilon}{1-\varepsilon}}, \quad \varepsilon = \tfrac{3}{10},
\end{aligned}
$$

The performance of the codes is presented in Table 6.5. An obvious conclusion which can be drawn, is that – at least for these three test examples – both PIRK codes are more efficient than DOPRI8; in the average, PIRK8 requires 3/4 of the number of f-evaluations that are needed by DOPRI8 to yield the same accuracy, whereas PIRK10 is almost twice as efficient. The superiority of PIRK10, especially in the high-accuracy range, is undoubtedly due to its higher order. Therefore, it would be interesting to compare this method with an embedded (sequential) Runge-Kutta pair of comparable order. Unfortunately, to the best of our knowledge, such formulae have not been constructed in the literature.

Table 6.5. Values of N for problem (6.3).

Method	$D=5$	$D=6$	$D=7$	$D=8$	$D=9$	$D=10$	$D=11$
DOPRI8	615	723	831	1062	1284	1780	2024
PIRK8	463	559	679	859	1099	1411	1876
PIRK10	378	448	540	662	784	911	1076

7. CONCLUSIONS

Iterated Runge-Kutta methods of arbitrarily high order have been constructed that are capable of efficiently exploiting the parallelism of an MIMD computer architecture. Assuming that sufficient processors are available, it is shown how to derive 'optimal methods', i.e., methods requiring a number of parallelised f-evaluations equal to the order. Within the class of optimal methods considered, the required number of processors s is least with respect to the order p if the algorithm is based on an iterated Gauss-Legendre RK method and this minimal number is given by $s=\frac{1}{2}p$. It is known that optimal methods exist requiring a smaller number of processors (an example is the fifth-order method of Butcher, mentioned in the Introduction), but it is not clear how to formulate a general construction procedure to arrive at such methods for arbitrary order.

A nice feature of the methods proposed is that they provide an embedded reference solution without additional f-evaluations. This advantage has been utilized to make a variable step implementation which has been compared with the code DOPRI8, nowadays considered as 'the state of the art' for the automatic integration of ODEs. On the basis of some test examples, the performance of the new code is compared with DOPRI8 and, in terms of the required number of f-evaluations, demonstrates a superior behaviour.

Another aspect is the simple implementation of the new algorithm. In the Appendix a FORTRAN subroutine is provided which accepts a general RK method of arbitrary order, defined in terms of its Butcher tableau. For example, if there is need for an automatic integration routine of order higher than 8, as is furnished by DOPRI8, then we can suffice to specify e.g. a high-order Gauss method (the construction of which is simple and fully described in [1]) and call this subroutine. Furthermore, for such accuracy demands, we remark that even in the case that the parallel evaluation of the derivatives is not possible (e.g. on a uniprocessor machine) or not relevant (e.g., because the evaluation of f is very inexpensive and offset by the overhead), this code may still be of value. Since classical embedded RK pairs of such

40

high orders are lacking, it may turn out that, even in the non-parallelised form, the present code is more efficient than DOPRI8, in spite of its large redundancy with respect to the number of f-evaluations (cf. the discussion following Theorem 2.1). It is easily verified that this approach can offer sequential embedded RK methods of arbitrary order p, using $m \cdot s + 1 = (p^2 - p + 2)/2$ stages. This aspect, which is a direct consequence of the simplicity of the PIRK algorithm, needs further investigation.

REFERENCES

[1] **Butcher, J.C.** (1964): *Implicit Runge-Kutta processes*, Math. Comp. **18**, 50-64.

[2] **Curtis, A.R.** (1975): *High-order explicit Runge-Kutta formulae, their uses, and limitations*, J. Inst. Maths. Applics. **16**, 35-55.

[3] **Fehlberg, E.** (1968): *Classical fifth-, sixth-, seventh-, and eighth-order Runge-Kutta formulas with stepsize control*, NASA Technical Report 287, extract published in Computing **4** (1969), 93-106.

[4] **Hairer, E.** (1978): *A Runge-Kutta method of order 10*, J. Inst. Math. Applics. **21**, 47-59.

[5] **Hairer, E., Nørsett, S.P. & Wanner, G.** (1987): *Solving ordinary differential equations I. Nonstiff problems*, Springer Series in Comp. Math., Vol. **8**, Springer-Verlag, Berlin.

[6] **Houwen, P.J. van der** (1977): *Construction of integration formulas for initial value problems*, North-Holland, Amsterdam.

[7] **Houwen, P.J. van der, Sommeijer, B.P. & Mourik, P.A. van** (1989): *Note on explicit parallel multistep Runge-Kutta methods*, J. Comp. Appl. Math. **27**, 411-420.

[8] **Hull, T.E., Enright, W.H. , Fellen, B.M. & Sedgwick, A.E.** (1972): *Comparing numerical methods for ordinary differential equations*, SIAM J. Numer. Anal. **9**, 603-637.

[9] **Iserles, A. & Nørsett, S.P.** (1990): *On the theory of parallel Runge-Kutta methods*, IMA J. Numer. Anal. **10**, 463-488.

[10] **Jackson, K.R. & Nørsett, S.P.** (1988): *Parallel Runge-Kutta methods*, to appear .

[11] **Lie, I.** (1987): *Some aspects of parallel Runge-Kutta methods*, Report No. 3/87, University of Trondheim, Division Numerical Mathematics.

[12] **Nørsett, S.P. & Simonsen, H.H.** (1989): *Aspects of parallel Runge-Kutta methods*, in: A. Bellen (ed.): Workshop on Numerical Methods for Ordinary Differential Equations, L'Aquila, 1987, Lecture Notes in Mathematics, Vol. **1386**, Springer-Verlag, Berlin, 103-117.

[13] **Prince, P.J. & Dormand, J.R.** (1981): *High-order embedded Runge-Kutta formulae*, J. Comp. Appl. Math. **7**, 67-75.

APPENDIX

Here we give the implementation (in FORTRAN 77) of the optimal PIRK methods of the form (2.5), including error control. This subroutine offers the user the facility to specify an arbitrary Runge-Kutta method by means of the matrix A and the vectors b^T and c (see also the description of these parameters).

Although this routine has been coded in standard FORTRAN 77, it will require machine-dependent amendment as to exploit the parallelism. Therefore we shall discuss in some detail the most important loop in this subroutine, i.e., the 80-loop. It is here, that the parallel calculation of the components of the iterate $r^{(j)}$ is to be performed (cf. (2.2)). A first observation is that this loop contains a call to another subprogram (viz., FCN). The separate compilation of subprograms prevents the compiler from actually parallelising this loop, since it is unknown what happens within FCN. Nevertheless, if the present source is offered to a compiler without giving any instructions, the outcome (i.e., the 'optimized' object code) will be the product of all kinds of operations, like unravelling, interchanging, distributing loops etc., and will certainly speed up the execution. However, the parallelisation will probably not completely fit in with the ideas as advocated in the present paper. Therefore, we have to insert an explicit specification concerning the way the compiler has to do its job; for example, we can specify that it is in this case without any danger to parallelise over the FCN-calls. Most parallel computers offer so-called 'directives' for this purpose (e.g., using an Alliant, one can specify: cvd$ cncall). Since these directives may differ for various parallel machines, we decided to code this loop in standard FORTRAN.

Another observation is that the 80-loop contains two nested innerloops: one over the components of the ODE and one to form the innerproduct of a row of A and the iterate vector $r^{(j-1)}$. If the parallel machine at hand has an architecture in which each processor is a vectorprocessor, then it may be advantageous to interchange these innerloops. Such considerations depend on the dimension of the ODE, the startup time of the particular vectorprocessor, the 'smartness' of the compiler, etc.

To sum up, in order to obtain an optimal performance, the user of the subroutine PIRK is advised to adjust the 80-loop to the specific situation he is dealing with, like the number of processors available (perhaps even larger than s), the dimension of the problems to be solved, etc.

```
      SUBROUTINE PIRK(N, NR, FCN, T, Y, TEND, TOL, H, S, P,
     +                NRA, A, B, C, YN, FN, RJ, RJM1, BIGY, YREF)
C-----------------------------------------------------------------
C  PIRK SOLVES AN INITIAL VALUE PROBLEM FOR A SYSTEM OF FIRST-
C  ORDER DIFFERENTIAL EQUATIONS OF THE FORM Y'(T)=F(T,Y(T)).
C  THE ROUTINE IS BASED ON AN ITERATED RUNGE-KUTTA METHOD AND
C  DESIGNED IN SUCH A WAY THAT PARALLELISM IS EXPLOITED.
```

```
C  IN COUNTING THE NUMBER OF REQUIRED F-EVALUATIONS, IT IS
C  ASSUMED THAT THE NUMBER OF STAGES IN THE RUNGE-KUTTA METHOD
C  DOES NOT EXCEED THE NUMBER OF PROCESSORS AVAILABLE.
C
C  MEANING OF THE PARAMETERS:
C  --------------------------
C  N       -   INTEGER VARIABLE
C                 THE DIMENSION OF THE SYSTEM
C  NR      -   INTEGER VARIABLE
C                 FIRST DIMENSION OF THE ARRAYS RJ, RJM1 AND BIGY AS
C                 DECLARED IN THE CALLING PROGRAM (NR .GE. N)
C  FCN     -   SUBROUTINE
C                 A USER-DEFINED SUBROUTINE COMPUTING THE DERIVATIVE
C                 F(T,Y(T))
C                 ITS SPECIFICATION READS:
C                     SUBROUTINE FCN(N,T,Y,F)
C                     DIMENSION Y(N),F(N)
C
C                 ON RETURN, F(I) (I=1,...,N) MUST CONTAIN THE VALUE OF
C                 THE I-TH COMPONENT OF THE DERIVATIVE VECTOR
C                 FCN MUST BE DECLARED EXTERNAL IN THE CALLING PROGRAM
C  T       -   REAL VARIABLE
C                 THE INDEPENDENT VARIABLE; ON ENTRY, T SHOULD BE SET
C                 TO THE INITIAL VALUE. ON RETURN, T CONTAINS THE VALUE
C                 FOR WHICH Y IS THE SOLUTION
C  Y       -   REAL ARRAY OF DIMENSION (AT LEAST) N
C                 THE DEPENDENT VARIABLE. ON ENTRY, Y SHOULD CONTAIN THE
C                 INITIAL VALUES OF THE DEPENDENT VARIABLES.
C                 ON RETURN, Y CONTAINS THE NUMERICAL SOLUTION AT T
C  TEND    -   REAL VARIABLE
C                 TEND SPECIFIES THE END POINT OF THE INTEGRATION INTERVAL
C  TOL     -   REAL VARIABLE
C                 TOL (>0) SPECIFIES A BOUND FOR THE LOCAL TRUNCATION
C                 ERROR
C  H       -   REAL VARIABLE
C                 ON ENTRY, H SHOULD BE GIVEN A VALUE WHICH IS USED AS A
C                 GUESS FOR THE INITIAL STEPSIZE
C  S       -   INTEGER VARIABLE
C                 NUMBER OF STAGES OF THE SPECIFIED RUNGE-KUTTA METHOD
C  P       -   INTEGER VARIABLE
C                 ORDER OF ACCURACY OF THE SPECIFIED RUNGE-KUTTA METHOD
C  NRA     -   INTEGER VARIABLE
C                 FIRST DIMENSION OF THE ARRAY A AS DECLARED IN THE
C                 CALLING PROGRAM (NRA .GE. S)
C  A       -   REAL ARRAY OF DIMENSION (NRA,L) WITH L .GE. S
C  B       -   REAL ARRAY OF DIMENSION (AT LEAST) S
C  C       -   REAL ARRAY OF DIMENSION (AT LEAST) S
C
C                 THE PARAMETERS A, B AND C DEFINE THE RUNGE-KUTTA
C                 METHOD, WRITTEN IN THE SO-CALLED BUTCHER-NOTATION
C                 (USUALLY, THE ELEMENTS OF C ARE EQUAL TO THE ROW-SUMS
C                 OF THE MATRIX A).
C                 IN PRINCIPLE, ANY RUNGE-KUTTA METHOD CAN BE USED.
C                 HOWEVER, THE OPTIMAL ORDER WITH RESPECT TO THE
C                 NUMBER OF STAGES IS OBTAINED IF A 'GAUSS-LEGENDRE'
C                 METHOD IS SELECTED. THE CORRESPONDING A, B AND C CAN
```

```
C              BE FOUND IN:
C              J.C. BUTCHER, IMPLICIT RUNGE-KUTTA PROCESSES,
C                         MATH. COMP. 18 (1964) PP. 50-64
C YN     -   REAL ARRAY OF DIMENSION (AT LEAST) N
C              USED AS SCRATCH ARRAY
C FN     -   REAL ARRAY OF DIMENSION (AT LEAST) N
C              USED AS SCRATCH ARRAY
C RJ     -   REAL ARRAY OF DIMENSION (NR,L) WITH L .GE. S
C              USED AS SCRATCH ARRAY
C RJM1   -   REAL ARRAY OF DIMENSION (NR,L) WITH L .GE. S
C              USED AS SCRATCH ARRAY
C BIGY   -   REAL ARRAY OF DIMENSION (NR,L) WITH L .GE. S
C              USED AS SCRATCH ARRAY
C YREF   -   REAL ARRAY OF DIMENSION (AT LEAST) N
C              USED AS SCRATCH ARRAY
C------------------------------------------------------------------
      DIMENSION Y(N),YN(N),FN(N),YREF(N),RJ(NR,*),RJM1(NR,*),
     +          BIGY(NR,*),A(NRA,*),B(*),C(*)
      INTEGER S,P
      LOGICAL REJECT
C------------------------------------------------------------------
C  THE COMMON BLOCK STAT CAN BE USED FOR STATISTICS CONCERNING
C  THE INTEGRATION PROCESS
C     NFCN        NUMBER OF EVALUATIONS OF THE DERIVATIVE FUNCTION F
C     NSTEPS      NUMBER OF INTEGRATION STEPS
C     NACCPT      NUMBER OF ACCEPTED STEPS
C     NREJCT      NUMBER OF REJECTED STEPS
C------------------------------------------------------------------
      COMMON/STAT/NFCN,NSTEPS,NACCPT,NREJCT
C------------------------------------------------------------
C  SMALLEST NUMBER SATISFYING 1.0 + UROUND > 1.0
C  UROUND MAY REQUIRE AMENDMENT ON DIFFERENT MACHINES
C----------------------------------------------------------
      DATA UROUND/7.1E-15/
C------------------
C  INITIALISATIONS
C------------------
      REJECT=.FALSE.
      NFCN=0
      NSTEPS=0
      NACCPT=0
      NREJCT=0
      TOL=MAX(TOL,10.0*UROUND)
C----------------------------------------------------------------
C  ON ITERATING THE RUNGE-KUTTA METHOD, WE USE A PREDICTION
C  OF FIRST-ORDER. THEREFORE, WE NEED M=P-1 ITERATIONS TO
C  OBTAIN A RESULT OF ORDER P.
C----------------------------------------------------------------
      M=P-1
C-------------------
C  INTEGRATION STEP
C-------------------
  10  CONTINUE
      IF (H .LT. 10.0*UROUND) THEN
         WRITE(6,1)T
  1      FORMAT(' THE ROUTINE HAS ADVANCED THE SOLUTION UP TO
```

```
+          T=',E16.8,/,'  AND STOPPED BECAUSE THE STEP SIZE HAS',
      +          ' BECOME TOO SMALL'/'   TRY A LESS STRINGENT VALUE',
      +          ' OF TOL OR CHANGE TO A HIGHER-ORDER METHOD')
            RETURN
         ENDIF
         IF (TEND-T .LT. UROUND) RETURN
         IF (T+H .GT. TEND) H=TEND-T
C----------------------
C  FORM THE PREDICTION
C----------------------
         DO 20 I=1,N
  20        YN(I)=Y(I)
         CALL FCN(N,T,YN,FN)
         NFCN=NFCN+1
  30     NSTEPS=NSTEPS+1
         DO 50 L=1,S
            DO 40 I=1,N
  40           RJM1(I,L)=FN(I)
  50     CONTINUE
C--------------------------------------------------
C  IN THE 110-LOOP, THE ITERATION IS PERFORMED
C--------------------------------------------------
         DO 110 J=1,M
C-----------------------------------------------------------------
C  IN THE 80-LOOP, THE S STAGES ARE PERFORMED CONCURRENTLY
C-----------------------------------------------------------------
            DO 80 L=1,S
               DO 70 I=1,N
                  BIGY(I,L)=YN(I)
                  DO 60 K=1,S
  60              BIGY(I,L)=BIGY(I,L)+H*A(L,K)*RJM1(I,K)
  70           CONTINUE
               CALL FCN(N,T+C(L)*H,BIGY(1,L),RJ(1,L))
  80        CONTINUE
            NFCN=NFCN+1
C----------------------
C  SHIFT THE ITERATES
C----------------------
            IF (J .LT. M) THEN
               DO 100 L=1,S
                  DO 90 I=1,N
  90                 RJM1(I,L)=RJ(I,L)
 100           CONTINUE
            ENDIF
 110     CONTINUE
C--------------------------------------------------
C  CALCULATE THE FINAL SOLUTION OF THIS STEP
C  AND A REFERENCE SOLUTION FOR ERROR CONTROL
C--------------------------------------------------
         DO 130 I=1,N
            Y(I)=YN(I)
            YREF(I)=YN(I)
            DO 120 K=1,S
               Y(I)=Y(I)+H*B(K)*RJ(I,K)
 120           YREF(I)=YREF(I)+H*B(K)*RJM1(I,K)
 130     CONTINUE
```

```
C----------------
C  ERROR CONTROL
C----------------
        ERROR=0.0
        DO 140 I=1,N
            DENOM=MAX(1.0E-6, ABS(Y(I)), ABS(YN(I)), 2.0*UROUND/TOL)
  140       ERROR=ERROR+((Y(I)-YREF(I))/DENOM)**2
        ERROR=SQRT(ERROR/N)
        FAC=MAX(1.0/6.0,MIN(3.0,(ERROR/TOL)**(1.0/P)/0.9))
        HNEW=H/FAC
        IF (ERROR .GT. TOL) THEN
C--------------------
C  STEP IS REJECTED
C--------------------
            IF (NACCPT .GE. 1) NREJCT=NREJCT+1
            REJECT=.TRUE.
            H=HNEW
            GOTO 30
        ELSE
C--------------------
C  STEP IS ACCEPTED
C--------------------
            NACCPT=NACCPT+1
            T=T+H
            IF (REJECT) THEN
                HNEW=MIN(HNEW,H)
                REJECT=.FALSE.
            ENDIF
            H=HNEW
            GOTO 10
        ENDIF
        END
```

CHAPTER II

Block Runge-Kutta methods on parallel computers

Reprinted from

Z. Angew. Math. Mech. **72** (1) (1992), 3-18

with granted permission from AKADEMIE VERLAG

Block Runge-Kutta methods on parallel computers

P.J. van der Houwen and B.P. Sommeijer

CWI: Centre for Mathematics and Computer Science
Post box 94079, 1090 GB Amsterdam, The Netherlands

Abstract. In this paper block methods for solving ODEs on parallel computers are constructed. Most block methods found in the literature produce approximations to the exact solution at equidistant points. Here, we allow that the approximations correspond to nonequidistant points like the intermediate approximations computed in Runge-Kutta methods. This approach enables us to improve the order of accuracy. We concentrate on explicit methods such that they are suitable for use on parallel computers.

1991 Mathematics Subject Classification: 65L06
1991 CR Classification: G.1.7
Key Words: numerical analysis, stability, block Runge-Kutta methods, parallelism.

1. INTRODUCTION

Block methods turned out to be efficient methods for solving the initial value problem for the system of ordinary differential equations (ODEs)

$$\frac{dy(t)}{dt} = f(y(t))$$

on parallel computers (cf. e.g. Worland [10] and Chu & Hamilton [3]). Most block methods occurring in the literature can be interpreted as block linear multistep methods (BLM methods), that is, they are derived from the linear multistep (LM) method

$$\rho(E)y_n = h\sigma(E)f(y_n),$$

in which y_n is replaced by an m-dimensional vector $Y_n := (y_{nm}, y_{nm+1}, \dots, y_{nm+m-1})^T$ and where the (scalar) coefficients of the polynomials ρ and σ are replaced by matrices. Thus, in BLM methods the components of the block vector Y_n represent approximations to the exact solution at *equidistant* points.

In this paper, we consider block methods where the components of the block vector represent approximations to the exact solution at *not necessarily equidistant* points. In this way, we obtain additional parameters for increasing the order of accuracy of the method. In the derivation of these methods it turns out to be convenient to start with a Runge-Kutta (RK) method, and, by analogy with BLM methods, to replace the y-values generated by the method by vectors the components of which represent approximations to the exact solution. If these vectors are k-dimensional, then the RK parameters are replaced by k-by-k matrices. We shall call these methods *block Runge-Kutta methods* (BRK methods).

In Section 2, we give a precise definition of BRK methods and we give examples of methods from the literature which can be written as BRK methods. The representation in BRK form provides a unifying way of describing all sorts of methods (including BLM methods) and is particularly convenient for describing block methods for use on parallel computers. In Section 3 the order conditions for explicit one-stage methods and implicit two-stage methods are given, and Section 4 is devoted to the construction of these BRK methods with $k=2, 3, 4$. We shall particularly be interested in explicit methods. For explicit methods with given k we tried to maximize the order and to minimize the number of processors without increasing the number of sequential right-hand side evaluations per step (we shall call this minimal number of processors the *optimal* number of processors). It is possible to derive explicit one-stage methods of order $2k-1$, using not more than 2 processors. However, if the requirement of zero-stability is imposed (which is crucial if the method is to be used as a method on its own), then the order reduces to $k+1$. We also derive zero-stable, explicit two-stage methods of order $2k$ for two-processor computers. In Section 5, the various methods are compared for a few test problems from the literature.

It turned out that, like for all block methods, stability is a critical aspect of BRK methods. In this paper, we did not concentrate on stability aspects. Only when free parameters were available which could not be used for increasing the order, we have employed them to increase the stability of the method.

2. BLOCK RUNGE-KUTTA METHODS

Let us start with the conventional s-stage RK method

$$y_{n+1}^{(i)} = y_n + h \sum_{j=1}^{s} b_{ij} f(y_{n+1}^{(j)}), \quad i = 1, \dots, s+1;$$

(2.1)

$$y_{n+1} = y_{n+1}^{(s+1)}, \quad n = 0, 1, \dots .$$

The general structure of the block Runge-Kutta (BRK) methods considered in this paper is a direct generalization of this conventional method. We introduce block vectors Y_n, the components of which are numerical approximations to the exact solution values at k points. To be more precise, let Y_{n+1} be defined by

$$Y_{n+1} := (y_{n,c_1}, y_{n,c_2}, \dots, y_{n,c_k})^{\mathrm{T}}, \qquad c_k = 1,$$

where $y_{n,c}$ denotes a numerical approximation to the exact solution value $y(t_n+ch)$. For scalar ODEs, we now define the s-stage block RK (BRK) method

(2.1')
$$Y_{n+1}^{(i)} = A_i Y_n + h \sum_{j=1}^{s} B_{ij}\, f\!\left(Y_{n+1}^{(j)}\right), \quad i = 1, \dots, s+1;$$
$$Y_{n+1} = Y_{n+1}^{(s+1)}, \quad n = 0, 1, \dots,$$

where A_i and B_{ij} are k-by-k matrices and where we use the convention that for any given vector $v = (v_j)$, $f(v)$ denotes the vector with entries $f(v_j)$. This method can be considered as the block analogue of (2.1). It is straightforwardly extended to systems of ODEs and therefore also to nonautonomous equations. In order to start the method, one needs the initial vector Y_0, which requires as many starting values as there are distinct values c_j ($j=1,\dots,k$).

In analogy with the Butcher array for describing the RK methods (2.1), i.e., the $(s+1)$-by-$(s+1)$ array

$$
\begin{array}{c|ccc}
b_{11} & \cdot & \cdot & \cdot & b_{1s} \\
\cdot & \cdot & \cdot & \cdot & \cdot \\
\cdot & \cdot & \cdot & \cdot & \cdot \\
\cdot & \cdot & \cdot & \cdot & \cdot \\
b_{s,1} & \cdot & \cdot & \cdot & b_{s,s} \\
\hline
b_{s+1,1} & \cdot & \cdot & \cdot & b_{s+1,s}
\end{array}
$$

we may describe the BRK methods (2.1') by the $k(s+1)$-by-$k(s+1)$ array

$$
\begin{array}{c|ccc}
A_1 & B_{11} & \cdot & \cdot & \cdot & B_{1s} \\
\cdot & \cdot & \cdot & \cdot & \cdot & \cdot \\
\cdot & \cdot & \cdot & \cdot & \cdot & \cdot \\
A_s & B_{s1} & \cdot & \cdot & \cdot & B_{ss} \\
\hline
A_{s+1} & B_{s+1,1} & \cdot & \cdot & \cdot & B_{s+1,s}
\end{array}
$$

This notation is particularly convenient when more than two stages are involved. It frequently happens that the two last rows of this array are identical. In such cases, we shall omit the last row in order to save space.

We call the method *explicit* if the matrices B_{ij} vanish for $j \geq i$, and *implicit* otherwise. In this paper, we are mainly interested in *explicit* methods. For explicit methods, the k components of the blocks $f(Y_{n+1}^{(j)})$ can be computed in parallel; hence if k processors are available, then (explicit) BRK methods require not more than s (sequential) right-hand side evaluations per step. However, the required number of processors is often less than k, without causing the number of (sequential) right-hand side evaluations per step to exceed s. For instance, it may happen that in the formula for a particular component of Y_{n+1} no right-hand side evaluations occur, that is, all rows in the matrices B_{ij} corresponding to this component vanish. In such cases, the processor assigned to this component is not needed. Similarly, if the rth column of all matrices B_{ij} vanishes, then the computation of the corresponding component of Y_{n+1} does not require any right-hand side evaluation not already occurring in the formulas for the other components, so that there is no need to assign a processor to this component. We define the *optimal number of processors* as the number of processors for which the number of (sequential) right-hand side evaluations per step is minimal. In the explicit case, the representation (2.1') is very convenient for implementing the method on a computer, because the actual code is a direct translation of the formula (2.1') and the instructions for the computer in order to exploit the built-in parallelism of the method are obvious.

The points t_n and $t_n + c_j h$ $(j \neq k)$ will respectively be called *step points* and *block points*. Block points coincide with step points if the corresponding value of c_j is an integer. Upon completion of the integration process, the accuracy of the numerical solution obtained does not necessarily be the same at all points $t_n + c_j h$. Points where the corresponding components of Y_{n+1} do have the same order as the components corresponding to the step points t_n will be called *output points*.

The general explicit one- and two-stage methods are respectively given by

$$\begin{array}{c|c} A_1 & 0 \\ \hline A_2 & B_{21} \end{array} \quad , \qquad \text{i.e.,} \quad Y_{n+1} = A_2 Y_n + h B_{21} f(A_1 Y_n),$$

and

$$\begin{array}{c|cc} A_1 & 0 & 0 \\ A_2 & B_{21} & 0 \\ \hline A_3 & B_{31} & B_{32} \end{array} \quad , \qquad \begin{aligned} \text{i.e.,} \quad Y_{n+1} &= A_3 Y_n + h B_{31} f(A_1 Y_n) \\ &\quad + h B_{32} f(A_2 Y_n + h B_{21} f(A_1 Y_n)). \end{aligned}$$

Here, O denotes the k-by-k matrix with zero entries.

As a numerical example of an (explicit) 3-stage method, we present the modified multistep method of Butcher [1] of order 5 as a BRK method: the block point vector is given by $c = (0,1)^T$ and the Butcher array assumes the form:

$$
\begin{array}{cc|cccccc}
1 & 0 & & & & & & \\
0 & 1 & & & & & & \\
& & & & & & & \\
1 & 0 & 3/8 & 9/8 & & & & \\
0 & 1 & 0 & 0 & & & & \\
& & & & & & & \\
-23/5 & 28/5 & -26/15 & 0 & 32/15 & -4 & & \\
0 & 1 & 0 & 0 & 0 & 0 & & \\
\hline
0 & 1 & 0 & 0 & 0 & 0 & 0 & 0 \\
-1/31 & 32/31 & -1/93 & 12/93 & 64/93 & 0 & 15/93 & 0 \\
\end{array}
\quad , \quad c = (0, 1)^T.
$$

The construction of higher-order BRK methods is rather difficult in the general case. In this paper, we shall construct high-order methods of a special form which are obtained by using the predictor-corrector (PC) technique. Our starting point is the special implicit two-stage method

$$
(2.2) \qquad
\begin{array}{c|cc}
I & O & O \\
A & B & C \\
\hline
A & B & C \\
\end{array}
=
\begin{array}{c|cc}
I & O & O \\
A & B & C \\
\hline
A & B & C \\
\end{array}
\quad ,
$$

i.e., $\quad Y_{n+1} = AY_n + hBf(Y_n) + hCf(Y_{n+1})$.

If C does not vanish, then we can use this method as corrector and if $C=O$, then it can be used as (a one-stage) predictor formula, e.g.,

$$
(2.2') \qquad
\begin{array}{c|c}
I & O \\
\hline
A & B \\
\end{array}
\quad , \qquad
\text{i.e., } \quad Y_{n+1} = AY_n + hBf(Y_n).
$$

From this pair we can generate higher-stage BRK methods by PC iteration provided that the block point vectors $c:=(c_1,...,c_k)^T$ are identical. For example, in PECE mode we obtain the special two-stage BRK method

$$
\text{(2.3)} \quad
\begin{array}{c|cc}
I & O & O \\
D & E & O \\
\hline
A & B & C
\end{array}
\quad , \text{ i.e., } Y_{n+1} = AY_n + hBf(Y_n) + hCf(DY_n + hEf(Y_n)).
$$

Finally, it should be remarked that (2.2) is also the representation of the so-called *general linear methods* introduced by Butcher in 1966 (see Butcher [2]). Most methods from the literature (including the general BRK method (2.1')) can be cast into the form (2.2). However, although the original method is explicit, the general linear method version is often implicit. For example, the explicit two-stage BRK method (2.3) can be rewritten in the form (2.2) by redefining the matrices A, B and C in (2.2), but C will not be a zero matrix. Thus, for implementation of higher-stage BRK methods on parallel computers, the representation (2.2) is less suitable.

In the following subsections, we present in BRK form a number of methods which have been proposed for use on parallel computers. In particular, we give examples of the predictor-corrector methods of Miranker and Liniger [8] and Shampine and Watts (cf. Worland [10]), and the multi-block methods of Chu and Hamilton [3]. A discussion of block methods for parallel computation may be found in Gear [5].

2.1. Methods of Miranker and Liniger

The methods of Miranker and Liniger [8] can be presented as explicit, one-stage BRK methods. For example, their second-order method can be represented by the array

$$
\text{(2.4)} \quad
\begin{array}{cc|cc}
1 & 0 & & \\
0 & 1 & & \\
\hline
0 & 1 & 2 & 0 \\
0 & 1 & 1/2 & 1/2
\end{array}
\quad , \quad c = (2,1)^T,
$$

and their fourth-order method by

$$
\text{(2.5)} \quad
\begin{array}{cccc|cccc}
1 & 0 & 0 & 0 & & & & \\
0 & 1 & 0 & 0 & & & & \\
0 & 0 & 1 & 0 & & & & \\
0 & 0 & 0 & 1 & & & & \\
\hline
0 & 1 & 0 & 0 & 0 & 0 & 0 & 0 \\
0 & 0 & 0 & 1 & 0 & 0 & 0 & 0 \\
0 & 0 & 0 & 1 & -1/3 & 4/3 & 8/3 & -5/3 \\
0 & 0 & 0 & 1 & 1/24 & -5/24 & 9/24 & 19/24
\end{array}
\quad , \quad c = (-1,0,2,1)^T.
$$

Both methods require only two processors and respectively two and four starting values when implemented in BRK form.

2.2. Predictor-Corrector method of Shampine and Watts

The PC method of Shampine and Watts [9] is based on the block method of Clippinger and Dimsdale (1958), which can be presented in the form (2.2) as

$$
(2.6)\quad
\begin{array}{cc|cccc}
1 & 0 & & & & \\
0 & 1 & & & & \\
& & & & & \\
0 & 1 & 0 & 5/24 & 1/3 & -1/24 \\
0 & 1 & 0 & 1/6 & 2/3 & 1/6 \\
\end{array}
\quad,\qquad c = (1/2,\,1)^{\mathrm{T}},
$$

and on the predictor method defined by

$$
(2.7)\quad
\begin{array}{cccc|cccc}
1 & 0 & 0 & 0 & & & & \\
0 & 1 & 0 & 0 & & & & \\
0 & 0 & 1 & 0 & & & & \\
0 & 0 & 0 & 1 & & & & \\
\hline
0 & 0 & 1 & 0 & 0 & 0 & 0 & 0 \\
0 & 0 & 0 & 1 & 0 & 0 & 0 & 0 \\
0 & 1/3 & 1/3 & 1/3 & 0 & 1/4 & -1/3 & 13/12 \\
0 & 1/3 & 1/3 & 1/3 & 0 & 29/24 & -3 & 79/24 \\
\end{array}
\quad,\qquad c = (-1/2,\,0,\,1/2,\,1)^{\mathrm{T}}.
$$

Method (2.6) is one of the oldest block methods proposed in the literature. Shampine and Watts proved that this corrector method is fourth-order accurate at the step points. They also proved that the predictor method is third-order accurate and possesses favourable stability properties. This predictor can also be applied as a method on its own and requires four starting values and one processor.

In order to apply the PC pair (2.7)-(2.6) using the BRK format, we rewrite the corrector in the form

$$
\begin{array}{cccc|cccccccc}
1 & 0 & 0 & 0 \\
0 & 1 & 0 & 0 \\
0 & 0 & 1 & 0 \\
0 & 0 & 0 & 1 \\[4pt]
0 & 0 & 1 & 0 & 0 & 0 & 0 & 0 & 0 & 0 & 0 & 0 \\
0 & 0 & 0 & 1 & 0 & 0 & 0 & 0 & 0 & 0 & 0 & 0 \\
0 & 0 & 0 & 1 & 0 & 0 & 0 & 5/24 & 0 & 0 & 1/3 & -1/24 \\
0 & 0 & 0 & 1 & 0 & 0 & 0 & 1/6 & 0 & 0 & 2/3 & 1/6
\end{array}
$$

(2.6') $\rule{6cm}{0.4pt}$, $c = (-1/2, 0, 1/2, 1)^{\mathrm{T}}$.

The PC method of Shampine and Watts was implemented by Worland [10] on two processors.

2.3. Multi-block methods of Chu and Hamilton

Chu and Hamilton [3] generalized the cyclic linear multistep methods of Donelson and Hansen [4]. Families of third- and fourth-order multi-block methods were derived. We give two examples of their $k=2$ methods which can be represented in the form (2.2) or (2.2'). The first example is the explicit third-order method

(2.8)
$$
\begin{array}{cc|cc}
1 & 0 \\
0 & 1 \\[4pt]
5 & -4 & 1 & 2 \\
28 & -27 & 6 & 9
\end{array}
$$
, $c = (1/2, 1)^{\mathrm{T}}$,

and the second example is the fourth-order implicit method

(2.9)
$$
\begin{array}{cc|cccc}
1 & 0 \\
0 & 1 \\[4pt]
0 & 1 & -1/48 & 13/48 & 13/48 & -1/48 \\
0 & 1 & 0 & 1/6 & 2/3 & 1/6
\end{array}
$$
, $c = (1/2, 1)^{\mathrm{T}}$.

2.4. Parallel MRK methods

An example of methods which can be written in the form (2.3), and which do not originate from PECE methods, is the family of first-order, explicit parallel MRK methods (cf. van der Houwen et al. [6])

$$(2.10) \quad
\left[
\begin{array}{ccc|ccc}
1 & 0 & 0 & 0 & 0 & 0 \\
0 & 0 & 1 & 0 & 0 & 0 \\
0 & 1-a_1 & a_1 & 0 & 0 & 0 \\
\hline
0 & 0 & 1 & 0 & 0 & 0 \\
0 & 0 & 1 & 0 & \dfrac{b_3}{(1-a_1)} & 0 \\
0 & 0 & 1 & 1-c-b_1 & b_1 & c
\end{array}
\right], \qquad c = (0, c, 1)^{\mathrm{T}},$$

where a_1, b_1, b_3 and c are free parameters. Third-order accuracy is obtained by setting

$$a_1 := \frac{1}{2} + \frac{5}{6c} \pm \frac{1}{2}\sqrt{1 + \frac{10}{3c}}, \qquad b_1 = \frac{7}{3} - ca_1, \qquad b_3 = -\frac{5}{6c},$$

with c as a free parameter. These methods require three starting values and only one sequential right-hand side evaluation on two processors. Notice that (2.10) is of the *general* explicit one-stage form in which the matrix A_1 has not been replaced by the identity matrix as was the case in (2.2').

3. ORDER CONDITIONS

In this section, we restrict our considerations to parameter arrays of the form (2.2) either with $C=O$ or $C \neq O$. Let the exact solution be substituted into (2.2). Then, in general, the order conditions are derived by requiring that the residual vector is of order h^{p+1} for all components (that is, we require that all components of Y_{n+1} are pth-order approximations to the corresponding exact solution values). In this way, we obtain the following condition for pth-order consistency:

$$(I - zC)\exp(zc) - (A + zB)\exp(zc - ze) = O(z^{p+1}),$$
$$e := (1, 1, \dots, 1)^{\mathrm{T}}, \qquad c := (c_1, c_2, \dots, c_k)^{\mathrm{T}}.$$

By defining the error vectors

$$(3.1a) \quad
\begin{aligned}
&C_0 := Ae - e; \qquad C_1 := A(c - e) + Be + Ce - c; \\
&C_j := A(c - e)^j + j[B(c - e)^{j-1} + Cc^{j-1}] - c^j, \qquad j = 2, 3, \dots,
\end{aligned}$$

the conditions for pth-order consistency take the form

$$(3.1b) \quad C_j = 0, \quad j = 0, 1, \dots, p.$$

Here, powers of vectors are meant to be componentwise powers.

In the construction of high-order formulas it is convenient to specify the matrix A in (2.2) in advance, because the eigenvalues of A should lie in a zero-stable configuration, that is, they should be on the unit disc, those on the unit circle being simple (such a zero-stability condition is difficult to satisfy simultaneously with the order conditions unless k is sufficiently small). A natural choice for the matrix A is suggested by observing that

$$Y_{n+1} - y_n e \approx \left(\int_{t_n}^{t_n+c_j h} f(y(t)) dt \right).$$

Replacing the integral term by a quadrature formula, we obtain a method where A is of the form

$$(3.2) \qquad A := \begin{pmatrix} 0 & \cdots & 0 & 1 \\ \cdot & \cdots & \cdot & \cdot \\ 0 & \cdots & 0 & 1 \end{pmatrix}.$$

This matrix has one eigenvalue 1 and $k-1$ zero eigenvalues, so that a reasonable stability region may be expected (cf. the analogous situation for linear multistep methods of Adams-type). BRK methods possessing a matrix A of the form (3.2) will be called *Adams-type methods*.

Assuming that A is given and is such that $Ae=e$, the most simple way to derive high-order formulas is to specify the vector c. This leaves us with a linear system of p equations for each component formula of the corrector formula. However, in this approach, the free parameters in the vector c are not exploited. These free parameters may be used for minimizing the error vector C_{p+1}. For instance, we may add to the order conditions (3.1) the condition that c is such that $\| C_{p+1} \|$ is minimal for some norm $\| \cdot \|$. Alternatively, one may sacrifice the linearity of the order conditions and choose c such that certain components of the error vector vanish, that is, it is not necessary that all components of Y_{n+1} are pth-order approximations.

To be more general, we denote the order of consistency of the formula for y_{n,c_i} by p_i and define the set $J_q := \{ i \in \{1, 2, ..., k\} | p_i = q \}$. Now, we introduce the following property:

Property 3.1.   (i) $J_p \cup J_{p-1} = \{1, 2, ..., k\}$,

              (ii)   for each $i \in J_p$, the matrix A has vanishing elements a_{ij} for all $j \in J_{p-1}$.

If this property is satisfied, then the method (2.2) produces pth-order results at the points t_n+c_ih, $n=1,2,...$ and all $i\in J_p$. One may interpret this as a form of super-convergence.

As an example, in the Adams-type BRK methods with matrix A of the form (3.2), the first $k-1$ components of Y_n only occur in the right-hand side as argument of the function f, so that these components are allowed to be of one order less than the order of y_n, without decreasing the order of the approximations at the points t_n.

We recall that from an explicit and implicit BRK method with identical block point vector $c:=(c_1,...,c_k)^T$, we can derive higher-stage BRK methods by PC iteration. By requiring that the explicit method (predictor) and the implicit method (corrector) provide approximations to $y(t_n+c_jh)$, respectively of orders q and p, for all j, we obtain after r iterations a method which provides approximations of order $p^*=\min\{p, q+r\}$. Since the predictor need not to be stable, one can employ the full freedom of the generating matrices, so that q is usually sufficiently large to get the maximal attainable order p of the corrector in just one correction (PECE mode). If not, then one may decide to continue the iteration.

4. CONSTRUCTION OF BRK METHODS

Since the implementational complexity of the BRK method is mainly determined by the number of starting values and the associated storage needed to implement the method, we shall distinguish the various methods by their number of starting values. The methods constructed in the following subsections will be compared with methods from the literature.

4.1. Methods requiring two starting values

In this subsection we consider methods where the block vector Y_n is defined by

$$Y_{n+1} := (y_{n,c}, y_{n+1})^T.$$

At first sight, it would be natural to choose $c=1/2$. However, as we shall see, a more judicious choice is possible.

4.1.1. Explicit one-stage methods. We shall construct the family of second-order BRK methods of Adams-type and the general family of third-order methods.

Second-order methods of Adams-type. The conditions (3.1) with $C=O$ and A defined by (3.2) can be satisfied for $p=2$ and yield

58

$$(4.1) \quad \frac{\begin{array}{cc} 1 & 0 \\ 0 & 1 \end{array}}{\begin{array}{cc|cc} 0 & 1 & \dfrac{-c^2}{2(1-c)} & \dfrac{c(2-c)}{2(1-c)} \\ 0 & 1 & \dfrac{-1}{2(1-c)} & \dfrac{3-2c}{2(1-c)} \end{array}} \quad , \quad c = (c, 1)^T, \; c \neq 1,$$

with error vector

$$(4.2) \qquad C_3 = \frac{1}{2} \begin{pmatrix} c^2(c-3) \\ 3c-5 \end{pmatrix}.$$

The following special cases of (4.1) will be tested in the numerical experiments at the end of this section:

$c = 0$	(4.1) reduces to the Adams-Bashforth method	$C_3 = (\,0.0, -2.5)^T$
$c = 1/2$	'natural choice'	$C_3 \approx (-0.3, -1.8)^T$
$c = 5/3$	Local error at t_{n+1} is $O(h^4)$	$C_3 \approx (-1.9, \; 0.0)^T$
$c = 2$	(4.1) reduces to Miranker-Liniger method (2.4)	$C_3 = (-2.0, +0.5)^T$
$c = 1+4^{1/3}$	$\|C_3\|_\infty$ minimized	$C_3 \approx (-1.4, +1.4)^T$
$c = 3$	Local error at t_n+ch is $O(h^4)$	$C_3 = (\,0.0, +2.0)^T$

We observe that the case $c=5/3$ will raise the order to 3 at all step points t_n, in spite of the second-order accuracy of $y_{n,c}$, because of the special form of the matrix A (cf. Property 3.1).

Third-order methods. Next we construct the family of one-stage BRK methods in which all components are at least of third order. We find the method

$$(4.3) \quad \frac{\begin{array}{cc} 1 & 0 \\ 0 & 1 \end{array}}{\begin{array}{cc|cc} \dfrac{c^2(3-c)}{(1-c)^3} & \dfrac{1-3c}{(1-c)^3} & \dfrac{c^2}{(1-c)^2} & \dfrac{c}{(1-c)^2} \\ \dfrac{5-3c}{(1-c)^3} & \dfrac{-c^3+3c^2-4}{(1-c)^3} & \dfrac{2-c}{(1-c)^2} & \dfrac{(2-c)^2}{(1-c)^2} \end{array}} \quad , \quad c = (c, 1)^T, \; c \neq 1,$$

with error vector

$$C_4 = \begin{pmatrix} -c^2 \\ -(2-c)^2 \end{pmatrix}.$$

This method is zero-stable for all values of c for which the eigenvalues of A are on the unit disc and are not both equal to 1. Since A has the eigenvalues 1 and $(c^2-2c-5)/(c-1)^2$, we obtain the condition

$$-1 \le \lambda < 1, \qquad \lambda := \frac{c^2-2c-5}{(c-1)^2}.$$

This leads to the necessary condition

(4.4) $\qquad c \le 1 - \sqrt{3}, \qquad c \ge 1 + \sqrt{3}.$

The parasitic eigenvalue λ vanishes for $c=1\pm\sqrt{6}$. Unfortunately, the value $c=2$ which makes y_{n+1} fourth-order accurate is not in the range (4.4). If $c=1/2$, then the method reduces to the method (2.8) of Chu and Hamilton.

A number of experiments was carried out in order to illustrate the effect of c on the accuracy of the methods (4.1) and (4.3). We chose the nonlinear initial value problem

(4.5) $\qquad y'(t) = \sin(y^5) - \sin(\sin^5(t)) + \cos(t), \qquad y(0) = 0, \qquad 0 \le t \le 1,$

with exact solution $y(t)=\sin(t)$.

In Table 4.1 the results are given. The absolute error obtained at the end point of the integration interval is written in the form 10^{-d} and the values of d are given in the table (d may be interpreted as the number of correct decimal digits). Each column contains results which required the same number of sequential right-hand sides. In these and subsequent experiments, the starting values incorporated in the initial vector Y_0 are taken from the exact solution.

These results show the theoretical order of accuracy. It is clear that the choice $c=1/2$ is not the best possible. Furthermore, the value $c=1+4^{1/3}$ (minimal-norm-value) does not improve the accuracy, so that we refrain from considering this special case in the subsequent sections. Notice that the method (4.1) with $c=5/3$ produces results which are comparable with the results of the method (4.3) with $c=1\pm\sqrt{6}$.

Table 4.1. Correct decimal digits at $t=1$ for problem (4.5) obtained by BRK methods with $k=2$ and $s=1$.

Sequential right-hand sides	6	12	24	48	96	order
Adams-Bashforth method	1.8	2.4	3.0	3.6	4.2	2
Miranker-Liniger method (2.4)	2.7	3.2	3.7	4.3	4.9	2
BRK method (4.1): $c=1/2$	2.0	2.5	3.1	3.7	4.4	2
BRK method (4.1): $c=1+4^{1/3}$	2.1	2.7	3.3	3.9	4.5	2
BRK method (4.1): $c=3$	1.9	2.5	3.1	3.7	4.3	2
BRK method (4.1): $c=5/3$	3.1	4.0	5.0	5.9	6.8	3
BRK method (4.3): $c=1+\sqrt{6}$	3.1	4.0	4.9	5.8	6.7	3
BRK method (4.3): $c=1-\sqrt{6}$	3.3	4.1	4.9	5.8	6.7	3

4.1.2. Implicit two-stage methods of Adams-type.

The conditions (3.1) with nonvanishing matrix C can be satisfied for $p=4$ by

$$(4.6) \quad
\begin{array}{cc|cccc}
1 & 0 & & & & \\
0 & 1 & & & & \\
0 & 1 & \dfrac{-c^3}{12(1-c)} & \dfrac{c(c^2-6c+6)}{12(1-c)} & \dfrac{c(c^2-6c+6)}{12(1-c)} & \dfrac{-c^3}{12(1-c)} \\[2ex]
0 & 1 & \dfrac{(1-2c)}{12(1-c)(2-c)} & \dfrac{-6c^2+10c-3}{12c(1-c)} & \dfrac{3-2c}{12c(1-c)} & \dfrac{6c^2-14c+7}{12(1-c)(2-c)} \\
\end{array}$$

with $c = (c, 1)^T$, $c \neq 0, 1, 2$.

The corresponding error vector is given by

$$C_5 = -\frac{1}{6} \begin{pmatrix} c^3(c^2 - 5c + 5) \\ 5c^2 - 10c + 4 \end{pmatrix}.$$

The following special cases of (4.6) will be considered:

$c = \dfrac{1}{2}$	(4.6) is equivalent with the corrector (2.9)	$C_5 = \left(-\dfrac{11}{192}, -\dfrac{8}{192}\right)^T$
$c = 1 - \dfrac{\sqrt{5}}{5}$	Local error at t_{n+1} is $O(h^6)$	$C_5 = \left(-\dfrac{4\sqrt{5}}{125}, 0\right)^T$

4.1.3. Predictor-corrector methods.

In order to 'solve' the corrector equation defined by (4.6) one may use a PC method with predictor defined by (4.3). The PC methods determined by the matrices (4.3)-(4.6) require two starting values and, in PECE mode, they all have at least order 4. For $c=1-\sqrt{5}/5$, we achieve order 5 in PE(CE)^2

mode. We remark that for the predictor formula, the value of c is not required to satisfy the inequalities (4.4).

We illustrate the performance of the PC method (4.3)-(4.6) by comparing it with the 2-step Adams PC method (notice that the BRK method (4.3)-(4.6) with $c=1/2$ is equivalent with the Chu-Hamilton pair (2.8)-(2.9)). In the Tables 4.2, the correct decimal digits at $t=1$ and the total numbers of sequential right-hand side evaluations are listed for the various methods in PECE mode and in $PE(CE)^2$ mode.

Table 4.2a. Correct decimal digits at $t=1$ for problem (4.5) obtained by BRK methods in PECE mode with $k=2$.

Sequential right-hand sides	6	12	24	48	96	order
Two-step Adams-PC method	2.1	3.1	4.1	5.0	5.9	3
Chu-Hamilton pair (2.8)-(2.9)	4.3	5.4	6.5	7.6	8.7	4
BRK method (4.3)-(4.6): $c=1-\sqrt{5}/5$	4.8	5.4	6.5	7.6	8.8	4

Table 4.2b. Correct decimal digits at $t=1$ for problem (4.5) obtained by BRK methods in $PE(CE)^2$ mode with $k=2$.

Sequential right-hand sides	6	12	24	48	96	order
Two-step Adams-PC method	1.8	3.1	4.2	5.1	6.0	3
Chu-Hamilton pair (2.8)-(2.9)	3.9	5.7	9.3	8.4	9.5	4
BRK method (4.3)-(4.6): $c=1-\sqrt{5}/5$	3.9	5.5	7.0	8.5	10.0	5

4.2. Methods requiring three starting values

The block vector Y_n is now defined by

$$Y_{n+1} := (y_{n,c_1}, y_{n,c_2}, y_{n+1})^T,$$

providing us with two free parameters. As before, equidistant output points need not to be the best choice. Because of the rapidly increasing complexity of the derivations if more than 2 starting values are used, we shall not consider the general case as in the preceding section, but we shall restrict our considerations to a few special cases.

4.2.1. Explicit one-stage methods. We consider Adams-type methods and a more general family of zero-stable methods.

Third-order methods of Adams-type. If $C=O$, then the following array satisfies the conditions (3.1) for $p=3$ and for all (distinct) values of c_1 and c_2 different from 1:

$$(4.7) \quad
\begin{array}{ccc|ccc}
1 & 0 & 0 & & & \\
0 & 1 & 0 & & & \\
0 & 0 & 1 & & & \\
\hline
0 & 0 & 1 & a_1 - (c_2-1)b_1 & (c_1-1)b_1 & c_1 - a_1 + (c_2-c_1)b_1 \\
0 & 0 & 1 & a_2 - (c_2-1)b_2 & (c_1-1)b_2 & c_2 - a_2 + (c_2-c_1)b_2 \\
0 & 0 & 1 & a_3 - (c_2-1)b_3 & (c_1-1)b_3 & c_3 - a_3 + (c_2-c_1)b_3
\end{array} \quad ,$$

where $c = (c_1, c_2, 1)^T$ and

$$a_i := \frac{c_i^2}{2(c_1 - 1)}, \qquad b_i := \frac{c_i^2(2c_i - 3c_1 + 3)}{6(c_1 - 1)(c_2 - 1)(c_2 - c_1)}, \qquad i = 1, 2, 3.$$

We restrict our considerations to the two-processor case, that is, we set $c_1=0$. By virtue of the special form of A we obtain order $p=4$ at the step points if the third formula has order 4 while the first and second formula have order 3. Setting the third error component equal to zero we find $c_2=17/10$.

Fourth-order methods. Let us consider methods of the form

$$(4.8) \quad
\begin{array}{ccc|ccc}
1 & 0 & 0 & & & \\
0 & 1 & 0 & & & \\
0 & 0 & 1 & & & \\
\hline
0 & 0 & 1 & 0 & 0 & 0 \\
a_{21} & a_{22} & a_{23} & b_{21} & b_{22} & b_{23} \\
a_{31} & a_{32} & a_{33} & b_{31} & b_{32} & b_{33}
\end{array} \quad , \qquad c = (0, c, 1)^T.$$

Solving the conditions (3.1) for $p=4$ with $c=1/2$ we obtain

$$
\begin{array}{ccc|ccc}
1 & 0 & 0 & & & \\
0 & 1 & 0 & & & \\
0 & 0 & 1 & & & \\
\hline
0 & 0 & 1 & 0 & 0 & 0 \\
-9-a & 9 & 1+a & (-10-a)/6 & (-22-4a)/6 & (8-a)/6 \\
-b & 64 & -63+b & (-9-b)/6 & (108-4b)/6 & (99-b)/6
\end{array} \quad , \qquad c = (0, 1/2, 1)^T,
$$

where a and b are free parameters. We could have used these parameters for increasing the order of accuracy to $p=5$. However, then the method turns out to be zero-unstable. Therefore, we shall employ them for improving the stability of the method. In particular, we choose a and b such that the parasitic roots of the characteristic equation of A vanish. This characteristic equation is given by

$$(\delta - 1)\left(\delta^2 + (55 - b)\delta + 9b - 64a - 576\right) = 0,$$

so that we are led to the values $a = -81/64$ and $b = 55$. The corresponding Butcher array becomes

(4.9)

$$
\begin{array}{ccc|ccc}
1 & 0 & 0 & & & \\
0 & 1 & 0 & & & \\
0 & 0 & 1 & & & \\
\hline
0 & 0 & 1 & 0 & 0 & 0 \\
-495/64 & 9 & -17/64 & -559/384 & -271/96 & 593/384 \\
-55 & 64 & -8 & -32/3 & -56/3 & 22/3
\end{array}
$$

, $c = (0, 1/2, 1)^T$.

The following table illustrates the performance of the above explicit, one-stage methods.

Table 4.3. Correct decimal digits at $t=1$ for problem (4.5) obtained by BRK methods with $k=3$ and $s=1$.

Sequential right-hand sides	6	12	24	48	96	order
Adams-Bashforth	3.2	3.9	4.8	5.6	6.5	3
BRK method (4.7): $(c_1,c_2) = (0,1/2)$	3.4	4.2	5.1	6.0	6.9	3
BRK method (4.7): $(c_1,c_2) = (0,17/10)$	4.1	5.3	6.5	7.7	8.9	4
BRK method (4.9)	4.0	5.1	6.4	7.6	8.8	4

4.2.2. Implicit two-stage methods. We assume the generating array of the form

(4.10)

$$
\begin{array}{ccc|ccc|ccc}
1 & 0 & 0 & & & & & & \\
0 & 1 & 0 & & & & & & \\
0 & 0 & 1 & & & & & & \\
\hline
0 & 0 & 1 & 0 & 0 & 0 & 0 & 0 & 0 \\
a_{21} & a_{22} & a_{23} & b_{21} & b_{22} & b_{23} & 0 & c_{22} & c_{23} \\
a_{31} & a_{32} & a_{33} & b_{31} & b_{32} & b_{33} & 0 & c_{32} & c_{33}
\end{array}
$$

with $c = (0, c, 1)^T$ and we derive a fifth-order method of Adams-type and a sixth-order method with increased stability interval which is not of Adams-type.

Adams-type method of order 5. We choose $c=1/2$ and A of the form (3.2), and find that the order conditions (3.1) can be satisfied for $p=5$ by

(4.11)

1	0	0							
0	1	0							
0	0	1							
0	0	1	0	0	0	0	0	0	
0	0	1	11/1440	−37/720	19/60	0	173/720	−19/1440	
0	0	1	−1/180	1/45	2/15	0	31/45	29/180	

with $c = (0, 1/2, 1)^T$.

4.2.3. Predictor-corrector methods. We consider two PC methods which are in PECE mode of orders 5 and 6, respectively.

Method of order 5. The fourth-order predictor (4.9) and the fifth-order corrector (4.11) determine a PC method of order $p=5$. It requires three starting values and, if two processors are available, then only two sequential right-hand side evaluations per step are needed.

Method of order 6. Next we consider PC methods where the predictor and corrector are generated by matrices of the form (4.8) and (4.10), and where c is still a free parameter. We try to construct a PC method which is of order 6 in PECE mode by choosing the free parameters such that the corrector formula for y_{n+1} becomes of order $p=6$, whereas the other corrector formula and the two predictor formulas have order $p=5$.

To that purpose, we have investigated methods where

$$A := \begin{pmatrix} 0 & 0 & 1 \\ 0 & 0 & 1 \\ a & 0 & 1-a \end{pmatrix}$$

(notice that A does not refer to the second component of the block vector so that the corrector formula corresponding to this component may be of one order less than that of the third component). This leads to a one-parameter family of sixth-order PECE methods which can be represented in the form (2.3), i.e.,

$$Y_{n+1} = AY_n + hBf(Y_n) + hCf(DY_n + hEf(Y_n)).$$

The free parameter will be used to improve the (linear) stability of the method. The (linear) stability of this two-stage BRK method can be investigated by applying the method to the test equation $y' = \lambda y$ to obtain the recursion

$$Y_{n+1} = R(z)\, Y_n, \qquad R(z) := A + z(B + CD) + z^2 CE, \qquad z := \lambda h,$$

and by requiring that the matrix R satisfies the simple Von Neumann stability condition, that is, it has its eigenvalues on the unit disc those on the unit circle being simple. Choosing c as the free parameter, we start with determining a range of relevant c-values by requiring that $R(0)$ satisfies the stability condition (zero-stability). Since the eigenvalues of $R(0)=A$ are given by 0, 1 and $-a$, we require $-1 \le -a < 1$. It can be shown that imposing the conditions for sixth-order accuracy on the corrector formula for y_{n+1} leads to

$$a = \frac{15c^2 - 31c + 13}{15c^2 + c - 3},$$

so that c should be not less that $1/2$ in order to ensure zero-stability. As before, we shall not consider the maximization of the general stability boundary. Instead we consider the simpler case of maximizing the *real* stability boundary. A numerical search reveals that the real stability boundary is maximized for $c \approx 4.16$ and is approximately given by 2.247. In order to obtain (simple) rational expressions for the entries of the various matrices, we do not choose this 'optimal' value of c, but we set $c = 4$ yielding the stability boundary 1.766.

The predictor is generated by the matrices

$$(4.12) \qquad \left[\begin{array}{ccc|ccc}
1 & 0 & 0 & & & \\
0 & 1 & 0 & & & \\
0 & 0 & 1 & & & \\
\hline
0 & 0 & 1 & 0 & 0 & 0 \\
\dfrac{27}{2} & \dfrac{-25}{54} & \dfrac{-325}{27} & 5 & \dfrac{25}{9} & \dfrac{100}{9} \\
\dfrac{3}{2} & \dfrac{5}{54} & \dfrac{-16}{27} & \dfrac{1}{2} & \dfrac{-1}{18} & \dfrac{16}{9}
\end{array}\right], \qquad c = (0, 4, 1)^{\mathrm{T}}$$

and the corrector by

(4.13)

$$
\begin{array}{ccc|cccccc}
1 & 0 & 0 & & & & & & \\
0 & 1 & 0 & & & & & & \\
0 & 0 & 1 & & & & & & \\
\hline
0 & 0 & 1 & 0 & 0 & 0 & 0 & 0 & 0 \\
0 & 0 & 1 & \dfrac{4}{75} & \dfrac{76}{45} & \dfrac{2}{45} & 0 & \dfrac{58}{225} & \dfrac{88}{45} \\
\dfrac{129}{241} & 0 & \dfrac{112}{241} & \dfrac{1141}{7230} & \dfrac{-47}{4338} & \dfrac{2110}{2169} & 0 & \dfrac{26}{10845} & \dfrac{896}{2169}
\end{array}
$$

with $c = (0, 4, 1)^{\mathrm{T}}$.

The following table is the $k=3$ analogue of the preceding tables:

Table 4.4. Correct decimal digits at $t=1$ for problem (4.5) obtained
by BRK methods in PECE mode with $k=3$.

Sequential right-hand sides	6	12	24	48	96	order
Three-step Adams-PC method	3.6	4.5	5.7	6.9	8.1	4
BRK method (4.9)-(4.11)	4.5	6.0	7.5	9.0	10.5	5
BRK method (4.12)-(4.13)	5.0	6.9	8.9	10.9	13.0	6

4.3. Predictor-Corrector method requiring four starting values

We have searched for two-processor predictors in the class of methods of the form

$$
\begin{array}{cccc|cccc}
1 & 0 & 0 & 0 & & & & \\
0 & 1 & 0 & 0 & & & & \\
0 & 0 & 1 & 0 & & & & \\
0 & 0 & 0 & 1 & & & & \\
\hline
0 & 1 & 0 & 0 & 0 & 0 & 0 & 0 \\
0 & 0 & 0 & 1 & 0 & 0 & 0 & 0 \\
a_{31} & a_{32} & a_{33} & a_{34} & b_{31} & b_{32} & b_{33} & b_{34} \\
a_{41} & a_{42} & a_{43} & a_{44} & b_{41} & b_{42} & b_{43} & b_{44}
\end{array}
\quad , \quad c = (-1, 0, c, 1)^{\mathrm{T}}.
$$

For a given value of c we can achieve order 7 by solving two linear systems of 8 equations each in 8 unknowns.

The corrector was chosen such that

$$
\left[
\begin{array}{cccc|cccc|cccc}
1 & 0 & 0 & 0 & & & & & & & & \\
0 & 1 & 0 & 0 & & & & & & & & \\
0 & 0 & 1 & 0 & & & & & & & & \\
0 & 0 & 0 & 1 & & & & & & & & \\
0 & 1 & 0 & 0 & 0 & 0 & 0 & 0 & 0 & 0 & 0 & 0 \\
0 & 0 & 0 & 1 & 0 & 0 & 0 & 0 & 0 & 0 & 0 & 0 \\
a_{31} & a_{32} & 0 & 1-a_{31}-a_{32} & b_{31} & b_{32} & b_{33} & b_{34} & 0 & 0 & c_{33} & c_{34} \\
a_{41} & a_{42} & 0 & 1-a_{41}-a_{42} & b_{41} & b_{42} & b_{43} & b_{44} & 0 & 0 & c_{43} & c_{44}
\end{array}
\right]
$$

with $c = (-1, 0, c, 1)^{\mathrm{T}}$.

By this choice we achieve that the order conditions (3.1) simplify considerably. Given the value of c, this method can be made order 8 accurate in each component equation, again by solving two linear systems of 8 equations in 8 unknowns. These four systems of 8 equations have been solved numerically in terms of the parameter c and for a range of c-values we computed the real stability boundary β_{real} of the PECE mode. We found that β_{real} was maximal for $c \approx 2.58$ ($\beta_{\mathrm{real}} \approx 0.358$). In order to obtain a method with (simple) rational parameter values we chose $c = 5/2$ resulting in $\beta_{\mathrm{real}} \approx 0.302$. The corresponding predictor is generated by

$$
(4.14) \quad
\left[
\begin{array}{cccc|cccc}
1 & 0 & 0 & 0 & & & & \\
0 & 1 & 0 & 0 & & & & \\
0 & 0 & 1 & 0 & & & & \\
0 & 0 & 0 & 1 & & & & \\
0 & 1 & 0 & 0 & 0 & 0 & 0 & 0 \\
0 & 0 & 0 & 1 & 0 & 0 & 0 & 0 \\
\dfrac{5975}{224} & \dfrac{1539}{20} & -\dfrac{537}{35} & -\dfrac{2793}{32} & \dfrac{225}{32} & \dfrac{567}{8} & 9 & \dfrac{2205}{32} \\
\dfrac{82}{343} & \dfrac{117}{125} & \dfrac{63232}{128625} & -\dfrac{2}{3} & \dfrac{3}{49} & \dfrac{18}{25} & -\dfrac{128}{1225} & 1
\end{array}
\right] ,
$$

with $c = (-1, 0, 5/2, 1)^{\mathrm{T}}$; the corresponding corrector is defined by

$$
\begin{array}{c|cc}
I & O & O \\
A & B & C
\end{array}
$$

(4.15)

where

$$
A = \frac{1}{30469}
\begin{pmatrix}
0 & 1 & 0 & 0 \\
0 & 0 & 0 & 1 \\
\frac{5^3 \cdot 7^3 \cdot 13 \cdot 83}{2^{10}} & \frac{3^6 \cdot 5^3 \cdot 263}{2^7} & 0 & -\frac{3^6 \cdot 7^3 \cdot 827}{2^{10}} \\
4549 & 3^3 \cdot 1039 & 0 & -3^3 \cdot 79
\end{pmatrix},
$$

$$
B = \frac{1}{30469}
\begin{pmatrix}
0 & 0 & 0 & 0 \\
0 & 0 & 0 & 0 \\
\frac{3^3 \cdot 5^4 \cdot 7^3}{2^9} & \frac{3^6 \cdot 5^2 \cdot 7 \cdot 17 \cdot 67}{2^{10}} & \frac{3^5 \cdot 5^2 \cdot 7^3}{2^5} & \frac{3^5 \cdot 5 \cdot 7^3 \cdot 13}{2^5} \\
\frac{23029}{3 \cdot 7} & \frac{3^3 \cdot 13 \cdot 1709}{5 \cdot 7} & -\frac{2^8 \cdot 3^2 \cdot 31}{5 \cdot 7} & \frac{3^2 \cdot 61 \cdot 337}{5}
\end{pmatrix},
$$

$$
C = \frac{1}{30469}
\begin{pmatrix}
0 & 0 & 0 & 0 \\
0 & 0 & 0 & 0 \\
0 & 0 & \frac{3^2 \cdot 5 \cdot 7 \cdot 809}{2^5} & -\frac{3^3 \cdot 5^3 \cdot 7^3 \cdot 37}{2^{10}} \\
0 & 0 & \frac{2^9 \cdot 11}{3 \cdot 5 \cdot 7} & 14369
\end{pmatrix},
$$

and $c = (-1, 0, 5/2, 1)^T$. Table 4.5 compares this method in PECE mode with the four-step Adams and four-step Shampine-Watts method.

Table 4.5. Correct decimal digits at $t=1$ for problem (4.5) obtained by BRK methods in PECE mode with $k=4$.

Sequential right-hand sides	6	12	24	48	96	order
Four-step Adams-PC method	3.3	4.8	6.4	7.9	9.5	5
Shampine-Watts pair (2.7)-(2.6')	3.6	4.8	6.0	7.2	8.4	4
BRK pair (4.14)-(4.15)	7.3	10.2	12.8			8

5. SUMMARY OF METHODS AND NUMERICAL EXAMPLES

The explicit, zero-stable methods and the PC combinations discussed in the preceding sections will be applied to a number of initial value problems. In addition, we give the results obtained by the classical Adams formulas. First, however, we summarize the main characteristics of the various methods.

5.1. Summary of methods

Below we have listed a few important features such as the block point vector c, the order p, and the number of processors P_{opt} needed to implement the method with only one right-hand side evaluation per step.

Table 5.1a. Survey of explicit one-stage BRK methods of the form (2.2').

Reference	c^T	P_{opt}	p	Remarks
Miranker-Liniger [8]	$(2,1)$	2	2	See (2.4)
	$(-1,0,2,1)$	2	4	See (2.5)
Shampine-Watts [9]	$(-1/2,0,1/2,1)$	1	3	See (2.7)
Chu-Hamilton [3]	$(1/2,1)$	2	3	See (2.8)
This paper	$(c,1)$	2	3	See (4.1) with $c=5/3$
	$(c,1)$	2	3	See (4.3)
	$(c_1,c_2,1)$	2	3	See (4.7)
	$(c_1,c_2,1)$	2	4	See (4.7) with $(c_1,c_2) = (0,17/10)$
	$(0,1/2,1)$	2	4	See (4.9)
	$(0,4,1)$	2	5	See (4.12)
	$(-1,0,5/2,1)$	2	7	See (4.14)

Table 5.1b. Survey of implicit BRK methods of the form (2.2).

Reference	c^T	P_{opt}	p	Remarks
Clippinger-Dimsdale	$(1/2,1)$	2	4	See (2.6)
Chu-Hamilton [3]	$(1/2,1)$	2	4	See (2.9)
This paper	$(c,1)$	2	5	See (4.6) with $c=1-\sqrt{5}/5$
	$(0,1/2,1)$	2	5	See (4.11)
	$(0,4,1)$	2	6	See (4.13)
	$(-1,0,5/2,1)$	2	8	See (4.15)

Table 5.1c. Survey of PC pairs in PE(CE)^r mode.

Predictor	Corrector	c^T	p	r
(2.7)	(2.6')	$(-1/2,0,1/2,1)$	4	1
(2.8)	(2.9)	$(1/2,1)$	4	1
(4.3) with $c=1-\sqrt{5}/5$	(4.6) with $c=1-\sqrt{5}/5$	$(c,1)$	5	2
(4.9)	(4.11)	$(0,1/2,1)$	5	1
(4.12)	(4.13)	$(0,4,1)$	6	1
(4.14)	(4.15)	$(-1,0,5/2,1)$	8	1

5.2. Nonlinear problem with rapidly increasing solution

The first test problem is the nonlinear problem

$$(5.1) \qquad y'(t) = -y^3 + t^9(10 + t^{21}), \quad y(0) = 0, \quad 0 \le t \le 1,$$

with exact solution $y(t)=t^{10}$. In Table 5.2 the results are listed. Since the number of sequential right-hand side evaluations per step varies from 1 to 3 for the various methods, we adapted the stepsize as to obtain that each column of this table contains results with an equal number of sequential right-hand side evaluations over the whole integration interval.

A first observation is that most parallel methods behave more efficiently than the corresponding one-processor Adams methods, showing that already on two-processor machines parallelism can be exploited. Furthermore, these results clearly demonstrate the superiority of the high-order methods, especially the 6th- and the 8th-order BRK methods. It should be remarked that these two methods produce unstable results (indicated by an '∗' in Table 5.2) for large stepsizes, in spite of their large real stability boundary. The reason is that these methods employ a block point t_n+ch, with c much larger than 1, viz. $c=4$ and $c=5/2$, respectively. Since the modulus of $\partial f/\partial y$, which determines the maximally allowed stepsize, is a rapidly increasing function of t (at the solution, $|\partial f/\partial y|$ behaves as $3 \cdot t^{20}$), it is clear that an evaluation of f beyond the endpoint $t=1$ may easily cause instabilities.

Table 5.2. Correct decimal digits at $t=1$ for problem (5.1).

Sequential right-hand sides	6	12	24	48	96	order
Two-step Adams-Bashforth method	0.3	0.8	1.3	1.9	2.5	2
Miranker-Liniger method (2.4)	0.6	1.2	1.9	2.5	3.1	2
BRK method (4.1): $c=5/3$	2.6	2.4	3.1	3.9	4.8	3
BRK method (4.3): $c=1-\sqrt{6}$	0.5	1.2	2.0	2.9	3.8	3
Two-step Adams pair: PECE	0.2	0.9	1.7	2.5	3.4	3
Chu-Hamilton pair (4.3)-(4.6): PECE, $c=1/2$	1.1	1.9	3.0	4.2	5.5	4
BRK pair (4.3)-(4.6): $PE(CE)^2$, $c=1-\sqrt{5}/5$	2.0	2.9	4.1	5.7	7.4	5
Three-step Adams-Bashforth method	0.5	1.1	1.9	2.7	3.6	3
Method (4.7): $(c_1,c_2) = (0,17/10)$	2.0	2.6	3.7	4.8	6.0	4
Three-step Adams pair: PECE	0.3	1.1	2.1	3.3	4.5	4
BRK pair (4.9)-(4.11): PECE	1.2	2.2	3.6	5.1	6.7	5
BRK pair (4.12)-(4.13): PECE	*	*	1.5	5.3	7.4	6
Four-step Adams-Bashforth method	0.6	1.4	2.5	3.6	4.8	4
Miranker-Liniger method (2.5)	1.1	2.3	3.5	4.7	5.9	4
Four-step Adams pair: PECE	1.3	2.6	4.0	5.5	7.0	5
Shampine-Watts pair (2.7)-(2.6'): PECE	1.1	1.8	2.9	4.1	5.3	4
BRK pair (4.14)-(4.15): PECE	*	1.3	5.6	9.0	11.6	8

5.3. Orbit equation

The second problem was taken from the test set of Hull et al. [7]:

$$(5.2) \quad \begin{array}{ll} y_1' = y_3, & y_1(0) = 1 - \varepsilon, \quad \varepsilon = 0.3 \\ y_2' = y_4, & y_2(0) = 0 \\ y_3' = -y_1 (y_1^2 + y_2^2)^{-3/2}, & y_3(0) = 0 \\ y_4' = -y_2 (y_1^2 + y_2^2)^{-3/2}, & y_4(0) = \sqrt{\dfrac{1+\varepsilon}{1-\varepsilon}} \end{array}$$

Table 5.3. Correct decimal digits at $t=20$ for problem (5.2).

Sequential right-hand sides	240	480	960	1920	3840	order
Two-step Adams-Bashforth method	0.3	0.7	1.2	1.7	2.3	2
Miranker-Liniger method (2.4)	0.5	2.1	2.1	2.5	3.1	2
BRK method (4.1): $c=5/3$	0.3	1.2	2.1	3.0	3.9	3
BRK method (4.3): $c=1-\sqrt{6}$	0.3	1.2	2.1	3.0	3.9	3
Two-step Adams pair: PECE	-0.1	0.6	1.4	2.3	3.2	3
Chu-Hamilton pair (4.3)-(4.6): PECE, $c=1/2$	-1.5	0.1	3.7	5.2	6.5	4
BRK pair (4.3)-(4.6): PE(CE)^2, $c=1-\sqrt{5}/5$	1.4	3.2	4.8	6.4	7.9	5
Three-step Adams-Bashforth method	0.1	1.0	1.9	2.8	3.7	3
Method (4.7): $(c_1,c_2) = (0,17/10)$	1.9	3.5	4.4	5.5	6.7	4
Three-step Adams pair: PECE	0.4	1.8	3.4	5.0	6.2	4
BRK pair (4.9)-(4.11): PECE	1.3	2.8	4.4	5.9	7.4	5
BRK pair (4.12)-(4.13): PECE	3.3	4.9	6.8	8.6	9.6	6
Four-step Adams-Bashforth method	1.4	2.3	3.4	4.6	5.8	4
Miranker-Liniger method (2.5)	2.0	4.4	4.8	5.8	6.9	4
Four-step Adams pair: PECE	0.8	2.0	3.5	5.0	6.5	5
Shampine-Watts pair (2.7)-(2.6'): PECE	1.1	2.9	4.1	5.1	6.2	4
BRK pair (4.14)-(4.15): PECE	3.9	6.8	9.0			8

For this example, which describes a *system* of ODEs, the errors are measured in the maximum norm. Since most methods nicely show their asymptotic order behaviour, the high-order BRK methods are again superior to the low-order ones. Hence, the conclusion can be drawn that the introduction of non-equally spaced block points t_n+c_jh favourably influences the performance of the BRK methods.

5.4. Euler's equation of motion

The third problem is Euler's equation of motion (cf. Hull et al. [7]):

$$(5.3) \quad \begin{array}{ll} y_1' = y_2\,y_3, & y_1(0) = 0 \\ y_2' = -y_1\,y_3, & y_2(0) = 1 \\ y_3' = -0.51\,y_1\,y_2, & y_3(0) = 1. \end{array}$$

Table 5.4. Correct decimal digits at $t=20$ for problem (5.3).

Sequential right-hand sides	120	240	480	960	1920	order
Two-step Adams-Bashforth method	1.2	1.9	2.5	3.1	3.7	2
Miranker-Liniger method (2.4)	1.6	2.4	3.1	3.8	4.4	2
BRK method (4.1): $c=5/3$	1.7	2.6	3.5	4.4	5.3	3
BRK method (4.3): $c=1-\sqrt{6}$	1.6	2.6	3.5	4.4	5.3	3
Two-step Adams pair: PECE	1.2	2.0	2.9	3.8	4.7	3
Chu-Hamilton pair (4.3)-(4.6): PECE, $c=1/2$	*	3.3	4.7	6.0	7.3	4
BRK pair (4.3)-(4.6): PE(CE)^2, $c=1-\sqrt{5}/5$	2.5	3.9	5.5	7.0	8.5	5
- -						
Three-step Adams-Bashforth method	1.5	2.4	3.3	4.2	5.1	3
Method (4.7): $(c_1,c_2) = (0,17/10)$	2.8	4.1	5.4	6.6	7.9	4
Three-step Adams pair: PECE	1.4	2.7	4.0	5.3	6.5	4
BRK pair (4.9)-(4.11): PECE	2.7	4.1	5.6	7.1	8.6	5
BRK pair (4.12)-(4.13): PECE	3.2	5.1	6.9	8.7	10.7	6
- -						
Four-step Adams-Bashforth method	3.3	3.8	4.8	6.0	7.1	4
Miranker-Liniger method (2.5)	3.1	5.0	6.3	7.2	8.3	4
Four-step Adams pair: PECE	2.5	3.4	4.8	6.2	7.7	5
Shampine-Watts pair (2.7)-(2.6'): PECE	1.9	3.3	4.6	5.9	7.2	4
BRK pair (4.14)-(4.15): PECE	2.9	7.4	9.8			8

This table gives rise to the same conclusions as formulated at the previous test problems.

To sum up, these examples clearly show that, even when only 2 processors are used, a substantial gain in efficiency can be obtained when compared with sequential (uniprocessor) methods. This especially holds for the high-order BRK methods.

REFERENCES

[1]   **Butcher, J.C.** (1965): *A modified multistep method for the numerical integration of ordinary differential equations*, J. ACM **12**, 124-135.

[2]   **Butcher, J.C.** (1987): *The numerical analysis of ordinary differential equations, Runge-Kutta and general linear methods*, Wiley, New York.

[3]   **Chu, M.T. & Hamilton, H.** (1987): *Parallel solution of ODE's by multi-block methods*, SIAM J. Sci. Stat. Comput. **8**, 342-353.

[4]   **Donelson, J. & Hansen, E.** (1971): *Cyclic composite multistep predictor-corrector methods*, SIAM J. Numer. Anal. **8**, 137-157.

[5]   **Gear, C.W.** (1988): *Parallel methods for ordinary differential equations*, Calcolo **25**, 1-20.

[6]   **Houwen, P.J. van der, Sommeijer, B.P. & Mourik, P.A. van** (1989): *Note on explicit parallel multistep Runge-Kutta methods*, J. Comput. Appl. Math. **27**, 411-420.

[7]   **Hull, T.E., Enright, W.H. , Fellen, B.M. & Sedgwick, A.E.** (1972): *Comparing numerical methods for ordinary differential equations*, SIAM J. Numer. Anal. **9**, 603-637.

[8]   **Miranker, W.L. & Liniger, W.** (1967): *Parallel methods for the numerical integration of ordinary differential equations*, Math. Comp. **21**, 303-320.

[9]   **Shampine, L.F. & Watts, H.A.** (1969): *Block implicit one-step methods*, Math. Comp. **23**, 731-740.

[10] **Worland, P.B.** (1976): *Parallel methods for the numerical solution of ordinary differential equations*, IEEE Trans. Comput. **C-25**, 1045-1048.

PART II

Parallel numerical methods for stiff ODEs

CHAPTER III

A-stable parallel block methods for ordinary and integro-differential equations

Reprinted from

Appl. Numer. Math. **9** (1992), 267-281

A-stable parallel block methods for ordinary and integro-differential equations

B.P. Sommeijer, W. Couzy and P.J. van der Houwen

Centre for Mathematics and Computer Science
Post box 94079, 1090 GB Amsterdam, The Netherlands

Abstract. In this paper we study the stability of a class of block methods which are suitable for integrating ordinary and integro-differential equations on parallel computers. A-stable methods of orders 3 and 4 and $A(\alpha)$-stable methods with $\alpha > 89.9°$ of order 5 are constructed. On multiprocessor computers these methods are of the same computational complexity as implicit linear multistep methods on one-processor computers.

1991 Mathematical Subject Classification: 65L06, 65L20
1991 C.R. Classification: G.1.7, G.1.9
Keywords: numerical analysis, block methods, parallelism

1. INTRODUCTION

Many algorithms for numerically solving initial value problems for ordinary differential equations (ODEs):

(1.1) $$\frac{dy(t)}{dt} = f(t, y(t)), \quad y(t_0) = y_0,$$

or Volterra integro-differential equations (VIDEs):

(1.2) $$\frac{dy(t)}{dt} = f\left(t, y(t), \int_{t_0}^{t} k(t, x, y(x))\, dx\right), \quad y(t_0) = y_0,$$

are based on implicit linear multistep methods (LM methods), in particular on Backward Differentiation methods (BDF methods). The main reason for their popularity is the relatively low computational effort per step, at least when compared with other suitable methods for stiff equations, such as implicit Runge-Kutta methods. However, the BDFs have one serious disadvantage: they are subject to the so-called 'second Dahlquist barrier', which says that the order cannot exceed two if the method has to be A-stable. Thus the higher-order BDFs lack the property of A-stability. This means that if a high-order formula is selected (dictated by accuracy considerations), then it may happen that – for certain types of stiff ODEs or VIDEs – the algorithm encounters stability problems which usually result in a dramatical degradation of the performance. To circumvent this behaviour it is highly desirable to have A-stable methods of high order without increasing the computational effort per step.

It is our aim to construct such methods. They are most easily formulated as so-called block methods. Block methods can be considered as a set of simultaneously applied linear multistep methods to obtain several numerical approximations within one application. Numerous block methods have been proposed in the literature including high-order A-stable ones (see e.g. Watts and Shampine [16]). However, these implicit methods require in each application an amount of work which by far exceeds the computational effort required by a BDF. In recent papers (cf. e.g. Chu and Hamilton [3]), block methods have been given which solve the huge implicit relations on a *parallel* computer which indeed significantly reduces the computational costs. However, all these techniques follow the approach of predictor-corrector iteration, which in fact restricts their application to nonstiff problems.

Like Chu and Hamilton, we will employ parallelism to obtain the afore-mentioned goals. We shall construct A-stable methods of orders three and four, and $A(\alpha)$-stable methods of order five with $\alpha \approx \pi/2$. Furthermore, by carefully segmenting the total work per step into a few subtasks of approximately equal computational length, these methods require an amount of work which is very similar to what a BDF requires when implemented on a uni-processor machine. In Section 5.3 we will see that a high degree of parallelization is obtained. Since the implicit relations are solved by a Newton-type process (as is the case in BDF implementations) rather than in a predictor-corrector fashion, the property of A-stability is preserved.

In Sections 2 and 3, we present the construction of block methods for ODEs, in Section 4, block methods for VIDEs employing these block ODE solvers are discussed, and in Section 5, numerical experiments are reported. The way of construction is based on extremely simple tools: firstly, certain order-conditions are imposed such that a number of parameters are left free, and secondly, a numerical search over the free parameters is carried out to give the method the optimal stability characteristics. So far, we did not succeed in developing more sophisticated search techniques by analytical means.

2. PARALLEL BLOCK METHODS FOR ODES

In order to simplify the formulas, we present the derivations of the block methods for scalar, autonomous ODEs. The extension of these methods to systems of ODEs, and therefore also to nonautonomous equations, is straightforward.

The block methods studied in this paper are a direct generalization of the implicit one-step method

(2.1) $y_{n+1} = a\,y_n + h\,b\,f(y_n) + h\,d f(y_{n+1})$, $n = 0, 1, \dots$,

where h is the stepsize and y_n an approximation to $y(t_n)$. By introducing block vectors

(2.2) $Y_{n+1} := (y_{n,1}, \dots , y_{n,k})^{\mathrm{T}}$, $c := (c_1, \dots , c_k)^{\mathrm{T}}$, $c_k = 1$,

where $y_{n,i}$ denotes a numerical approximation to the exact solution value $y(t_n+c_ih)$, and assuming that (1.1) is a scalar equation, we can define the block method

(2.3) $Y_{n+1} = AY_n + hBf(Y_n) + hDf(Y_{n+1})$,

where A, B and D are k-by-k matrices. Here we use the convention that for any given vector $v = (v_j)$, $f(v)$ denotes the vector with entries $f(v_j)$. This method can be considered as the block analogue of (2.1). A characteristic of these methods is that, unlike conventional block methods based on linear multistep methods, the block point vector c is allowed to have $k-1$ *noninteger* components. In order to start the method, one needs the initial vector Y_0, which requires, in general, as many starting values as there are distinct values c_j ($j=1,\dots,k$). Notice that the last component of Y_{n+1} contains the step point value y_{n+1}. Furthermore, we remark that, in general, $y_{n,i} \neq y_{m,j}$, even if $n+c_i = m+c_j$.

The method (2.3) is suitable for direct use on parallel computers if the matrix D is *diagonal*, since such a form uncouples the various components as far as implicitness is concerned; the corresponding methods will be called *parallel block methods*. Using k processors, each processor has to evaluate a component of $f(Y_n)$ and to solve a system of equations whose dimension is that of the system of ODEs (1.1). If Newton's method is used for solving the system of equations, then each processor needs the Jacobian matrix $I - h\,d_{jj}\,\partial f/\partial y$ and its *LU*-decomposition. Either the various processors have to compute themselves the data they need, or one may consider the use of additional processors for computing the Jacobian matrices and their *LU*-decompositions. Let us consider the second strategy. As soon as the additional processors have completed an update of the matrix $\partial f/\partial y$ and computed the *LU*-decompositions of the k matrices $I - h\,d_{jj}\,\partial f/\partial y$, then the first k processors can replace their data by the new data. However, usually the computational job of computing Jacobian matrices and *LU*-decompositions is so substantial that the speed of updating may not be great enough. In such cases, the use of matrices D with equal diagonal elements is recommendable, because then the Jacobian matrices $I - h\,d_{jj}\,\partial f/\partial y$

are all identical, so that only one instead of k decompositions are required. Therefore, methods where D is of the form $d \cdot I$, I being the identity matrix, have some advantage.

If D is a full matrix, then the block method is not directly suitable for use on parallel computers. However, (2.3) allows the application of an iteration process that has a high degree of parallelism. This iteration method is of the one-level form

$$\left[I - h\,C\,\frac{\partial f(y_n)}{\partial y}\right]Y^{(j+1)} - h\,E f(Y^{(j+1)}) =$$
$$AY_n + h\,Bf(Y_n) - h\,C\,\frac{\partial f(y_n)}{\partial y}\,Y^{(j)} + h\,[D - E]\,f(Y^{(j)}),$$

where C and E are suitable iteration matrices. There are several possibilities for choosing these matrices in order to achieve parallelism and to preserve stability. We mention:

(i) C diagonal and $E=O$ (linear diagonal iteration),

(ii) $C=O$ and E diagonal (nonlinear diagonal iteration), and

(iii) $C=D$, $E=O$ combined with diagonalization of C (diagonalized Newton).

A survey of properties of diagonal iteration in the case where (2.3) corresponds to Runge-Kutta methods can be found in [10]. The diagonalized Newton process was proposed by Lubich [12]. In passing we remark, that one might also consider higher-level iteration methods. For example, the 'pipeline' iteration proposed by Feldstein [5] fits into the family of three-level iteration methods.

In a forthcoming paper, we will study the above iteration process if the matrix D in (2.3) is a full matrix. In the present paper, we assume that D is diagonal.

The conditions for pth-order consistency for methods of the form (2.3) are extremely simple and read (cf. [9])

(2.4) $C_j = 0, \quad j = 0, 1, ..., p,$

with

$$C_0 := Ae - e; \quad C_1 := A(c - e) + Be + De - c;$$
$$C_j := A(c - e)^j + j[B(c - e)^{j-1} + Dc^{j-1}] - c^j, \quad j = 2, 3, ... \,,$$

where e denotes the vector with unit entries and where powers of vectors are meant to be componentwise powers.

In order to compare the components of these vectors with the error constants corresponding to conventional linear multistep methods, we introduce the *normalized* error vectors [8]

(2.5) $\qquad E_j := \dfrac{C_j}{j!\,(B+D)e}\ ,$

where the division of vectors is meant component wise. When a linear k-step method is written in the form (2.3) with $c = (-k+2,..., -2,-1,0,1)^{\mathrm{T}}$, then the last component of E_j equals the normalized error constant of the linear k-step method. Since these block methods are in fact a composition of k conventional linear multistep methods, the theory developed for the latter class of methods (see Henrici [8] or Hairer, Nørsett and Wanner [7]), is to a large extent also applicable in the case of block methods. In particular, this theory can be used to determine the order of convergence of the block methods, that is the behaviour of $Y_{n+1} - Y(t_{n+1})$, with $Y(t_{n+1}) := \big(y(t_n+c_1 h),\ y(t_n+c_2 h),...,y(t_n+h)\big)^{\mathrm{T}}$, for $h \to 0$ and $t_n = t_0 + nh$ fixed (see also Cooper [4]).

3. STABILITY

The (linear) stability of block methods can be investigated by applying the method to the test equation $y' = \lambda y$. This leads to a recursion of the form

(3.1) $\qquad Y_{n+1} = M(z)\,Y_n, \qquad M(z) := [I - zD]^{-1}[A + zB], \qquad z := \lambda h.$

M will be called the *amplification matrix* and its eigenvalues the *amplification factors*. Here we observe that, by requiring the elements of the diagonal matrix D to be positive, the matrix $I - zD$ is nonsingular for all z on the negative real axis. Therefore, in the sequel we will assume that the (diagonal) elements of D are positive.

In our stability analysis we shall use the following result on the power of a matrix N (cf., Varga [15, p. 65]):

(3.2) $\qquad \| N^n \| = O(n^{q-1}[\rho(N)]^n) \quad$ as $n \to \infty,$

where $\| \cdot \|$ and $\rho(N)$ are the spectral norm and radius of N and where all diagonal submatrices of the Jordan normal form of N which have spectral radius $\rho(N)$ are at most q-by-q. If $\rho(N) < 1$ or $\rho(N) = q = 1$, then N is said to be *power bounded*.

Following the familiar stability definitions used for RK and LM methods, we shall call the region where the amplification matrix $M(z)$ is power bounded, the *stability region* of the block method. If the stability region contains the origin, then the method is called *zero-stable*. The region where $\|M^n\|$ tends to zero will be called the *strong stability region*. If the (strong) stability region of a block method contains the left half plane, then the block method is called *(strongly) A-stable*; furthermore, if the amplification matrix of an A-stable method has vanishing eigenvalues at infinity, then the method is called *L-stable*.

84

For some methods (i.e., the BDF methods) a less demanding definition of stability is more appropriate. Therefore the notion of $A(\alpha)$-stability has been introduced The angle α defines a wedge in the left half plane and the method is stable if z lies inside this wedge. This is, however, a rather crude way to describe the stability region, since for the higher-order BDF methods the part of the left half plane which is not included in the stability region is a small lobe near the imaginary axis. To provide more detailed information on the stability region, we introduce two additional parameters leading to the notion of $A(\alpha, \beta, \gamma)$-stability:

Definition 3.1. A method is said to be $A(\alpha, \beta, \gamma)$-*stable* if
(i) its region of stability contains the infinite wedge $\{z: -\alpha < \pi - \arg(z) < \alpha\}$, $0 < \alpha \le \pi/2$, and all points in the nonpositive halfplane with $|z| > \beta$, and
(ii) $1+\gamma$ is the maximum value of the spectral radius of $M(z)$ when z runs through the region of instability lying in the nonpositive halfplane.   []

Note that $A(\pi/2, 0, 0)$-stability implies A-stability. The degree of instability of the method is measured by γ.

If we set $A = D = I$ and $B = O$ in (2.3), then the method reduces to a set of k completely uncoupled one-step methods of the Backward Euler type, each advancing the solution from $t_{n-1}+c_i h$ to $t_n+c_i h$ $(i=1,2,...,k)$. Evidently, these k formulas can be efficiently implemented on a k-processor machine (in fact, they could equally well run on k separate computers). Such methods have excellent stability properties (e.g., the property of L-stability), but are only of first order. However, by using full matrices A and B, that is the k formulas of the block method share the same information from the previous step, the order can be considerably increased. In the next two subsections, we investigate for $k = 2$ ('two-dimensional block methods') and $k = 3$ ('three-dimensional block methods') to what values the order can be raised while preserving the favourable stability properties of Backward Euler (stability plots may be found in [14]).

3.1. Two-dimensional block methods
First we consider the case $k=2$ and choose the coefficient matrices of the form

$$(3.3) \quad A = \begin{pmatrix} a_1 & 1-a_1 \\ a_2 & 1-a_2 \end{pmatrix}, \quad B = \begin{pmatrix} b_{11} & b_{12} \\ b_{21} & b_{22} \end{pmatrix}, \quad D = \begin{pmatrix} d_1 & 0 \\ 0 & d_2 \end{pmatrix}, \quad c = (c,1)^T.$$

Imposing the conditions for second-order consistency we can express the entries of the matrix B in terms of the five free parameters c, a_1, a_2, d_1 and d_2:

(3.4a) $\quad b_{j1} = \frac{1}{2}(1-c)\,a_j + \frac{c_j(2d_j - c_j)}{2(1-c)}, \quad b_{j2} = c_j + (1-c)a_j - b_{j1} - d_j, \quad j = 1, 2,$

where $c_1 = c$ and $c_2 = 1$. The components C_{ij} of the vectors C_i $(i \geq 3)$ are given by

$$C_{ij} = (1 - \frac{i}{2})\,(c-1)^i\,a_j + i\,c_j^{i-1}d_j + \frac{i}{2}c_j\,(c_j - 2d_j)\,(c-1)^{i-2} - c_j^i, \quad j = 1, 2.$$

An elementary calculation shows that C_{3j} vanishes if

(3.4b) $\quad a_j = \frac{c_j}{(c-1)^3}\,[3\,(c-1)\,(c_j - 2d_j) + 2\,c_j\,(3d_j - c_j)],$

and that C_{4j} also vanishes if, in addition,

(3.4c) $\quad d_1 = \frac{c}{2(c+1)}, \quad d_2 = \frac{c-2}{2(c-3)}.$

The characteristic equation of the amplification matrix in (3.1) can be written in the form

(3.5) $\quad P(\zeta, z) := \det\left[A + zB - \zeta(I - zD)\right] =$

$$\det\begin{pmatrix} a_1 + b_{11}z - \zeta(1 - d_1 z) & 1 - a_1 + b_{12}z \\ a_2 + b_{21}z & 1 - a_2 + b_{22}z - \zeta(1 - d_2 z) \end{pmatrix} = 0.$$

We shall determine the z-region where this polynomial has its roots ζ within the unit circle, that is, the region of strong stability. In addition, we should impose the condition of zero-stability, i.e., the condition that the two eigenvalues $\alpha = 1$ and $\alpha = a_1 - a_2$ of A are on the unit disk those on the unit circle being simple, i.e.,

(3.6) $\quad -1 \leq a_1 - a_2 < 1.$

A further restriction on the range of the free parameters is obtained by imposing the 'stability at infinity' condition. By this we mean that the roots of the polynomial $P(\zeta, \infty)$ are on the unit disk (which is of course anyhow a necessary condition for A-stability). By virtue of the Hurwitz-criterion we obtain (recall that d_1 and d_2 are assumed to be positive)

(3.7) $\quad |\,b_{11}d_2 + b_{22}d_1\,| \leq d_1 d_2\,[d_1 d_2 + \det(B)], \quad \det(B) \leq d_1 d_2.$

3.1.1. Second-order methods. If we are satisfied with second-order accuracy, then we may choose the free parameters a_j and d_j in (3.4a) such that the matrix B vanishes while preserving the property of A-stability. For example, if $c=0$ then the method is equivalent with the familiar two-step Backward Differentiation Formula generated by

$$(3.8) \qquad A = \begin{pmatrix} 0 & 1 \\ -1/3 & 4/3 \end{pmatrix}, \quad B = \begin{pmatrix} 0 & 0 \\ 0 & 0 \end{pmatrix}, \quad D = \begin{pmatrix} 0 & 0 \\ 0 & 2/3 \end{pmatrix}, \quad c = (0,1)^{\mathrm{T}}.$$

3.1.2. Third-order methods. Third-order accuracy is achieved by choosing $C_{31}=C_{32}=0$, leaving us with three free parameters for monitoring the stability of the method. We find

$$a_1 = \frac{c(c^2 - 3c + 6d_1)}{(c-1)^3}, \qquad\qquad a_2 = \frac{3c + 12d_2 - 6cd_2 - 5}{(c-1)^3},$$

$$(3.9) \qquad b_{11} = \frac{c^2 - 2cd_1 - c^2 d_1}{(c-1)^2}, \qquad\qquad b_{12} = \frac{c - 2cd_1 - d_1}{(c-1)^2},$$

$$b_{21} = \frac{2 - 5d_2 - c + 2cd_2}{(c-1)^2}, \qquad\qquad b_{22} = \frac{(c-2)^2 - d_2(c^2 - 6c + 8)}{(c-1)^2},$$

leaving c, d_1 and d_2 as the free parameters. Taking into account the conditions of zero-stability and 'stability at infinity' (conditions (3.6) and (3.7)), we performed a numerical search in the (c,d_1,d_2)-space. It turned out that the regions of A-stable (c,d_1,d_2)-values are so small that A-stable points and strongly unstable points are close together, that is, a small perturbation of these values causes the method to violate the A-stability conditions. For example, the values

$$(3.10) \qquad c = 0.917387, \quad d_1 = 0.319523, \quad d_2 = 0.347067,$$

generate such a 'marginally' A-stable method. There is, however, an alternative approach. It is easily verified that putting $a_2=C_{32}=0$ yields methods providing third-order approximations at the step points t_n and second-order approximations at the points t_n+ch. It turns out that in the space of free parameters the regions of A-stable methods are larger so that it is easier to find A-stable methods by a numerical search. For example, we found the A-stable, third-order method

$$(3.11) \quad A = \begin{pmatrix} 0 & 1 \\ 0 & 1 \end{pmatrix}, \quad B = \begin{pmatrix} \dfrac{147}{220} & \dfrac{161}{220} \\ -\dfrac{50}{33} & \dfrac{23}{66} \end{pmatrix}, \quad D = \begin{pmatrix} \dfrac{7}{10} & 0 \\ 0 & \dfrac{13}{6} \end{pmatrix}, \quad c = \tfrac{1}{10}(21, 10)^T$$

with the normalized error vectors $E_3 \approx (0.19, 0)^T$ and $E_4 \approx (0.20, -0.017)^T$. The amplification factors at the origin equal 0 and 1, and the maximal amplification factor at infinity is ≈ 0.94.

3.1.3. Fourth-order methods. Fourth-order accuracy for both components is obtained by choosing $C_{31} = C_{32} = C_{41} = C_{42} = 0$. Alternatively, replacing $C_{41} = 0$ by $a_2 = 0$, reduces the order of the first component to 3, without affecting the order of the second component. In both approaches we are left with one free parameter for monitoring the stability of the method. Unfortunately, the stability regions of these fourth-order methods are rather limited and do not even allow for $A(\alpha)$-stability. Thus, in the class (3.3) the fourth-order methods seem to be of no interest.

3.2. Three-dimensional block methods

For $k=3$ we expect to find A-stable methods of order four and we may hope for $A(\alpha)$-stable methods of order five. These two cases will be investigated in the following subsections.

3.2.1. Fourth-order methods. Let us choose the matrix A such that $a_{i3} = 1 - a_{i1} - a_{i2}$, $i = 1, 2, 3$, so that C_0 vanishes. The vectors C_j vanish for $j = 1, 2, 3, 4$ if the entries b_{ij} and d_j satisfy the linear systems

$$\begin{pmatrix} 1 & 1 & 1 & 1 \\ c_1-1 & c_2-1 & 0 & c_i \\ (c_1-1)^2 & (c_2-1)^2 & 0 & c_i^2 \\ (c_1-1)^3 & (c_2-1)^3 & 0 & c_i^3 \end{pmatrix} \begin{pmatrix} b_{i1} \\ b_{i2} \\ b_{i3} \\ d_i \end{pmatrix} =$$

$$(3.12) \qquad \begin{pmatrix} c_i - a_{i1}(c_1-1) - a_{i2}(c_2-1) \\ \frac{1}{2}[c_i^2 - a_{i1}(c_1-1)^2 - a_{i2}(c_2-1)^2] \\ \frac{1}{3}[c_i^3 - a_{i1}(c_1-1)^3 - a_{i2}(c_2-1)^3] \\ \frac{1}{4}[c_i^4 - a_{i1}(c_1-1)^4 - a_{i2}(c_2-1)^4] \end{pmatrix}, \quad i = 1, 2, 3.$$

This shows that there is a family of fourth-order block methods with eight free parameters: a_{i1}, a_{i2} ($i = 1, 2, 3$), c_1 and c_2.

In order to ensure zero-stability, we require that the matrix A has its two parasitic eigenvalues within the unit circle. Writing the characteristic equation of A in the form $(\zeta - 1)(\zeta^2 + q_0\zeta + r_0) = 0$, we find that we have zero-stability if

(3.13) $|q_0| < r_0 + 1, \qquad r_0 < 1,$

$$q_0 := a_{31} + a_{32} - a_{11} - a_{22},$$
$$r_0 := a_{11}a_{12} + a_{31}a_{12} + a_{32}a_{21} - a_{11}a_{32} - a_{21}a_{12} - a_{22}a_{31}.$$

Taking this constraint into account, we performed a numerical search over the free parameters to obtain the A-stable method

$$A = \begin{pmatrix} -1 & \frac{1}{2} & \frac{3}{2} \\ \frac{1}{2} & 1 & -\frac{1}{2} \\ -1 & \frac{1}{2} & \frac{3}{2} \end{pmatrix}, \qquad D = \begin{pmatrix} \dfrac{13 \cdot 1303}{2^9 \cdot 5 \cdot 11} & 0 & 0 \\ 0 & \dfrac{277}{2 \cdot 3^2 \cdot 13} & 0 \\ 0 & 0 & \dfrac{16001}{2^9 \cdot 3^2 \cdot 5} \end{pmatrix},$$

(3.14)

$$B = \begin{pmatrix} \dfrac{5 \cdot 13 \cdot 43}{2^{11}} & \dfrac{15161}{2^5 \cdot 3^2 \cdot 11} & \dfrac{29 \cdot 43 \cdot 83}{2^{11} \cdot 3^2 \cdot 5} \\ \dfrac{-73}{2 \cdot 3^2 \cdot 7} & \dfrac{-467}{2 \cdot 3^3 \cdot 7} & \dfrac{-7 \cdot 37}{2 \cdot 3^3 \cdot 13} \\ \dfrac{5 \cdot 16069}{2^{11} \cdot 3^2 \cdot 7} & \dfrac{54419}{2^5 \cdot 3^3 \cdot 5 \cdot 7} & \dfrac{41927}{2^{11} \cdot 3^3} \end{pmatrix},$$

with $c = (5, 13/4, 1)^{\mathrm{T}}$ and with normalized error vector $E_5 \approx (0.13, 0.27, 0.075)^{\mathrm{T}}$. Its amplification factors at the origin are 0, 1/2 and 1, and at infinity the maximal amplification factor is ≈ 0.92.

The above direct search method is rather expensive, and therefore we also applied an alternative approach where

(3.15) $$\sum_{i=1}^{m} \sum_{j=1}^{k} |\mu_{ij}|^{q_{ij}}$$

was minimized over the free parameters b_{i2} and d_i ($i = 1, 2, 3$), c_1 and c_2. Here, $k = 3$, the q_{ij} are control parameters and μ_{ij}, $j = 1, \dots, k$ denote the eigenvalues of the amplification matrix $M(z_i)$ defined in (3.1) with z_i running through a set of m points lying on the imaginary axis. In this way we found the A-stable method

$$A = \frac{1}{1600} \begin{pmatrix} 2820 & -183 & -1037 \\ -7100 & -3423 & 12123 \\ -1020 & -1607 & 4227 \end{pmatrix}, \quad D = \frac{1}{5} \begin{pmatrix} 8 & 0 & 0 \\ 0 & 8 & 0 \\ 0 & 0 & 8 \end{pmatrix},$$

(3.16)

$$B = \frac{1}{400} \begin{pmatrix} -398 & -92 & -177 \\ 6282 & -92 & 2143 \\ 1098 & 272 & 507 \end{pmatrix}, \quad c = (3,5,1)^{\mathrm{T}}$$

with normalized error vector $E_5 \approx (3.67, 0.19, 0.064)^{\mathrm{T}}$. At the origin the amplification factors are 0.81, 0.81 and 1, and at infinity the maximal amplification factor is ≈ 0.37.

3.2.2. Fifth-order methods. Along the same lines as we constructed the fourth-order method (3.16), we proceeded with the fifth-order case. Now only five free parameters are available, say d_i ($i = 1, 2, 3$), c_1 and c_2. Imposing the constraint (3.13), we found a few $A(\alpha, \beta, \gamma)$-stable methods which may be considered as A-stable in most practical applications.

We mention the $A(\alpha, \beta, \gamma)$-stable method with $\alpha \approx 89.9988°$, $\beta \approx 0.16$ and $\gamma \approx 2.6 \cdot 10^{-6}$ generated by

$$A = \begin{pmatrix} -.37354856915573 & 1.3772028209449 & -.0036542517891531 \\ .45636214490330 & .58957191150098 & -.045934056404276 \\ -71.558907928027 & 69.945110840701 & 2.6137970873262 \end{pmatrix},$$

(3.17) $B = \begin{pmatrix} -.089579683013023 & -.020791477924637 & .0023118793010643 \\ .037434812789650 & .78549538208108 & .024702269787981 \\ -18.279469309687 & -29.674965823418 & -1.6401568285440 \end{pmatrix},$

$$D = \begin{pmatrix} .261 & 0 & 0 \\ 0 & .581 & 0 \\ 0 & 0 & .832 \end{pmatrix}, \quad c = \begin{pmatrix} -2.747 \\ -2.122 \\ 1 \end{pmatrix},$$

with normalized error vector $E_6 \approx (0.007, 0.0038, -0.015)^{\mathrm{T}}$. At the origin the amplification factors are 0.92, 0.92, and 1, and at infinity the maximal amplification factor is ≈ 0.993.

Finally, we present the $A(\alpha, \beta, \gamma)$-stable method with $\alpha \approx 89.98°$, $\beta \approx 0.30$ and $\gamma \approx 6.9 \cdot 10^{-5}$ generated by

$$A = \begin{pmatrix} .58694824150708 & -.042737729478577 & .45578948797150 \\ 73.394943213338 & 2.5499812910344 & -74.944924504372 \\ 1.3881897627759 & -.0035265226034516 & -.38466324017241 \end{pmatrix},$$

$$(3.18) \quad B = \begin{pmatrix} .78434821208875 & .023439431423946 & .033345158796322 \\ -30.332265183768 & -1.5938561820999 & -18.934741340575 \\ -.012761141648945 & .0022604702667178 & -.092097195902230 \end{pmatrix},$$

$$D = \begin{pmatrix} .57487 & 0 & 0 \\ 0 & .83102 & 0 \\ 0 & 0 & .2618 \end{pmatrix}, \quad c = \begin{pmatrix} 1.6153 \\ 4.7871 \\ 1 \end{pmatrix},$$

and with normalized error vector $E_6 \approx (0.004, -0.016, 0.007)^T$. At the origin the amplification factors are 0.88, 0.88 and 1, and at infinity the maximal amplification factor is ≈ 0.89.

3.3. Survey of method characteristics

We conclude with a survey of the parameters α, β and γ characterizing the stability regions of the block methods derived in this paper (see Definition 3.1) and compare them with those of the BDFs (details about the BDF methods can be found in [6]). In Table 3.1 these values are listed (an '$*$' in the γ-column means that the corresponding value is not relevant). In addition, we give the normalized error vectors defined in (2.5) of all methods. For a uniform presentation, we first formulated the BDFs as block methods. We recall that a k-step BDF method can be cast in the form (2.3) with block point vector $c = (2-k, ..., -1, 0, 1)^T$.

Finally, we remark that a k-step, kth-order BDF requires k starting values, independent of its formulation, whereas the block methods of this paper need only 2 (for $p = 3$) or 3 (for $p = 4, 5$) starting values.

Table 3.1. Normalized error vectors and values of α, β and γ.

Method	Order p	$E_{p+1}{}^T$	α	β	γ
BDF$_3$	3	$(0, 0, 1/4)$	88.4°	1.94	0.046
(3.11)	3	$(0.20, -0.017)$	90°	0	$*$
BDF$_4$	4	$(0, 0, 0, 1/5)$	73.2°	4.72	0.191
(3.14)	4	$(0.13, 0.27, 0.075)$	90°	0	$*$
(3.16)	4	$(3.67, 0.19, 0.064)$	90°	0	$*$
BDF$_5$	5	$(0, 0, 0, 0, 1/6)$	51.8°	9.94	0.379
(3.17)	5	$(0.007, 0.0038, -0.015)$	$>89.9°$	0.16	0.0000026
(3.18)	5	$(0.004, -0.016, 0.007)$	$>89.9°$	0.30	0.000069

4. APPLICATION TO VOLTERRA INTEGRO-DIFFERENTIAL EQUATIONS

Consider the initial value problem for VIDEs given by (1.2). The most straightforward way of solving numerically this problem replaces the integral term in (1.2) by a quadrature formula and integrates the resulting ODE by some ODE integrator. This 'direct quadrature' method will be indicated by DQ method. The stability of DQ methods strongly depends on the quadrature formula used for approximating the integral term, particularly if the VIDE in (1.2) is stiff. For example, DQ methods using Gregory quadrature formulas become easily unstable (see, e.g., [1]).

A more stable approach is based on the approximation of the integral term by converting it into a differential equation and by integrating this differential equation by an ODE solver. For that purpose, we introduce the function

$$(4.1) \qquad z(t,s) := \int_{t_0}^{s} k(t, x, y(x)) \, dx,$$

and we write the initial value problem (1.2) in the form

$$(4.2a) \qquad \frac{dy(t)}{dt} = f(t, y(t), z(t,t)), \qquad y(t_0) = y_0.$$

The method now consists of the application of an ODE solver to the initial value problem (4.2a), where the values of $z(t,t)$ needed by the ODE solver are obtained by integrating the initial value problem

$$(4.2b) \qquad \frac{\partial z(t,s)}{\partial s} = k(t, s, y(s)), \qquad z(t,t_0) = 0$$

from $s=t_0$ until $s=t$. This method still belongs to the class of DQ methods, however, it uses a special quadrature formula derived from an ODE solver. If the ODE solver is an LM method (ρ,σ), then the quadrature formula is called (ρ,σ)-reducible (cf. Matthys [13]). Similarly, we shall call the DQ method (ρ,σ)-reducible if both initial value problems (4.2a) and (4.2b) are solved by the same LM method (ρ,σ), and (A, B, D)-reducible if (4.2a) and (4.2b) are solved by the same block method (2.3) generated by the matrices A, B and D.

Let us consider the stability of (A, B, D)-reducible DQ methods. Following the usual stability analysis of VIDE solvers (cf., e.g., Brunner and Lambert [2] and Matthys [13]), we shall consider stability with respect to the basic test problem

$$(4.3) \qquad \frac{dy(t)}{dt} = \xi y(t) + \eta \int_{t_0}^{t} y(x)\ dx, \qquad y(t_0) = y_0.$$

Using the representation (4.2) and writing $z(t,t)=z(t)$, this problem can be represented in the form

$$(4.4) \qquad \frac{dy(t)}{dt} = \xi y(t) + \eta z(t), \quad y(t_0) = y_0, \qquad \frac{dz(t)}{dt} = y(t), \quad z(t_0) = 0.$$

Application of the block method (2.3) to each of these equations yields the recursions

$$Y_{n+1} = AY_n + hB[\xi Y_n + \eta Z_n] + hD[\xi Y_{n+1} + \eta Z_{n+1}],$$

(4.5)

$$Z_{n+1} = AZ_n + hBY_n + hDY_{n+1}.$$

We shall show that (4.5) is algebraically equivalent with the recursion obtained by applying (2.3) to the system (4.4). Writing (4.4) in the form

$$(4.4') \qquad \frac{d}{dt} u(t) = \begin{pmatrix} \xi & \eta \\ 1 & 0 \end{pmatrix} u(t), \qquad u(t) := \begin{pmatrix} y(t) \\ z(t) \end{pmatrix},$$

the block method (2.3) takes the form

$$U_{n+1} = A \circ U_n + hB \circ f(U_n) + hD \circ f(U_{n+1}), \quad U_{n+1} := (y_{n,1}, z_{n,1}; \ldots ; y_{n,k}, z_{n,k})^{\mathrm{T}},$$

(4.5')

$$f(U_{n+1}) := (\xi y_{n,1} + \eta z_{n,1}, y_{n,1}; \ldots ; \xi y_{n,k} + \eta z_{n,k}, y_{n,k})^{\mathrm{T}},$$

with $y_{n,j}$ and $z_{n,j}$ denoting the components of the (column) vectors Y_{n+1} and Z_{n+1} used in (4.5), and where the tensor products $A \circ U_n$ and $B \circ f(U_n)$ are defined according to

$$A \circ U_n := (a_1 Y_n, a_1 Z_n; \ldots ; a_k Y_n, a_k Z_n)^{\mathrm{T}},$$

(4.6)

$$B \circ f(U_n) := (b_1(\xi Y_n + \eta Z_n), b_1 Y_n; \ldots ; b_k(\xi Y_n + \eta Z_n), b_k Y_n)^{\mathrm{T}},$$

with a_j and b_j denoting the jth row vectors of the matrices A and B, respectively. It is now readily verified that by reordering the equations occurring in (4.5') such that the first, third, fifth, ... equations come first and the second, fourth, sixth, ... equations come next, we obtain the recursions (4.5).

Hence, if λ and μ denote the eigenvalues of the Jacobian matrix associated with (4.4'), then the recursion (4.5) is stable if both $h\lambda$ and $h\mu$ are in the stability region of the block method (2.3). The corresponding region of $(h\xi, h^2\eta) = (h\lambda + h\mu, -h^2\lambda\mu)$-values will be called the *stability region of the (A, B, D)-reducible DQ method.* Furthermore, if this stability region contains the set $\{(h\xi, h^2\eta): \xi < 0, \eta < 0\}$, then the DQ method is called A_0-*stable.* The preceding considerations can be summarized in the following theorem which generalizes a result for LM methods originally given by Brunner and Lambert [2].

Theorem 4.1. Let S be the stability region of the block method (2.3) generated by the matrices A, B and D, and let λ and μ be defined by $\lambda + \mu = \xi$, $\lambda\mu = -\eta$. Then the set $\{(h\xi, h^2\eta): h\lambda \in S, h\mu \in S\}$ defines the region of stability of the (A, B, D)-reducible DQ method. []

From this theorem it follows that the (A, B, D)-reducible DQ method is A_0-stable if, and only if, the generating block method (A, B, D) is A-stable. Thus, the use of the block methods constructed in this paper avoids the so-called 'second Dahlquist barrier' which applies to A_0-stable (ρ, σ)-reducible DQ methods for VIDEs (cf. [13, Theorem 5]).

5. NUMERICAL EXPERIMENTS

5.1. Accuracy test

To verify the order of the various methods we integrated the test problem proposed by Kaps [11]:

(5.1)
$$\frac{dy_1}{dt} = -(2 + \varepsilon^{-1})y_1 + \varepsilon^{-1}(y_2)^2, \qquad y_1(0) = 1,$$

$$\frac{dy_2}{dt} = y_1 - y_2(1 + y_2), \qquad y_2(0) = 1,$$

with $0 \leq t \leq T$. The exact solution is given by $y_1 = \exp(-2t)$ and $y_2 = \exp(-t)$ for all values of the parameter ε. In Table 5.1, we have listed the values Δ, where Δ denotes the number of correct decimal digits at the endpoint (i.e., we write the maximum norm of the error at $t = T$ in the form $10^{-\Delta}$). In all experiments the theoretical order of the method is shown for sufficiently small values of h (if p is the order of the method, then, on halving the step size, the value of Δ should increase by $\approx 0.3 p$).

Table 5.1. Values of Δ for problem (5.1) with $T=1$, $\varepsilon=10^{-8}$.

Method	p	$h=1/4$	$h=1/8$	$h=1/16$	$h=1/32$	$h=1/64$	$h=1/128$
BDF$_3$	3	2.8	3.7	4.6	5.5	6.5	7.4
(3.11)	3	2.8	3.6	4.4	5.2	6.1	7.0
BDF$_4$	4	3.4	4.7	5.9	7.1	8.4	9.6
(3.14)	4	3.8	5.2	9.5	7.9	8.9	10.0
(3.16)	4	3.1	3.9	4.8	5.9	7.1	8.2
BDF$_5$	5	4.0	5.6	7.2	8.7	10.2	12.0
(3.17)	5	2.6	4.0	5.5	7.3	9.2	10.3
(3.18)	5	4.7	5.4	6.4	7.7	9.2	10.1

5.2. Stability test

We tested the stability of the methods by integrating a problem in which the Jacobian matrix has purely imaginary eigenvalues:

$$(5.2) \qquad \frac{dy_1}{dt} = -\alpha y_2 + (1+\alpha)\cos(t), \qquad \frac{dy_2}{dt} = \alpha y_1 - (1+\alpha)\sin(t), \qquad 0 \le t \le T,$$

with initial conditions $y_1(0)=0$, $y_2(0)=1$ and exact solution $y_1=\sin(t)$ and $y_2=\cos(t)$ for all values of the parameter α.

In Table 5.2, the results are listed for $T=100$. Values of Δ corresponding to stepsizes that are theoretically unstable are in boldface and overflow is indicated by $*$. The unstable results of the BDFs are in agreement with their regions of instability indicated in Table 3.1 (the phenomenon that BDF$_5$ becomes stable again for sufficiently small h is due to the fact that its imaginary interval of instability is given by $i\,[0.71, 9.94]$).

Table 5.2. Values of Δ for problem (5.2) with $T=100$, $\alpha=10$.

Method	p	$h=4/5$	$h=2/5$	$h=1/5$	$h=1/10$	$h=1/20$	$h=1/40$
BDF$_3$	3	2.0	2.9	3.9	$*$	$*$	**4.9**
(3.11)	3	2.1	2.8	3.4	4.0	4.6	5.3
BDF$_4$	4	2.2	$*$	$*$	$*$	**2.9**	**8.2**
(3.14)	4	2.8	4.0	4.9	5.8	6.8	8.0
(3.16)	4	1.6	2.7	3.8	4.9	5.8	6.8
BDF$_5$	5	-0.1	$*$	$*$	$*$	8.5	10.3
(3.17)	5	1.2	2.0	3.4	4.7	6.2	7.6
(3.18)	5	2.9	3.9	5.1	6.4	7.6	**8.6**

Next, we show that the 'almost' A-stable fifth-order methods (3.17) and (3.18) behave as A-stable methods in practice. We performed experiments for $\alpha=1$ and $\alpha=4$ with $h=1/8$: for $\alpha=1$ both integration processes are *theoretically* unstable, and for $\alpha=4$ the processes are stable. In Table 5.3 the results are listed for increasing length of the integration interval: these results clearly show that both methods perform perfectly stably for $\alpha=1$ and the T-values chosen.

Table 5.3. Values of Δ for problem (5.2) for $h=1/8$.

Method	$\alpha=1$: theoretically unstable			$\alpha=4$: theoretically stable		
	$T=10$	$T=100$	$T=1000$	$T=10$	$T=100$	$T=1000$
(3.17)	3.6	3.8	3.6	4.0	3.9	3.9
(3.18)	4.5	4.3	4.8	5.4	5.4	5.4

5.3. Volterra integro-differential equation

Consider the initial value problem

$$(5.3) \quad \frac{dy(t)}{dt} = -\frac{1 + \alpha t(1+t)^2}{(1+t)^2} + \frac{\alpha}{y(t)} \ln\left(\frac{2+2t}{2+t}\right) + \alpha \int_0^t \frac{dx}{1+(1+t)y(x)}, \quad y(2) = \tfrac{1}{3},$$

with $2 \le t \le T$ and $\alpha > 0$. The exact solution is given by $y(t)=1/(1+t)$. For $\alpha=1$, this problem has been discussed in [2]. From the expressions

$$\xi := \frac{\partial f}{\partial y} = -\frac{\alpha}{y^2(t)} \ln\left(\frac{2+2t}{2+t}\right), \quad \eta := \frac{\partial f}{\partial z}\frac{\partial k}{\partial y} = -\alpha \frac{1+t}{(1+(1+t)y)^2},$$

it follows that (5.3) is stable if $t > 0$ and $y \ge 0$. Furthermore, we see that in the vicinity of the exact solution we have $\xi \approx -\alpha(1+t)^2$ and $\eta \approx -\alpha(1+t)$, so that the stiffness of this problem increases with α and t. For example, if $\alpha=T=10$, then an A_0-stable method is highly desirable.

Table 5.4 lists results for various methods and values of the stepsize h. Notice that the results for the stiff problem ($\alpha = 10$) are not less accurate (even more accurate) than the results for the nonstiff problem ($\alpha=1$), showing that stiffness does not cause any problem. Similar to the ODE case (cf. Table 5.1), the method (3.14) performs very accurately, whereas (3.17) is significantly less accurate.

Table 5.4. Values of Δ for problem (5.3) at $T=10$.

Method	Order p	$\alpha=1$ $h=1/2$	$h=1/4$	$h=1/8$	$\alpha=10$ $h=1/2$	$h=1/4$	$h=1/8$
BDF$_3$	3	5.7	6.8	7.9	6.0	6.9	7.8
(3.11)	3	5.5	6.5	7.3	5.4	6.5	7.3
BDF$_4$	4	5.4	7.0	8.3	6.5	8.1	9.4
(3.14)	4	6.0	8.3	9.1	6.4	8.6	10.9
(3.16)	4	5.2	6.2	7.2	6.7	7.9	8.5
BDF$_5$	5	5.1	7.2	8.9	6.1	8.2	9.9
(3.17)	5	2.5	5.2	7.2	2.9	5.3	7.5
(3.18)	5	6.0	6.9	8.2	6.8	8.5	9.3

5.4. Performance test on the ALLIANT FX/4

Finally, we tested the methods (3.11) and (3.18) on the ALLIANT FX/4 by integrating the problem (5.1) of Kaps. In Table 5.5, we have listed timings on P processors and the rate of efficiency of a k-processor method, i.e., the execution time on one processor divided by k times the execution time on k processors. These results show that the gain factor is close to its optimal value.

Table 5.5. Timings (in seconds) for problem (5.1) at $T=1$ with $\varepsilon=10^{-8}$ and $h=1/256$.

method	k	$P=1$	$P=2$	$P=3$	$P=4$	Efficiency rate
(3.11)	2	0.43	0.23	0.23		0.93
(3.18)	3	0.66	0.45	0.25	0.25	0.88

From this table we conclude that the performance is close to its optimum, that is, the gain factor obtained for a k-processor method is almost equal to k. Table 5.5 also lists timings in cases where methods have the disposal of one more processor (i.e., $k+1$) than the number (i.e., k) they are designed for. We see that this additional processor is not utilized, since the k processors (concurrently) solve the k implicit relations and the extra processor is idle. As mentioned before, it could have been exploited for updating the Jacobian matrix, but in this test we did not include such a technique.

It should be noted that the efficiency rate is slightly dependent on implementation strategies, such as how accurately the nonlinear systems are solved. For example, it may happen that the first (or any other) implicit relation requires less Newton iterations than the other implicit relations (e.g., because of a more accurate initial approximation); in such cases this first processor will be idle for some time, which of course, has a bad influence on the efficiency rate.

REFERENCES

[1] **Brunner, H. & Houwen, P.J. van der** (1986): *The numerical solution of Volterra equations*, CWI Monograph No.**3**, North-Holland, Amsterdam.

[2] **Brunner, H. & Lambert, J.D.** (1974): *Stability of numerical methods for Volterra integro-differential equations*, Computing **12**, 75-89.

[3] **Chu, M.T. & Hamilton, H.** (1987): *Parallel solution of ODE's by multi-block methods*, SIAM J. Sci. Stat. Comput. **8**, 342-353.

[4] **Cooper, G.J.** (1978): *The order of convergence of general linear methods for ordinary differential equations*, SIAM J. Numer. Anal. **15**, 643-661.

[5] **Feldstein, A.** (1990): Oral communication at the *International Conference on the Numerical Solution of Volterra and Delay Equations*, Arizona State University, May 25-28.

[6] **Gear, C.W.** (1971): *Numerical initial value problems in ordinary differential equations*, Prentice Hall, Englewood Cliffs, N.J.

[7] **Hairer, E., Nørsett, S.P. & Wanner, G.** (1987): *Solving ordinary differential equations I. Nonstiff problems*, Springer Series in Comp. Math., Vol. **8**, Springer-Verlag, Berlin.

[8] **Henrici, P.** (1962): *Discrete variable methods in ordinary differential equations*, Wiley, New York.

[9] **Houwen, P.J. van der & Sommeijer, B.P.** (1992): *Block Runge-Kutta methods on parallel computers*, Z. Angew. Math. Mech. **72**, 3-18.

[10] **Houwen, P.J. van der & Sommeijer, B.P.** (1990): *Parallel ODE solvers*, in: Proc. of the International Conference on Supercomputing, Amsterdam, June 11-15, ACM Press, 71-81.

[11] **Kaps, P.** (1981): *Rosenbrock-type methods*, in: *Numerical methods for stiff initial value problems* (eds.: G.Dahlquist & R. Jeltsch), Bericht Nr.9, Inst. für Geometrie und Praktische Mathematik der RWTH Aachen.

[12] **Lubich, Chr.** (1990): Oral communication at the *International Conference on the Numerical Solution of Volterra and Delay Equations*, Arizona State University, May 25-28.

[13] **Matthys, J.** (1976): *A-stable linear multistep methods for Volterra integro-differential equations*, Numer. Math. **27**, 85-94.

[14] **Sommeijer, B.P., Couzy, W. & Houwen, P.J. van der** (1989): *A-stable parallel block methods*, Report NM-R8918, Centre for Mathematics and Computer Science, Amsterdam.

[15] **Varga, R.S.** (1962): *Matrix iterative analysis*, Prentice Hall, Englewood Cliffs, N.J.

[16] **Watts, H.A. & Shampine, L.F.** (1972): *A-stable block implicit one-step methods*, BIT **12**, 252-266.

CHAPTER IV

Embedded diagonally implicit Runge-Kutta algorithms on parallel computers

Reprinted from
Embedded diagonally implicit Runge-Kutta algorithms
on parallel computers,
P.J. van der Houwen, B.P. Sommeijer and W. Couzy,
Mathematics of Computation, Volume 58, pp 135-159, 1992,
by permission of the American Mathematical Society

Embedded diagonally implicit Runge-Kutta algorithms on parallel computers

P.J. van der Houwen, B.P. Sommeijer and W. Couzy

Centre for Mathematics and Computer Science
P.O. Box 94079, 1090 GB Amsterdam, The Netherlands

Abstract. This paper investigates diagonally implicit Runge-Kutta methods in which the implicit relations can be solved in parallel and are singly diagonal-implicit on each processor. The algorithms are based on diagonally implicit iteration of fully implicit Runge-Kutta methods of high order. The iteration scheme is chosen in such a way that the resulting algorithm is $A(\alpha)$-stable or $L(\alpha)$-stable with α equal or very close to $\pi/2$. In this way, highly stable, singly diagonal-implicit Runge-Kutta methods of orders up to 10 can be constructed. Because of the iterative nature of the methods, embedded formulas of lower orders are automatically available allowing a strategy for varying the stepsize and the order.

1991 Mathematics Subject Classification: 65L06, 65L20
1991 C.R. Classification: G.1.7
Key Words: numerical analysis, Runge-Kutta methods, parallelism.

1. INTRODUCTION

In Nørsett and Simonsen [21], Jackson and Nørsett [16], and Iserles and Nørsett [15], it was observed that on parallel computers, predictor-corrector methods (PC methods) based on implicit Runge-Kutta (RK) correctors are particularly attractive for solving initial value problems for the system of ordinary differential equations (ODEs)

(1.1) $\qquad \dfrac{dy(t)}{dt} = f(y(t)).$

On sequential computers, implicit RK methods are seldom used as corrector equation, because of the large number of implicit relations to be solved when using these correctors. However, matters are different when parallel computers are used, since PC methods, being a form of functional iteration, possess a high degree of parallelism. First results based on the PC approach were reported by Lie [18], who uses a fourth-order, two-stage Gauss-Legendre corrector and a third-order Hermite extrapolation predictor. In [12], these 'parallel, iterated' RK methods (which we shall briefly call *PIRK methods*) have been investigated for a variety of predictor methods and it was concluded that, from an implementational point of view, one-step predictors are preferable. Related PC methods were studied by Tam in his thesis [24]. In particular, families of methods were constructed with elliptically shaped stability regions. An analysis of the error behaviour of a very general class of PC methods, including all methods indicated above, was given by Burrage [2].

An attractive feature of PIRK methods is the availability of embedded formulas of lower orders allowing a strategy for step and order variation without additional costs. On the other hand, owing to their explicit character, PIRK methods have rather limited regions of stability and are therefore only suitable for integrating *nonstiff* systems.

In this paper, we shall be interested in integrating *stiff* systems, and we will investigate the possibility of constructing methods that are more stable than PIRK methods by *diagonally implicit iteration* of fully implicit RK methods. After a fixed number of iterations, such methods belong to the class of DIRK methods, and are therefore essentially different from the explicit PIRK methods studied in the aforementioned papers. DIRK methods resulting from diagonally implicit iteration have the property that *effectively* they are singly diagonal-implicit RK (SDIRK) methods when run on parallel computers. Furthermore, like the PIRK methods, they possess embedded formulas of lower order which make them an ideal starting point for developing variable order/variable step codes. We shall call the 'Parallel, Diagonal-implicitly Iterated' RK methods *PDIRK methods*.

In the literature, various (S)DIRK methods were published for the integration of stiff systems of ODEs. The most recent contributions are the parallel DIRK methods of Iserles and Nørsett [15], which are, like PDIRK methods, effectively of SDIRK-type on multi-processor computers (these methods are the first and, as far as we know, the only parallel DIRK methods published in the literature). However, the order of most DIRK methods is limited to $p = 4$ (the only DIRK methods exceeding this order are those of Cooper and Sayfy [5]). By diagonal iteration of implicit RK methods it is possible to construct highly stable PDIRK methods of orders up to 10.

Table 1.1 presents the characteristics of a number of SDIRK methods from the literature together with the most stable PDIRK methods of order $p > 4$ derived in the present paper. In this table, DIRK II denotes the Type II methods of Iserles and Nørsett [15], p_{emb} indicates that embedded methods of orders $\leq p_{emb}$ are available and s denotes the number of stages of the underlying corrector in the PDIRK methods (by choosing Gauss-Legendre or Radau IIA correctors we may set $s = \lfloor (p+1)/2 \rfloor$, where $\lfloor \cdot \rfloor$ denotes the integer part function). Furthermore, the number of sequential stages is defined as the number of implicit systems to be solved on each processor in each step. Finally, we introduce the concept of L^2-stability, which means that the method possesses an A-acceptable stability function for which the degree of the numerator is two less than the degree of the denominator.

Table 1.1. (S)DIRK and PDIRK methods.

Method	Order	Stages	Seq. Stages	Processors	Stability	p_{emb}	Reference
SDIRK	$p=3$	$p-1$	$p-1$	1	A-stable	1	[19]
SDIRK	$p=3$	$p-1$	$p-1$	1	Strongly A-stable	1	[6]
SDIRK	$p=4$	$p-1$	$p-1$	1	A-stable	1	[6], [1]
SDIRK	$p=5,6$	5	5	1	A-stable	1	[5]
SDIRK	$p=3$	p	p	1	S-stable	$p-1$	[4]
SDIRK	$p=3$	$p+1$	$p+1$	1	L-stable	$p-1$	[22]
SDIRK	$p=4$	$p+1$	$p+1$	1	S-stable	$p-1$	[4]
DIRK II	$p=4$	p	$p-2$	2	L-stable	$p-1$	[15]
PDIRK	$p=5$	$3(p-1)$	$p-1$	3	Strongly A-stable	$p-1$	§ 3.2
PDIRK	$p=6$	$3(p-1)$	$p-1$	3	Strongly $A(\alpha)$-stable	$p-1$	§ 3.2, $\alpha>89.9°$
PDIRK	$p=7$	$4(p-1)$	$p-1$	4	$A(\alpha)$-stable	$p-1$	§ 3.2, $\alpha>89.9°$
PDIRK $p\leq4,p=6$		$s(p-1)$	$p-1$	s	A-stable	$p-1$	§ 3.1
PDIRK $p\leq6,p=8$		sp	p	s	L-stable	$p-1$	§ 3.1
PDIRK $p\leq8,p=10$		$s(p+1)$	$p+1$	s	L^2-stable	$p-1$	§ 3.1

This table shows that the PDIRK methods constructed in this paper have the advantages of high order, good stability and embedded formulas, but the disadvantage of quite a large number of sequential stages per step. For example, in spite of its inherent parallelism, the number of sequential stages per step of an L^2-stable, eighth-order PDIRK method is 3 times as large as that of the A-stable, fourth-order SDIRK method of Crouzeix [6] and Alexander [1], and 9 times as large as that of the BDF methods. However, due to the iterative nature of PDIRK methods, the 'later' stages are relatively cheap because there are accurate initial iterates available for solving the associated implicit relations. This feature, and in particular their high order and unconditional stability, make PDIRK methods a promising starting point to base a code on. This is confirmed by a few preliminary experiments reported in Section 4, where we show by means of two 'difficult' test problems taken from the literature, that a provisional implementation of an L^2-stable, seventh-order, four-processor PDIRK method is already far superior to the SDIRK code SIMPLE of Nørsett and Thomsen [22] and at least competitive with the BDF code LSODE of Hindmarsh [11]. The development of a more sophisticated code based on PDIRK-type methods and much more extensive comparisons with existing sequential codes on a significant class of stiff problems will be subject of our future research and should provide more reliable data on the efficiency of PDIRK-based codes.

2. PDIRK METHODS

For notational convenience, we shall assume in the following that the equation (1.1) is a scalar equation. However, all considerations below are straightforwardly extended to systems of ODEs, and therefore, also to nonautonomous equations. Our starting point is the s-stage, implicit, one-step RK method

$$(2.1a) \qquad y_{n+1} = y_n + h\, b^T f(Y),$$

where Y is implicitly defined by the set of algebraic equations

$$(2.1b) \qquad Y := y_n e + h A f(Y).$$

Here, h is the integration step, e is a column vector of dimension s with unit entries, b is an s-dimensional vector and A is an s-by-s matrix. Furthermore, we use the convention that for any given vector $v=(v_j)$, $f(v)$ denotes the vector with entries $f(v_j)$.

By iterating, say m times, the equation for Y by diagonally implicit iteration, we obtain the method

$$(2.2) \qquad Y^{(j)} = y_n e + h\, [A - D]\, f(Y^{(j-1)}) + h D f(Y^{(j)}), \qquad y^{(j)} = y_n + h\, b^T f(Y^{(j)}),$$

where $j = 1, 2, \ldots, m$, and D is a diagonal matrix with arbitrary, nonnegative diagonal elements and $Y^{(0)}$ denotes an initial approximation to the vector Y. Notice that after each iteration the current approximation $y^{(j)}$ to y_{n+1} can be computed. As we shall see in Section 2.1, the order of these approximations increases by 1 in each iteration. Therefore, the mth iterate will be used to continue the integration process and the preceding iterates can be used for error control.

Since the matrix D is of diagonal form, the s components of each vector $Y^{(j)}$ can be computed in parallel, provided that s processors are available. Thus, effectively, we obtain a method which requires per integration step the computational time needed for computing one component of the initial approximation $Y^{(0)}$ and the successive solution of m equations. In the following, we always assume that we have s processors at our disposal and we shall speak about computational effort per step when we mean the computational time required per step if s processors are available. We shall call the method providing $Y^{(0)}$ the *predictor method* and (2.1) the *corrector method*.

There are several possibilities for choosing the matrix D. The most simple choice sets $D = O$ to obtain an explicit iteration method (fixed point or functional iteration). This approach was followed in, e.g., Nørsett and Simonsen [21], in Lie [18], and in van der Houwen and Sommeijer [12]. These papers deal with the iteration of implicit methods for solving *nonstiff* ODEs. As stated in the introduction, we are aiming at *stiff* ODEs, which requires the use of matrices $D \neq O$. One possibility of exploiting nonzero matrices D is improving the rate of convergence of the iteration process. For example, by identifying the diagonal elements of D with those of A we obtain the nonlinear Jacobi iteration method. Alternatively, one may choose D such that the stability region of the iterated method rapidly converges to that of the corrector (cf. [13]). In this paper, however, we choose D such that we have for a prescribed number of iterations favourable stability characteristics, such as A-stability or L-stability (as far as we know, this approach has not yet been investigated in the literature). We restrict our considerations to the case where the predictor method is itself an RK-type method. Hence, by performing m iterations with (2.2) and by accepting $y^{(m)}$ as the final approximation to y_{n+1}, we obtain an RK method with a fixed number of stages. Furthermore, we assume that the predictor is explicit or at most diagonally implicit. Then, the resulting parallel RK method belongs to the class of DIRK methods (Diagonally Implicit RK methods), and will be briefly called the *PDIRK method*.

2.1. Order of PDIRK methods

Assuming that the iteration process (2.2) converges as $m \rightarrow \infty$, the values $y^{(j)}$ approximate the solution of the corrector method (2.1), i.e., $y^{(\infty)} = y_{n+1}$. The approximation $y^{(j)}$ differs from $y^{(\infty)}$ by the amount

$$y^{(j)} - y^{(\infty)} = y^{(j)} - y_{n+1} = h\, b^{\mathrm{T}} \left[f(Y^{(j)}) - f(Y) \right].$$

If the right-hand side function is sufficiently smooth, then the iteration error $Y^{(j)} - Y$ satisfies the approximate recursion

$$Y^{(j)} - Y \approx h\, [I - h \frac{\partial f}{\partial y} D]^{-1} \frac{\partial f}{\partial y} [A - D][Y^{(j-1)} - Y] =$$
$$h^j \left([I - h \frac{\partial f}{\partial y} D]^{-1} \frac{\partial f}{\partial y} [A - D] \right)^j [Y^{(0)} - Y],$$

so that

(2.3) $\qquad y^{(m)} - y_{n+1} \approx h^{m+1} \frac{\partial f}{\partial y} b^{\mathrm{T}} \left([I - h \frac{\partial f}{\partial y} D]^{-1} \frac{\partial f}{\partial y} [A - D] \right)^m [Y^{(0)} - Y].$

Let the predictor be of order q, i.e.,

(2.4) $\qquad Y^{(0)} - Y = O(h^q) \quad \Rightarrow \quad y^{(0)} - y_{n+1} = O(h^{q+1}),$

then

$$y^{(m)} - y_{n+1} = O(h^{q+m+1}),$$

so that $y^{(m)}$ has (global) order $q+m$.

In this paper, we shall study PDIRK methods with predictors of the form

(2.5) $\qquad Y^{(0)} := y_n e + h E f(y_n e) + h B f(Y^{(0)})$.

Because this predictor is *implicit*, we will choose the matrix B of diagonal form in order to exploit parallelism. Since

$$Y^{(0)} - Y = y_n e + h E f(y_n e) + h B f(y_n e + h E f(y_n e) + h B f(y_n e)) -$$

$$y_n e - h A f(y_n e + h A f(y_n e)) + O(h^3),$$

it is easily verified that the predictor (2.5) is always first-order accurate; it becomes of order two if $(E + B - A) e$ vanishes and of order three if, in addition, $(BA - A^2) e$ vanishes.

By defining y_{n+1} according to

(2.6) $\qquad y_{n+1} := y^{(m)} = y_n + h b^T f(Y^{(m)})$,

the PDIRK method is completely determined. For this method, we summarize the above order considerations in the following theorem:

Theorem 2.1. Let the corrector be of order p^*; then the approximation y_{n+1} generated by the PDIRK method $\{(2.5), (2.2), (2.6)\}$ has order $\min\{p^*, m+1\}$ for all matrices B and E, order $\min\{p^*, m+2\}$ if $(E+B)e = Ae$, and order $\min\{p^*, m+3\}$ if, in addition, $BAe = A^2 e$. []

We remark that correctors of any order are explicitly available. Correctors of any *even* order p^* are provided by the $p^*/2$-stage Gauss-Legendre methods and correctors of any *odd* order p^* are provided by the $(p^*+1)/2$-stage Radau methods.

2.2. Stiffly accurate PDIRK methods

As was discussed by Alexander [1], when integrating stiff equations it may be advantageous to use RK methods $\{A, b\}$ of which b^T equals the last row of A, i.e., $b^T = e_s^T A$, where s is the number of stages of the RK method. Such RK methods are termed *stiffly accurate*. Therefore, it is of interest to look for PDIRK methods possessing the property of stiff accuracy. Formally, we can associate with any PDIRK method a new PDIRK method possessing the property of stiff accuracy, simply by replacing (2.6) with

(2.7) $\qquad y_{n+1} = e_s^T Y^{(m)}$.

Of course, this only yields a feasible method if the last component of the vector $Y^{(m)}$ provides an approximation to y_{n+1}. For example, this is true if the corrector itself is stiffly accurate, i.e., $b^T = e_s^T A$. We shall call the two versions corresponding to (2.6) and (2.7) PDIRK methods of Type I and II, and denote them by PDIRK^I and PDIRK^{II}, respectively. Thus,

Type I : PDIRK method {(2.5), (2.2), (2.6)}

Type II : PDIRK method {(2.5), (2.2), (2.7)}.

The following theorem is the analogue of Theorem 2.1:

Theorem 2.2. Let the corrector be stiffly accurate ($b^T = e_s^T A$) and be of order p^*; then the approximation y_{n+1} generated by the PDIRK^{II} method is also stiffly accurate, and has order $\min\{p^*, m\}$ for all matrices B and E, order $\min\{p^*, m+1\}$ if $(E+B)e = Ae$, and order $\min\{p^*, m+2\}$ if, in addition, $BAe = A^2e$.   []

2.3. Various types of PDIRK methods and their Butcher arrays

Given the generating RK method (corrector) $\{A, b\}$ defined by (2.1), we shall investigate three special families of PDIRK methods, either of Type I or of Type II, which differ from each other by the way in which the predictor is defined, i.e., in choosing the matrices B and E. Let O denote the s-by-s matrix with zero entries, then we distinguish:

Type A : Last-step-value predictor $(E=B=O)$ $Y^{(0)} := y_n e$,

Type B : Backward Euler predictor $(E=O, B=D)$ $Y^{(0)} := y_n e + h\, Df(Y^{(0)})$,

Type C : Theta method predictor $(B=D)$ $Y^{(0)} := y_n e + h\, Ef(y_n e) + h\, Df(Y^{(0)})$.

Notice that the matrix B either vanishes or is chosen equal to D. Although, in general, B and D may be different (diagonal) matrices, the particular choice $B = D$ has advantages with respect to the implementation of the method. Typically for stiff equations, the implicit relations in which the matrix $D = \text{diag}(d_1, d_2, ..., d_s)$ is involved, will be solved by some form of Newton iteration, which requires (in the case of systems of ODEs) the LU-decomposition of the matrices $I - d_i h\, \partial f/\partial y$. Clearly, if $B = D$ then these decompositions can also be used in solving the predictor (see also the discussion below). In the remainder of this paper, the analysis is performed in terms of a general matrix B and concrete results are only specified for $B = O$ or $B = D$.

For future reference, we specify the various PDIRK^I families of methods in terms of their Butcher arrays and give the corresponding orders of accuracy p^I:

Type IA:

1. $D \neq O$: $\quad p^I = \min\{p^*, m+1\}$

$j=0$	O						
$j=1$	$A{-}D$	D					
$j=2$	O	$A{-}D$	D				
$j=3$	O	O	$A{-}D$	D			
.	.		.	.			
.	.			.	.		
.	.				.	.	
$j=m$	O	.	.	.	O	$A{-}D$	D
	$\mathbf{0}^T$	.	.	.	$\mathbf{0}^T$	$\mathbf{0}^T$	b^T

Type IB:

1. $D \neq O$: $\quad p^I = \min\{p^*, m+1\}$
2. $D := \operatorname{diag}(Ae)$: $\quad p^I = \min\{p^*, m+2\}$

$j=0$	D						
$j=1$	$A{-}D$	D					
$j=2$	O	$A{-}D$	D				
$j=3$	O	O	$A{-}D$	D			
.	.		.	.			
.	.			.	.		
.	.				.	.	
$j=m$	O	.	.	.	O	$A{-}D$	D
	$\mathbf{0}^T$	.	.	.	$\mathbf{0}^T$	$\mathbf{0}^T$	b^T

Type IC:

1. $D \neq O, E \neq O$: $\quad p^I = \min\{p^*, m+1\}$
2. $D := \operatorname{diag}(Ae - Ee), E \neq O$: $\quad p^I = \min\{p^*, m+2\}$
3. $D := \operatorname{diag}(Ae - Ee), DAe = A^2 e$: $\quad p^I = \min\{p^*, m+3\}$

	O						
$j=0$	E	D					
$j=1$	O	$A{-}D$	D				
$j=2$	O	O	$A{-}D$	D			
.	.		.	.			
.	.			.	.		
.	.				.	.	
$j=m$	O	.	.	.	O	$A{-}D$	D
	$\mathbf{0}^T$	.	.	.	$\mathbf{0}^T$	$\mathbf{0}^T$	b^T

In these arrays, $\mathbf{0}$ denotes the s-dimensional nullvector. Type II versions are obtained by defining y_{n+1} by means of (2.7) instead of by (2.6), and, if the weights of the corrector satisfy $\mathbf{b}^T = \mathbf{e}_s^T A$, then by virtue of Theorem 2.2, we may replace p^I by p^{II} and m by $m-1$. Notice that the $\mathbf{b}$-vector is not actually needed if the algorithm is based on Type II methods. Furthermore, we remark that methods of Type B.2 are completely determined by the generating corrector, and that those of Type C.3 prescribe the matrix D and the row sums of the matrix E.

As already observed, PDIRK methods all belong to the class of DIRK methods (since the name DIRK is not consistently used in the literature, we remark that we shall call an RK method of DIRK type if the strict upper triangular part of its Butcher tableau vanishes). Moreover, the ith processor ($i=1,2,...,s$) is faced with solving a sequence of implicit relations in each of which the decomposition of the matrix $I - d_i h\, \partial f/\partial y$ is required (in case of systems of ODEs). Since this decomposition can be used in all m iterations in (2.2), we shall say that PDIRK methods are *singly* diagonally implicit RK methods (SDIRK methods). Here we remark that this terminology is often reserved for methods in which *all* stages are implicit with the same diagonal entry in their Butcher array. However, the zero diagonal entries in PDIRK methods of the Types A and C (originating from $B=O$) do not exclude these methods from the class of SDIRK methods, since these zeros mean that $f(y_n)$ has to be evaluated prior to the iteration process. Because the bulk of the computational effort per step consists in solving the implicit relations, the costs of this explicit stage are relatively negligible.

Therefore, taking parallelism into account, we shall say that PDIRK methods require k *sequential stages* if each processor has to solve k implicit relations per step. Thus, Type A methods require m sequential stages, whereas for Type B and Type C methods this number is given by $m+1$.

Finally, we observe that if the diagonal matrix D has *equal* diagonal entries, then all processors need the same LU-decomposed matrix in their solution processes. In such cases, this decomposition, as well as the evaluation of the Jacobian matrix $\partial f/\partial y$, may be performed by an additional processor, providing a 'fresh' decomposition for *all* processors as soon as it is available.

3. STABILITY

Applying the PDIRK method to the test equation

(3.1) $y'(t) = \lambda y(t),$

yields a relation of the form

$$y_{n+1} = R_m(z)y_n,$$

where $z := \lambda h$ and $R_m(z)$ is a rational function, the so-called *stability function*. The stability functions corresponding to PDIRK^I and PDIRK^{II} methods will be denoted by $R^I_m(z)$ and $R^{II}_m(z)$, respectively. They can be directly derived from the Butcher arrays by using the familiar 'determinant formula' (cf., e.g., [7, p.72]). However, the dimension of these arrays is usually so high that the evaluation of the determinants is rather tedious, even for small values of the number of iterations m. Therefore, we shall derive these stability functions by alternative techniques.

From (2.6) and (2.7) we see that the stability functions are respectively determined by

$$(3.2) \qquad y_{n+1} = y_n + z\, b^T\, Y^{(m)} = R^I_m(z)y_n \quad \text{and} \quad y_{n+1} = e_s^T\, Y^{(m)} = R^{II}_m(z)y_n.$$

In order to derive an expression for $Y^{(m)}$ we write

$$Y^{(j)} = [I - zD]^{-1}Q_j y_n e,$$

where the matrix Q_j follows from

$$Y^{(j)} = \begin{aligned}[t] &[I - zD]^{-1}\left[y_n e + z[A - D]Y^{(j-1)}\right] = \\ &[I - zD]^{-1}\left[y_n e + z[A - D][I - zD]^{-1}Q_{j-1}y_n e\right]. \end{aligned}$$

Introducing the matrix function

$$Z = Z(z) := z[A - D][I - zD]^{-1},$$

we find that Q_j satisfies the recursion

$$Q_0 = [I - zD][I - zB]^{-1}[I + zE], \qquad Q_j = I + ZQ_{j-1}, \quad j \geq 1.$$

Hence, the stability functions are given by

$$R^I_m(z) = 1 + zb^T[I - zD]^{-1}Q_m(z)e, \qquad R^{II}_m(z) = e_s^T[I - zD]^{-1}Q_m(z)e,$$

(3.3)

$$Q_m = Q_m(z) := I + Z + Z^2 + \dots + Z^{m-1} + Z^m[I - zD][I - zB]^{-1}[I + zE].$$

We shall separately consider the case where the diagonal matrices B and D have *constant* diagonal elements, and the case where the matrices B and D are *arbitrary* diagonal matrices.

3.1. PDIRK methods with constant diagonal elements

First, we consider the effect of setting $D=d \cdot I$ on the attainable order of those PDIRK methods which already impose conditions on the matrix D. Assuming that the generating corrector always satisfies the condition $Ae=c$, we find, according to the specification of PDIRK methods in Section 2.3, that

Type B.2: $\qquad D = \text{diag}(Ae) \qquad \Rightarrow \qquad de = c,$

Type C.3: $\qquad DAe = A^2 e \qquad \Rightarrow \qquad dc = Ac.$

By observing that third-order correctors require that $b^T e=1$, $b^T c=1/2$, $b^T Ac=1/6$ and $b^T c^2=1/3$, we see that PDIRK methods of Type B.2 cannot satisfy these conditions, so that their order is limited to $p^*= 2$, which is obtained for $d=1/2$. A necessary condition for Type C.3 methods to satisfy these third-order conditions requires $d=1/3$. However, the fourth-order condition $b^T A^2 c = 1/24$ cannot be satisfied, so that the order of Type C.3 methods is limited to $p^*= 3$. Obviously, we are not interested in such low-order methods. Furthermore, as will be shown below, we shall exclude methods of Type C.1, because the number of sequential stages is not optimal with respect to the order p. Thus, in this section we shall concentrate on PDIRK methods of Type A.1, Type B.1 and Type C.2.

Next, we return to the stability functions (3.3). For $B=b \cdot I$ and $D=d \cdot I$ the matrix $Q_m(z)$ can be written as

$$Q_m(z) = \frac{N_m(z)}{(1 - bz)(1 - dz)^{m-1}} \; ,$$

where $N_m(z)$ is a polynomial in z with matrix-valued coefficients; (3.3) becomes

(3.4) $\qquad R^I{}_m(z) = 1 + \dfrac{b^T z N_m(z) e}{(1 - bz)(1 - dz)^m} \; , \qquad R^{II}{}_m(z) = \dfrac{e_s{}^T N_m(z) e}{(1 - bz)(1 - dz)^m} \; .$

This representation shows that both stability functions are of the form

(3.5a) $\qquad R(z) := (1 - dz)^{-q} P(dz), \qquad P(dz) := \displaystyle\sum_{j=0}^{r} c_j \, (dz)^j,$

where the coefficients c_j depend on q and d (recall that either $b=0$ or $b=d$). For future reference, it is convenient to specify the values of r and q for the various types of methods. In Table 3.1 these values are listed for general values of d.

Table 3.1. Values of r and q in the stability function (3.5a).

Type	IA	IB	IC	IIA	IIB	IIC
$r=$	$m+1$	$m+1$	$m+2$	m	m	$m+1$
$q=$	m	$m+1$	$m+1$	m	$m+1$	$m+1$

For an arbitrary given value of d the order of consistency of the stability function (3.5a) cannot exceed r, hence, by choosing m such that the order p of the PDIRK method equals r, we achieve that the number of sequential stages is minimal with respect to the order p.

3.1.1. Derivation of A-acceptable and L-acceptable stability functions. The following theorem defines an explicit representation of the stability function.

Theorem 3.1. Let p be the order of the method and let m be such that $r=p$; then the coefficients of (3.5a) are given by

$$(3.5b) \qquad c_j = \sum_{i=0}^{j} \binom{q}{j-i} \frac{(-1)^{j-i}}{i! \, d^i}, \; j = 0, 1, \dots, q; \qquad c_j = \sum_{i=0}^{q} \binom{q}{i} \frac{(-1)^i}{(j-i)! \, d^{j-i}},$$

where $j = q+1, q+2, \dots, p$, and $0! := 1$.

Proof. Since it is assumed that the method is of order p we necessarily have $R(z) = \exp(z) + O(z^{p+1})$. By expanding the function $(1-dz)^q \exp(z)$ in a Taylor series at $z=0$ and by equating corresponding coefficients in this expansion and in the polynomial $P(z)$, defined in (3.5a), we can find the first $p+1$ coefficients of P. Hence, all coefficients of P are uniquely determined and are given by (3.5b) (see also Nørsett [19] and Butcher [3, p. 246] for expressions in terms of derivatives of Laguerre polynomials). []

Notice that the condition $r=p$ excludes methods of Type C.1, because for Type I and Type II variants the maximal order is $m+1$ and m, respectively, which is one lower than the corresponding value of r. As a consequence, for methods of Type C with stability functions of the form (3.5), the order should be increased by one, which is obtained by requiring the matrix E to satisfy the condition $Ee = Ae - de$.

By means of Theorem 3.1 the stability analysis is now rather straightforward. Following Nørsett [20] and Butcher [3], we write $u=y^2$ and define the so-called E-polynomial

$$E(u) := |(1-iy)^q|^2\left[1-|R(iy/d)|^2\right] = |(1-iy)^q|^2 - |P(iy)|^2$$

$$= (1+u)^q - [c_0 - c_2u + c_4u^2 - \ldots]^2 - u[c_1 - c_3u + c_5u^2 - \ldots]^2.$$

From the condition $R(z)=\exp(z)+O(z^{p+1})$ it follows that $|R(iy/d)|^2=1+O(y^{p+1})$, so that $E(y^2)=O(y^{p+1})$. Hence, all terms of $E(y^2)$ of degree less than $p+1$ in y vanish, so that

$$E(u)= \sum_{j=\lfloor p/2 \rfloor+1}^{q} e_j\, u^j, \qquad e_j = e_j(d) := \binom{q}{j} - c_j^2 - 2\sum_{i=1} (-1)^i\, c_{j-i}\, c_{j+i},$$

with $c_j := 0$ if $j>p$ or $j<0$.

Because of the maximum principle, we have A-stability if $|R(iy)|$ is bounded by 1 for all real y, so that the method is A-stable if, and only if, $E(u)$ is nonnegative for $u \geq 0$.

Values of d for which $R(z)$ is A-acceptable will be called A-acceptable. Let the range of d-values which are A-acceptable be denoted by I_{pq}, i.e., $I_{pq}:=\{d\colon E(u)\geq 0$ for all $u \geq 0\}$; then the following summary is easily obtained by using Table 3.1 and the order results obtained for the various types of methods (p^* denotes the order of the corrector $\{A, b\}$):

Table 3.2. Summary of properties of PDIRK methods with constant diagonal elements.

Type	Condition	Order	Sequential stages	A-acceptable d-values
IA.1	$m \leq p^*-1$	$m+1$	m	$I_{m+1,m}$
IB.1	$m \leq p^*-1$	$m+1$	$m+1$	$I_{m+1,m+1}$
IC.2	$m \leq p^*-2$	$m+2$	$m+1$	$I_{m+2,m+1}$
IIA.1	$m \leq p^*$	m	m	$I_{m,m}$
IIB.1	$m \leq p^*$	m	$m+1$	$I_{m,m+1}$
IIC.2	$m \leq p^*-1$	$m+1$	$m+1$	$I_{m+1,m+1}$

Notice that $R(z)$ is L-acceptable if $R(z)$ is A-acceptable and if $q>p$. From Table 3.2 we see that the methods of Type IIB.1 possess L-acceptable stability functions. Since L-stable methods are usually more suitable for integrating stiff equations than

A-stable methods, the methods of Type IIB.1 are of interest in spite of the additional sequential stage when compared with the other methods. However, just as in the case of SDIRK methods, it is possible that an A-stable method can be made L-stable if the interval of A-acceptable d-values contains a value for which c_p vanishes. For $q = p \leq 15$, this has been investigated by Wolfbrandt [25] and it was found that such values of d exist for $p \leq 6$ and $p = 8$. This information is summarized in Table 3.3a.

In a similar way, L-acceptable ranges of d-values can be found in the case $q = p+1$. These ranges turn out to be nonempty for $p \leq 8$ and for $p=10$, and are given in Table 3.3b. Moreover, we list the values of $d_{p,p+1}$, which are inside these L-acceptable ranges and cause c_p to vanish, resulting in even stronger damping at 'infinity' (L^2-stability).

Finally, we considered the case $q = p-1$, resulting from IA.1 and IC.2 type methods. Since now the degree of the numerator in $R(z)$ is larger than that of the denominator, a necessary condition for this case to yield A-stability, is that c_p vanishes. For $p = 2, 3, ..., 10$ we determined the zeros of $c_p(d)$ and checked the resulting stability function on A-acceptability. Only for $p=2$ ($d=1/2$), $p=3$ ($d=(3+\sqrt{3})/6$), $p=4$ ($d=1.0685790213$), and $p=6$ ($d=0.47326839126$) A-stability can be obtained. Hence, in this way we have found A-stable methods of orders $p \leq 4$ and $p=6$ requiring $p-1$ sequential stages. This result is similar to what is possible in the case of RK methods for sequential computers (cf. [1] for $p \leq 4$ and [5] for $p=6$); however, the present methods contain embedded formulas of lower order.

Table 3.3a. A-acceptable and L-acceptable values of d for $p = q$.

$p = q$	Range I_{pp}	d_{pp}
1	[1/2, ∞]	1
2	[1/4, ∞]	$1 \pm \sqrt{1/2}$
3	[1/3, 1.068]	0.43586650
4	[0.395, 1.280]	0.5728160625
5	[0.247, 0.361] + [0.421, 0.473]	0.2780538410
6	[0.285, 0.54]	0.3341423671
7	empty	
8	[0.218, 0.264]	0.2343731596
9	empty	
10	empty	

Notice that any s-stage, pth-order corrector (even explicit corrector methods) can be used for generating A-stable methods of Type IB, and any pth-order corrector satisfying the condition $b^T = e_s^T A$ for generating the A-stable methods of Type IIA and IIC, or the L-stable methods of Type IIB.

Furthermore, we have seen that the stability can be improved by selecting special d-values. Another possibility, which might be useful in a variable-stepsize implementation, is to exploit the *length* of the A- and L-acceptable ranges: for small changes in the stepsize h, the value of $h \cdot d$ could be kept fixed (as long as the corresponding d-value is still in the allowed range, of course), so that a new decomposition of $I - h\,d\,\partial f/\partial y$ can be avoided.

Table 3.3b. Ranges of L-acceptable values of d for $p = q - 1$.

$p = q - 1$	Range $I_{p,p+1}$	$d_{p,p+1}$
1	$[1-\sqrt{1/2},\ 1+\sqrt{1/2}]$	0.5
2	$[0.181, 2.185]$	$0.5 \pm \sqrt{1/12}$
3	$[0.224, 0.572]$	0.3025345782
4	$[0.248, 0.676]$	0.3888576711
5	$[0.184, 0.334]$	0.2168805435
6	$[0.205, 0.378]$	0.2579552416
7	$[0.157, 0.2029] + [0.2052, 0.234]$	0.1690246379
8	$[0.171, 0.259]$	0.1929778040
9	empty	
10	$[0.147, 0.165] + [0.1938, 0.1961]$	0.1541460739

3.1.2. Accuracy test. It is well known [7] that, when integrating general stiff systems, the actually observed order is usually much lower than the *classical order p*. In fact, the order behaviour is often dictated by the so-called *stage order r* (for a definition of this notion and its consequences the reader is referred to [7]). Since most (P)DIRK methods have stage order $r = 1$, one might question the relevance of PDIRK methods possessing a high classical order. And indeed, for a general stiff problem, this order reduction phenomenon has great impact on the accuracy of this type of methods.

However, in [10], Hairer, Lubich and Roche give a thorough analysis of the behaviour of RK methods when applied to a singular perturbed problem of the form

$$(3.6) \qquad \varepsilon\frac{dy_1}{dt} = f_1(y_1, y_2), \qquad \frac{dy_2}{dt} = f_2(y_1, y_2), \qquad \text{with } \varepsilon \ll 1,$$

and show that for special RK methods the classical order may still dominate the global error, especially if stiffness increases (i.e., if $\varepsilon \to 0$). The motivation for considering this particular problem class is that it has practical significance and has been extensively studied in the literature (see the references cited in [10]). An important characteristic of problems of the form (3.6) is that the eigenvalues of the Jacobian matrix can be clustered into two groups, and behave as $O(1)$ and $O(\varepsilon^{-1})$, respectively. Here we give the essential result of Hairer et al. concerning the global error (cf. [10, Theorem 1 on p. 680]):

Theorem 3.2. Let the RK method be A-stable and let $\varepsilon \leq$ Constant$\cdot h$; then the global error for the stiff component y_1 behaves as $O(\varepsilon h^r) + O(h^p)$ if $b^T = e_s^T A$ and as $O(h^{r+1})$ if $|R(\infty)| < 1$. For both cases, the global error for the nonstiff component y_2 behaves as $O(\varepsilon h^{r+1}) + O(h^p)$. []

This result indicates that Type II methods are to be preferred if $\varepsilon \to 0$, since then the global error is dominated by the classical order, whereas methods of Type I will behave according to their (low) stage order.

To illustrate these properties, we applied a few of the PDIRK methods derived in the preceding subsection to a problem of the form (3.6), proposed by Kaps [17]:

$$
(3.6') \qquad
\begin{aligned}
\frac{dy_1}{dt} &= -(2 + \varepsilon^{-1})y_1 + \varepsilon^{-1}(y_2)^2, & y_1(0) &= 1, \\
\frac{dy_2}{dt} &= y_1 - y_2(1 + y_2), & y_2(0) &= 1,
\end{aligned}
\qquad 0 \leq t \leq 1,
$$

with the smooth exact solution $y_1 = \exp(-2t)$ and $y_2 = \exp(-t)$ for all values of the parameter ε.

The methods we have used in our tests are based on correctors of different classical order (a specification of these correctors can be found in the appendix to the report [14]). Moreover, all methods were equipped with the special d_{pp} or $d_{p,p+1}$ values given in the Tables 3.3 and, consequently, are L-stable and L^2-stable, respectively.

For $\varepsilon = 10^{-8}$ the absolute error for the stiff component y_1 at the end point $t=1$ is given in Table 3.4; here, the error is written in the form $10^{-\Delta}$ and the values of Δ are listed. Notice that the Type II methods require a stiffly accurate corrector (such as the Radau IIA formulas) and that L-stable, seventh-order PDIRK methods are only possible within the family of Type IIB.1 methods (cf. Tables 3.2 and 3.3b). This table clearly demonstrates the superiority of the stiffly accurate Type II methods over the Type I methods, which show only a second-order behaviour for the global error (recall that $r=1$ for the Type IB.1 methods). On the other hand, the stiffly accurate methods exhibit the classical order in the error behaviour and thus both results are in perfect agreement with the estimates in the theorem of Hairer et al.

From this experiment we may conclude that it is relevant indeed to have high-order PDIRK methods for integrating stiff systems of the form (3.6), in spite of their low stage order.

Comparing the efficiency of the various parallel methods of Type II, we observe that schemes of Type A and C are equally efficient, since they require the same number of sequential stages (cf. Table 3.2). The Type IIB.1 methods yield slightly more accurate results, but need an additional stage to reach the same order (we remark that the seventh-order method of this type does not show full advantage, since the integration process was impeded by the machine precision).

Table 3.4. Values of Δ at $t=1$ for the first component of problem (3.6') with $\varepsilon=10^{-8}$.

Type	Corrector	Order	$h=1/4$	$h=1/8$	$h=1/16$	$h=1/32$	$h=1/64$	Seq. Stages per step	Proc.
IB.1	Radau IIA	3	3.7	4.1	4.6	5.2	5.8	3	2
	Gauss-Legendre	4	2.9	3.6	4.2	4.8	5.4	4	2
	Explicit RK	4	3.0	3.7	4.3	4.9	5.5	4	4
	Radau IIA	5	3.6	4.3	4.9	5.5	6.1	5	3
	Gauss-Legendre	6	3.1	3.7	4.4	5.0	5.6	6	3
IIA.1	Radau IIA	3	4.0	4.9	5.8	6.7	7.6	3	2
	Radau IIA	5	6.9	8.4	9.8	10.6	11.0	5	3
IIB.1	Radau IIA	3	4.3	5.2	6.1	7.0	7.9	4	2
	Radau IIA	5	7.2	8.7	10.3	11.8	11.8	6	3
	Radau IIA	7	9.7	10.2	10.6	10.9	11.2	8	4
IIC.2	Radau IIA	3	4.0	4.9	5.8	6.7	7.6	3	2
	Radau IIA	5	6.9	8.4	9.8	10.6	11.0	5	3

3.2. PDIRK methods with arbitrary diagonal matrices

In the case where B and D are allowed to be arbitrary diagonal matrices, it is convenient to express $Q_m(z)$ in the form

$$Q_m(z) = [I - Z]^{-1}[I - Z^m] + Z^m Q_0$$
$$= [I - Z]^{-1}[I - Z^m] + Z^m[I - zD][I - zB]^{-1}[I + zE].$$

Since $[I - zD]^{-1} = [I - zA]^{-1}[I - Z]$, we find

$$Q_m(z) = [I - zD][I - zA]^{-1}\big[I - Z^m + [I - Z]Z^m[I - zD][I - zB]^{-1}[I + zE]\big],$$

so that (3.3) yields

(3.3')

$$R^I_m(z) = 1 + zb^T[I - zA]^{-1}\big[I - Z^m + [I - Z]Z^m[I - zD][I - zB]^{-1}[I + zE]\big]e,$$

$$R^{II}_m(z) = e_s^T[I - zA]^{-1}\big[I - Z^m + [I - Z]Z^m[I - zD][I - zB]^{-1}[I + zE]\big]e =$$

$$= 1 + e_s^T[I - zA]^{-1}\big[zA - Z^m + [I - Z]Z^m[I - zD][I - zB]^{-1}[I + zE]\big]e.$$

In the following two subsections, a representation for the stability functions without inverses of matrices will be given, and stability characteristics of PDIRK methods of the Types IB.2, IIB.2 and IIC.3 are presented.

3.2.1. Representation theorems. The following theorem gives a representation of the stability functions in terms of determinants containing only inverses of diagonal matrices:

Theorem 3.3. The stability functions (3.3') can be represented by

$$
R^I_m(z) = \frac{\det\left\{I - zA + z\left[I - Z^m + [I - Z]Z^m[I - zD][I - zB]^{-1}[I + zE]\right]eb^T\right\}}{\det\{I - zA\}},
$$

(3.7)

$$
R^{II}_m(z) = \frac{\det\{I - zA + \left[zA - Z^m + [I - Z]Z^m[I - zD][I - zB]^{-1}[I + zE]\right]ee_s^T\}}{\det\{I - zA\}}.
$$

Proof. Applying the identity

$$
1 + x^T N^{-1} y = \frac{\det\{N + yx^T\}}{\det\{N\}}
$$

to the stability functions, (3.3') straightforwardly leads to the representations (3.7). []

The expressions (3.7) can be simplified for the respective Types A, B and C:

Corollary 3.1. Let the matrix Z be given by $Z = z[A - D][I - zD]^{-1}$; then the following assertions hold:

(a) The stability function of PDIRK methods of Type A.1 are given by

$$
(3.8a) \qquad R^I_m(z) = \frac{\det\left\{I - zA + z[I - zZ^m A]eb^T\right\}}{\det\{I - zA\}},
$$

$$
R^{II}_m(z) = \frac{\det\left\{I - zA + z[I - Z^m]Aee_s^T\right\}}{\det\{I - zA\}}.
$$

(b) The stability function of PDIRK methods of Type B are given by

$$
(3.8b) \qquad R^I_m(z) = \frac{\det\left\{I - zA + z[I - Z^{m+1}]eb^T\right\}}{\det\{I - zA\}},
$$

$$
R^{II}_m(z) = \frac{\det\left\{I - zA + [zA - Z^{m+1}]ee_s^T\right\}}{\det\{I - zA\}}.
$$

(c) The stability function of PDIRK methods of Type C.2 or Type C.3 are given by

$$(3.8c) \quad R^{\mathrm{I}}_m(z) = \frac{\det\{I - zA + z[I - zZ^{m+1}A]eb^{\mathrm{T}}\}}{\det\{I - zA\}},$$

$$R^{\mathrm{II}}_m(z) = \frac{\det\{I - zA + z[I - Z^{m+1}]Aee_s^{\mathrm{T}}\}}{\det\{I - zA\}}. \quad []$$

Notice that these expressions no longer explicitly depend on E and B and are completely determined by the corrector and the matrix Z.

3.2.2. Stability characteristics. In this subsection, we consider the stability of PDIRK methods. We shall distinguish between methods based on Radau IIA correctors and on Gauss-Legendre correctors.

The Radau IIA correctors have order $p=2s-1$, where s is the number of stages, and satisfy the condition $b^{\mathrm{T}}=e_s^{\mathrm{T}}A$ (their Butcher arrays for $s=1,...,4$ are given in the appendix to [14]). Owing to this property, PDIRK methods of Type I and Type II are both relevant. We confine our considerations to types which require (with respect to their order) less sequential stages than the corresponding methods indicated in Table 3.2, that is, we consider methods of the Types IB.2, IIB.2, and IIC.3. For these types of methods, the stability functions are completely determined.

Table 3.5. Characteristics of PDIRK methods

Type	Corrector	Order	Seq.Stages	Processors	Stability
IB.2	Radau IIA	3	2	2	Strongly A-stable
	Gauss-Legendre	4	3	2	Strongly A-stable
	Radau IIA	5	4	3	Strongly A-stable
	Gauss-Legendre	6	5	3	Strongly $A(\alpha)$-stable, $\alpha=89.97°$
	Radau IIA	7	6	4	Strongly $A(\alpha)$-stable, $\alpha=83.3°$
IIB.2	Radau IIA	3	3	2	$L(\alpha)$-stable, $\alpha=89.75°$
	Radau IIA	5	5	3	$L(\alpha)$-stable, $\alpha=89.12°$
	Radau IIA	7	7	4	$L(\alpha)$-stable, $\alpha=89.02°$
IIC.3	Radau IIA	3	2	2	A-stable
	Radau IIA	5	4	3	$A(\alpha)$-stable, $\alpha=89.997°$
	Radau IIA	7	6	4	$A(\alpha)$-stable, $\alpha=89.95°$

In Table 3.5, we present a summary of the characteristics of these methods for several orders. Based on the stability functions (3.8), the stability region of the methods was determined numerically. It turned out that some stability functions are only $A(\alpha)$-acceptable. However, in these cases α is very close to $90°$ (in the Appendix to [14], a set of stability regions is given, including the regions of the embedded lower-order methods).

Furthermore, we considered PDIRK methods based on Gauss-Legendre correctors. Such s-stage correctors have order $2s$, but are not stiffly accurate and, hence, only Type I methods are relevant. In Table 3.5 we have included the characteristics of fourth- and sixth-order methods of Type IB.2 (the generating correctors can be found in [3, p. 219]).

In comparison with the PDIRK methods constructed in Section 3.1, we observe that the above PDIRK methods of Types IB.2 and IIC.3 require one sequential stage less to obtain a given order of accuracy. Moreover, with the exception of the 7th-order method of Type IB.2, these methods possess almost the same good stability properties.

For the methods of Type IIB.2 (for which the order equals the number of sequential stages), only the seventh-order is relevant, since in Section 3.1 it turned out to be impossible to construct an L-stable method of order 7 with 7 sequential stages; the third- and fifth-order methods of Type IIB.2 do not have an advantage over the L-stable methods described in Section 3.1.

3.2.3. Accuracy test. We conclude this section by applying the methods specified in Table 3.5 to the problem (3.6'). Using the same notation as described in Section 3.1.3, the results are given in Table 3.6.

Again, the stiffly accurate Type II methods are much more efficient than the methods of Type I. Moreover, the order behaviour nicely illustrates the results of the theorem of Hairer et al. (cf. Section 3.1.2). Furthermore, within the class of stiffly accurate methods, the C-variant is superior to the B-variant, since it is cheaper and yields, for this example, more accuracy.

Table 3.6. Values of Δ at $t=1$ for the first component of problem (3.6') with $\varepsilon=10^{-8}$.

Type	Corrector	Order	$h=1/4$	$h=1/8$	$h=1/16$	$h=1/32$	$h=1/64$	Seq. Stages per step	Proc.
IB.2	Radau IIA	3	2.8	3.8	4.1	4.7	5.3	2	2
	Gauss-Legendre	4	2.7	3.4	4.0	4.6	5.3	3	2
	Radau IIA	5	2.4	2.8	3.4	4.1	4.8	4	3
	Gauss-Legendre	6	3.0	3.5	4.1	4.8	5.4	5	3
	Radau IIA	7	4.2	4.6	5.2	5.8	6.4	6	4
IIB.2	Radau IIA	3	3.4	4.1	4.9	5.8	6.7	3	2
	Radau IIA	5	4.9	6.1	7.5	9.0	10.4	5	3
	Radau IIA	7	6.4	8.2	10.1	11.9	12.5	7	4
IIC.3	Radau IIA	3	4.3	5.2	6.1	7.0	7.9	2	2
	Radau IIA	5	6.6	8.0	9.4	10.8	11.6	4	3
	Radau IIA	7	8.7	10.6	12.0	12.3	12.6	6	4

4. EFFICIENCY TESTS

Finally, we will investigate the performance of PDIRK methods when run on a parallel computer. Because it is highly desirable to use an unconditionally stable method of high order, we selected a PDIRK method of Type IIB.1 with a D-matrix of the form $D = d \cdot I$. On the basis of the accuracy test described in Section 3.1.2, we decided to choose the seventh-order, four-point Radau IIA corrector (see (A.3) in the Appendix to [14]), with $m=7$ iterations. The resulting method is of order seven (cf. Theorem 2.2) and by choosing $d = 0.1690246379$ we achieve strong damping at infinity (L^2-stability, cf. Table 3.3b). Hence, taking into account the (implicit) predictor, the method requires eight sequential stages per step. We have implemented this method on an ALLIANT FX/4 computer, having four parallel (vector-) processors, shared memory and approximately 16 digits arithmetic precision. Since the underlying Radau method has four stages, we may expect an efficient use of this machine.

In order to be able to test problems with a strongly fluctuating solution, we equipped the above fixed-order PDIRK method with a simple strategy for error control and stepsize selection. Since the PDIRK approach provides a whole set of embedded reference solutions of lower order, we can construct an estimate of the local truncation error without additional costs. For this purpose we take $\| e_4^T Y^{(m)} - e_4^T Y^{(m-1)} \|$ as an estimate for the local error. All implicit relations are iterated using modified Newton iteration. If convergence happens to fail within a fixed number of iterations (in our version, we choose this number equal to 10), then we update the Jacobian and, if still no convergence can be obtained, we halve the stepsize (repeatedly, if necessary). Furthermore, the Newton process to solve for $Y^{(j)}$ is started with the initial guess $Y^{(j-1)}$, which is of increasing accuracy for increasing j. It should be observed that this provisional implementation certainly can be improved by a better tuning of the separate elements (for example, all kinds of thresholds and strategy parameters should be tuned on the basis of extensive testing). Since it is not the aim of this paper to present such a 'production code', we will give results for our 'research version'.

The goal of our tests is twofold:

(i) We want to investigate to what extent the theoretical parallelization can be realized in practice; in other words, what speedup factor can be obtained on this four-processor machine. Obviously, the ideal factor of four will be too optimistic, due to some unavoidable overhead, like communication and sequential parts in the program.

(ii) We want to compare the performance of the parallelized PDIRK code with that of a good sequential ODE solver. Within the class of sequential solvers based on unconditionally stable methods, we selected the code SIMPLE of Nørsett and Thomsen [22]. The method underlying this robust and reliable code is closely related to the PDIRK method, i.e., it is also based on an unconditionally stable, diagonally implicit Runge-Kutta method. Furthermore, SIMPLE is, like PDIRK, equipped with embedding techniques to control the local error. A disadvantage of this code is that its order is rather low; it is based on a third-order DIRK method. However, high-order A-stable DIRK-codes are not available in the literature. Since many problems are more efficiently integrated if high-order formulas are available, we also looked for a code based on methods of various orders. This leads us to LSODE of Hindmarsh [11]. This BDF based code has enjoyed very successful usage over a long period. However, the fact that only the first- and second-order formula in this code are unconditionally stable, makes LSODE less robust as a *general* stiff solver. It is well known that the performance of this code may decrease significantly when it is applied to problems with eigenvalues in the vicinity of the imaginary axis (see, for example, Stewart [23]). On the other hand, since LSODE is generally accepted as being a good sequential ODE solver, we decided to include it in our tests.

In the next subsections, we describe the results obtained when the aforementioned three codes are applied to some hard problems. Since the codes are different in nature (low order versus high order, onestep versus multistep), we refrain from specifying the traditional statistical output of an automatic ODE solver, like number of steps, number of LU-decompositions etc. It should be observed that the work involved per step is quite different for the various codes: for instance, the sequential number of implicit relations to be solved per step equals 1 for LSODE, 4 for SIMPLE, and 8 for PDIRK. Since the codes do not yield equal accuracy for the same value of the local error control parameter TOL, we list results for various values of TOL and measured the accuracy produced as well as the CPU-time required. All accuracies are given in terms of Δ, the number of correct digits in the endpoint of the integration interval (see Section 3.1.2), and the CPU-times are given in seconds.

4.1. Robertson kinetics example

In our first example we solve a set of reaction-rate equations:

$$
\begin{aligned}
\frac{dy_1}{dt} &= -0.04 \, y_1 + 10^4 \, y_2 \, y_3, \\
(4.1) \quad \frac{dy_2}{dt} &= 0.04 \, y_1 - 10^4 \, y_2 \, y_3 - 3 \cdot 10^7 \, (y_2)^2, \\
\frac{dy_3}{dt} &= 3 \cdot 10^7 \, (y_2)^2,
\end{aligned}
$$

defined on the interval $[0,10^8]$ with initial conditions $y_1(0) = 1$, $y_2(0) = y_3(0) = 0$. This problem is also used by Hindmarsh and Nørsett-Thomsen to illustrate the performance of LSODE and SIMPLE.

Initially, the solution changes rapidly and small stepsizes are required; gradually the solution reaches a steady state and the stepsize can be increased considerably. In a typical situation we observed stepsizes in the range $[10^{-3}, 10^6]$. Hence this problem imposes a severe test on the stepsize selection procedure. The results obtained by the various codes are collected in Table 4.1. Here T_1 means the CPU-time when only one processor is used, and T_4 denotes the CPU-time required when the program is run on four processors.

Table 4.1. Δ-values and CPU-times for problem (4.1)

Method	TOL	Δ	T_1	T_4
SIMPLE	10^{-4}	6.5	0.63	0.85
	10^{-5}	7.8	1.38	$>T_1$
	10^{-6}	9.5	3.67	$>T_1$
LSODE	10^{-5}	7.4	0.35	$>T_1$
	10^{-7}	8.6	0.80	$>T_1$
	10^{-9}	10.3	1.71	$>T_1$
PDIRK	10^2	8.5	0.51	0.19
	10^0	11.1	1.08	0.37

These results give rise to the following conclusions:

(i) Concerning the parallelization of the PDIRK code we observe a speedup with a factor $(T_1/T_4 \approx)$ 2.68 and 2.91 for the two values of TOL that we have used. One reason why these numbers are less than the optimal speedup factor 4, is the introduction of inevitable overhead (and of scalar code). Another reason is algorithmic in nature. Each component of the prediction $Y^{(0)}$ is a numerical approximation to the ODE solution at the point $t_n+d\,h$ (actually, all processors have solved exactly the same implicit relation in this predictor stage). These components are used as an initial guess in the various Newton processes computing $Y^{(1)}$. Since the components of $Y^{(1)}$ are approximations to the ODE solution at *different* points (i.e., the Radau points), these initial guesses do not have equal accuracy, so that we may expect different numbers of Newton iterations on the various processors. In the case TOL = 1, we measured the actual numbers of Newton iterations over the whole integration interval and found, for the four processors, 848, 924, 1012 and 1043, respectively. This means that in some steps a few processors have met the convergence criterion in the Newton process, and thus have been idle for some time while waiting for the other processors to complete solving their implicit relation. Taking this aspect into account, the optimal parallelization cannot exceed a speedup factor equal to (848+924+1012+1043)/1043 $\approx$ 3.67. The measured speedup in this case equals 2.91 (i.e., 79%), showing that the overhead (communication, scalar code etc.) only slightly degrades the performance. The reduction of the ideal factor 4 to

3.67 is a price we have to pay in choosing a PDIRK method. We may conclude that the actual efficiency of the method as a whole, defined as the total speedup divided by the number of processors used, equals $2.91/4 = 0.73$.

(ii) Concerning the scalar codes SIMPLE and LSODE, we observe that they run faster on one processor than on four (see the result obtained by SIMPLE for $TOL=10^{-4}$). Apparently, the parallelization and vectorization overhead does not pay for this problem (this might be different in case of an ODE with many components). Therefore, we only give timings for the uniprocessor experiments.

(iii) When compared with PDIRK, we see that SIMPLE needs much more time in the high-accuracy range. This is obviously due to its low order. LSODE, which can utilize higher orders, is more efficient in this range but, when compared to PDIRK, its CPU-time is approximately four times larger to obtain 8.5 digits precision and this factor increases if still higher-precision results are requested (notice that even on one processor, PDIRK is faster than LSODE on this problem).

(iv) Finally, we observe that the value for TOL used by PDIRK is several orders of magnitude larger than the value used by either SIMPLE or LSODE to achieve the same global error. This can be explained as follows: Owing to its high order, the local truncation error of PDIRK is usually relatively small. Therefore, if crude tolerances are used, the error control mechanism signals that a large stepsize can be used in order to balance the estimated and the requested local error. On the other hand, the Newton process imposes a limitation on the stepsize. In our implementation, the Newton processes to solve for $Y^{(0)}$ are given the value y_n as initial iterate. Unfortunately, for large values of h (as suggested by the error estimator) this initial iterate is not always inside the contraction domain for the Newton process, resulting in an adequate reduction of the stepsize. As a consequence, this high-order scheme, using a small(er) stepsize, will produce a local error which is much smaller than requested.

In conclusion, for this test problem (and also for the problem to be discussed in the next subsection), the restriction on the stepsize imposed by the Newton process is more stringent than that imposed by the local error control, unless very small values for TOL are used. We have also integrated some *linear* ODEs (for which the convergence problems are not relevant, of course) and observed a relation between TOL and the global error similar to that of SIMPLE and LSODE.

Summarizing, for obtaining highly accurate results, the above experiment shows that the high order of the PDIRK method is worth the large amount of redundancy introduced in its construction. In this connection we remark that the order of these methods can still be raised to 10, whereas an increase of the order is not possible for BDF methods and not feasible for embedded DIRK methods underlying the SIMPLE code.

4.2. Van der Pol's equation

Our second example is given by the van der Pol equation

(4.2) $y'' - \mu (1 - y^2) y' + y = 0.$

For $\mu=5$, this is problem E2 from the test set of Enright et al. [8]. However, as reported there, on the interval [0,1] the spectral radius of the Jacobian does not exceed 15, so that the problem is not really stiff. Therefore, we set this parameter to 50. For this μ-value the equation exhibits so called 'relaxation oscillations', which means that the solution possesses internal boundary layers. Furthermore, we consider an integration interval sufficiently large to capture such an internal layer, which again requires an adequate stepsize selection procedure. The problem tested in this section is defined by

(4.2')
$$\frac{dy_1}{dt} = y_2, \qquad\qquad y_1(0) = 2,$$
$$\frac{dy_2}{dt} = 50 \left(1 - (y_1)^2\right) y_2 - y_1, \qquad y_2(0) = 0, \qquad 0 \le t \le 41.5 .$$

This test example has also been discussed by Gottwald and Wanner in [9]. At approximately $t = 40.7$, the solution y_1 drops from 1 to -2 on a very short interval, forcing the codes to reduce their steplengths dramatically (several orders of magnitude). The results of the various codes applied to this problem can be found in Table 4.2.

Table 4.2. Δ-values and CPU-times for problem (4.2')

Method	TOL	Δ	T_1	T_4
SIMPLE	10^{-6}	5.6	1.07	$>T_1$
	10^{-8}	6.9	5.64	$>T_1$
	10^{-10}	7.8	25.5	$>T_1$
LSODE	10^{-6}	4.3	0.24	$>T_1$
	10^{-8}	6.3	0.42	$>T_1$
	10^{-10}	7.8	0.83	$>T_1$
PDIRK	10	5.1	0.56	0.20
	10^{-2}	6.1	1.20	0.41
	10^{-5}	7.2	2.44	0.82

Again, we see that PDIRK can take advantage from the availability of four processors: on the average, the speedup is 2.9 (or, equivalently, the efficiency is ≈ 0.72). For this problem the loss in efficiency due to overhead is less than

124

$(1 - 0.72 =)$ 0.28, because the various processors required a different number of Newton iterations (viz., for TOL=10^{-5} we found 3186, 3561, 3882 and 4092 iterations, respectively, thus reducing the optimal speedup factor from 4 to 3.6).

Furthermore, it is quite clear that the low-order SIMPLE code becomes excessively more expensive for smaller values of TOL. On the other hand, LSODE behaves rather efficient for this problem and is approximately equally efficient as PDIRK.

4.3. Conclusions

On the basis of these (difficult) problems we may draw the following conclusions:

- the actually obtained degree of parallelization of the PDIRK method is fairly close to its ideal value.
- the reason that SIMPLE is less efficient than the other two codes, especially in the high accuracy range, is because of its low order.
- it is well known that the higher-order BDF formulas lack the property of L-stability. This may result in serious difficulties for LSODE in the case that the Jacobian has eigenvalues in the vicinity of the imaginary axis. However, the two test problems do not belong to this category; hence, LSODE has not been faced with the limitation of the stability regions of the higher-order BDFs.
- unlike the implementation of SIMPLE and LSODE, the implementation of PDIRK does not require additional costs in calculating a reference solution.
- the present research version of the PDIRK code is at least as efficient as the well-balanced, extensively tested LSODE code.
- a future version of a PDIRK code can be improved as follows:
    (i)   better tuning of the stepsize strategy parameters and, particularly, finding more accurate initial iterates for the Newton process in the prediction stage;
    (ii)   implementation of a variable-order strategy; L-stable PDIRK formulas of orders up to 10 (excluding order 9) are available;
    (iii) implementation of a stiffness detector, like the one in SIMPLE, and switching to parallel fixed-point iteration (PIRK methods, cf. [12]) in nonstiff regions of the integration interval.

Acknowledgement. The authors like to thank dr. W.H. Hundsdorfer for the fruitful discussions on the order reduction phenomenon and drs. W.M. Lioen for assisting them with the experiments on the ALLIANT FX/4.

REFERENCES

[1] **Alexander, R.** (1977): *Diagonally implicit Runge-Kutta methods for stiff ODEs*, SIAM J. Numer. Anal. **14**, 1006-1021.

[2] **Burrage, K.** (1991): *The error behaviour of a general class of predictor-corrector methods*, Appl. Numer. Math. **8**, 201-216.

[3] **Butcher, J.C.** (1987): *The numerical analysis of ordinary differential equations*, Runge-Kutta and general linear methods, Wiley, New York.

[4] **Cash, J.R.** & **Liem, C.B.** (1980): *On the design of a variable order, variable step diagonally implicit Runge-Kutta algorithm*, J. Inst. Maths. Applics. **26**, 87-91.

[5] **Cooper, G.J.** & **Sayfy, A.** (1979): *Semiexplicit A-stable Runge-Kutta methods*, Math. Comp. **33**, 541-556.

[6] **Crouzeix, M.** (1975): *Sur l'approximation des équations différentielles opérationnelles linéaires par des méthodes de Runge-Kutta*, Ph. D. Thesis, Université de Paris.

[7] **Dekker, K.** & **Verwer J.G.** (1984): *Stability of Runge-Kutta methods for stiff nonlinear differential equations*, CWI Monograph 2, North-Holland, Amsterdam-New York-Oxford.

[8] **Enright, W.H., Hull, T.E.** & **Lindberg, B.** (1975): *Comparing numerical methods for stiff systems of ODEs*, BIT **15**, 10-48.

[9] **Gottwald, B.A.** & **Wanner, G.** (1981): *A reliable Rosenbrock integrator for stiff differential equations*, Computing **26**, 355-360.

[10] **Hairer, E., Lubich, Ch.** & **Roche, M.** (1988): *Error of Runge-Kutta methods for stiff problems studied via differential algebraic equations*, BIT **28**, 678-700.

[11] **Hindmarsh, A.C.** (1980): *LSODE and LSODI, two new initial value ordinary differential equation solvers*, ACM/SIGNUM Newsletter **15** (4), 10-11.

[12] **Houwen, P.J. van der** & **Sommeijer, B.P.** (1990): *Variable step iteration of high-order Runge-Kutta methods on parallel computers*, J. Comp. Appl. Math. **29**, 111-127.

[13] **Houwen, P.J. van der** & **Sommeijer, B.P.** (1990): *Iterated Runge-Kutta methods on parallel computers*, SIAM J. Sci. Stat. Comput. **12**, 1000-1028.

[14] **Houwen, P.J. van der, Sommeijer, B.P.** & **Couzy, W.** (1989): *Embedded diagonally implicit Runge-Kutta algorithms on parallel computers*, Report NM-R8912, Centre for Mathematics and Computer Science, Amsterdam.

[15] **Iserles, A.** & **Nørsett, S.P.** (1990): *On the theory of parallel Runge-Kutta methods*, IMA J. Numer. Anal. **10**, 463-488.

[16] **Jackson, K.R.** & **Nørsett, S.P.** (1988): *Parallel Runge-Kutta methods* (manuscript).

[17] **Kaps, P.** (1981): *Rosenbrock-type methods*, in: *Numerical methods for stiff initial value problems*, G. Dahlquist and R. Jeltsch (eds.), Bericht nr. 9, Inst. für Geometrie und Praktische Mathematik der RWTH Aachen.

[18] **Lie, I.** (1987): *Some aspects of parallel Runge-Kutta methods*, Report No. 3/87, Division Numerical Mathematics, University of Trondheim.

[19] **Nørsett, S.P.** (1974): *Semi-explicit Runge-Kutta methods*, Report Mathematics and Computation No.6/74, Dept. of Mathematics, University of Trondheim.

[20] **Nørsett, S.P.** (1975): *C-polynomials for rational approximation to the exponential function*, Numer. Math. **25**, 39-56.

[21] **Nørsett, S.P.** & **Simonsen, H.H.** (1989): *Aspects of parallel Runge-Kutta methods*, in: *Numerical methods for ordinary differential equations*, A. Bellen, C.W. Gear & E. Russo (eds.), Proceedings L'Aquila 1987, Lecture Notes in Mathematics **1386**, Springer-Verlag, Berlin, 103-117.

[22] **Nørsett, S.P.** & **Thomsen, P.G.** (1984): *Embedded SDIRK-methods of basic order three*, BIT **24**, 634-646.

[23] **Stewart, K.** (1990): *Avoiding stability-induced inefficiencies in BDF methods*, J. Comput. Appl. Math. **29**, 357-367.

[24] **Tam, H.W.** (1989): *Parallel methods for the numerical solution of ordinary differential equations*, Report No. UIUCDCS-R-89-1516, Computer Science Department, University of Illinois.

[25] **Wolfbrandt, A.** (1977): *A study of Rosenbrock processes with respect to order conditions and stiff stability*, Ph. D. Thesis, Chalmers University of Technology, Göteborg.

CHAPTER V

Iterated Runge-Kutta methods on parallel computers

Reprinted with permission from the
SIAM Journal on Scientific and Statistical Computing,
volume 12, number 5, pp. 1000-1028.

Iterated Runge-Kutta Methods on Parallel Computers

P.J. van der Houwen and B.P. Sommeijer

Centre for Mathematics and Computer Science
P.O.Box 94079, 1090 GB Amsterdam, The Netherlands

Abstract. This paper examines diagonally implicit iteration methods for solving implicit Runge-Kutta methods with high stage order on parallel computers. These iteration methods are such that after a finite number of m iterations, the iterated Runge-Kutta method belongs to the class of diagonally implicit Runge-Kutta methods (DIRK methods) using mk implicit stages where k is the number of stages of the generating implicit Runge-Kutta method (corrector method). However, a large number of the stages of this DIRK method can be computed in parallel, so that the number of stages that have to be computed sequentially is only m. The iteration parameters of the method are tuned in such a way that fast convergence to the stability characteristics of the corrector method is achieved. By means of numerical experiments it is also shown that the solution produced by the resulting iteration method converges rapidly to the corrector solution so that both stability and accuracy characteristics are comparable with those of the corrector. This implies that the reduced accuracy often shown when integrating stiff problems by means of DIRK methods already available in the literature (which is caused by a low stage order) is not shown by the DIRK methods developed in this paper provided that the corrector method has a sufficiently high stage order.

1991 Mathematics Subject Classification: 65L06, 65L20

1991 C.R. Classification: G.1.7

Key Words: Diagonally implicit Runge-Kutta methods, parallelism, stability.

1. INTRODUCTION

1.1. Runge-Kutta methods

Suppose that we want to solve stiff initial value problems for systems of first-order, ordinary differential equations (ODEs), i.e.,

$$(1.1) \qquad \frac{dy(t)}{dt} = f(t, y(t)), \quad y(t_0) = y_0, \quad y : \mathbb{R} \to \mathbb{R}^d, \quad f : \mathbb{R} \times \mathbb{R}^d \to \mathbb{R}^d,$$

by means of a Runge-Kutta (RK) method. Then the stiffness of the problem requires that the RK method should be sufficiently stable, preferably A-stable, and therefore

130

implicit. This leads us to fully implicit RK methods (IRK methods) in which the Butcher array

(1.2)
$$\begin{array}{c|c} c & A \\ \hline & b^{\mathrm{T}} \end{array}$$

has a full A-matrix. Most widely used are the IRK methods based on Gaussian quadrature formulas (such as Gauss-Legendre, Lobatto and Radau methods), which are known to be A-stable for any order of accuracy. However, the high degree of implicitness of these methods implies that solving the implicit relations is rather costly. In general, a k-stage IRK method (that is, b and c are k-dimensional vectors and A is a k-by-k matrix) requires in each step the solution of a system of dimension kd, so that the computational complexity is of order $(kd)^3$. This compares unfavourably with implicit linear multistep methods which require in each step the solution of a system of dimension d.

In order to reduce the computational labour involved when using implicit RK methods, various people have considered diagonally implicit RK methods (DIRK methods) possessing a lower triangular A matrix and therefore requiring (in general) in each step the solution of k systems of dimension d. Hence, the computational complexity is now of order kd^3 instead of order $(kd)^3$. Unfortunately, the price we have to pay for the less expensive DIRK methods is a considerable drop in accuracy in many stiff problems. This is caused by the phenomenon of order reduction (cf., e.g., [21], [9], [11]) which reduces the observed order of RK methods to their stage order (or their stage order plus one). Most DIRK methods are particularly sensitive to order reduction because their stage order is only one or two, which is much smaller than for k-stage Gauss-Legendre, Lobatto IIIA and Radau IIA methods which have all stage order k.

An alternative for the DIRK methods are the singly implicit RK methods (SIRK methods) of Burrage [2] which possess a high stage order. By means of a transformation technique due to Butcher (see [5], [6]), these SIRK methods can be transformed into methods that are, like DIRK methods, only diagonally implicit. However, the additional transformations required in each step cause that the total costs per step are considerably higher than for DIRK methods.

Yet another possibility is the use of parallel processors. In this paper, we shall show that on parallel computers the fully implicit relations associated with IRK methods can be solved efficiently by using the highly parallelizable iteration methods of diagonally implicit type proposed in van der Houwen et al. [13]. This brings us back to using IRK methods as corrector method instead of using DIRK or SIRK methods. In particular, we shall concentrate on iterating IRK methods possessing high *stage* orders.

1.2. IRK methods with high stage orders

Most IRK methods are designed in such a way that they have a high order at the step points. However, as already remarked above, a high order at step points is often spoiled by order reduction, so that it seems more natural to look for IRK methods with as high a stage order as possible. In order to achieve this, we shall consider $(k+1)$-stage IRK methods of the type

$$(1.3) \quad \begin{array}{c|cc} 0 & 0 & 0^T \\ c & a & A \\ \hline & b_0 & b^T \end{array}$$

where b_0 is a scalar, a, b and c are k-dimensional vectors, and A is again a k-by-k matrix. IRK methods of this type have roughly the same computational complexity as the IRK methods of type (1.2), but they possess the additional parameter vector a which can be used for increasing the stage order. To see that (1.2) and (1.3) are (almost) equally expensive, let us assume (for simplicity of notation) that (1.1) is a scalar problem (i.e., $d=1$), and let us introduce the vectors

$$Y_{n+1} := (y_{n,1}, \dots, y_{n,k})^T, \quad c := (c_1, \dots, c_k)^T,$$

where $y_{n,i}$ denotes a numerical approximation to the exact solution value $y(t_n+c_ih)$, h being the stepsize. Then we can write (1.3) in the form

$$Y_{n+1} - hAf(et_n+ch, Y_{n+1}) = ey_n + haf(t_n, y_n),$$
$$(1.3') \qquad y_{n+1} = y_n + hb_0f(t_n, y_n) + hb^Tf(et_n+ch, Y_{n+1}).$$

Here, e is the vector with unit entries, and we used the convention that for any given vectors $v=(v_j)$ and $t=(t_j)$, $f(t,v)$ denotes the vector with entries $f(t_j,v_j)$. If $b_0 = 0$ and $a = 0$, then it follows from (1.3') that (1.3) reduces to (1.2), so that in each step the computational complexity of (1.2) and (1.3) differ by the evaluation of $f(t_n,y_n)$, but both methods require the solution of a system of dimension kd. Since the bulk of the computational effort goes in solving this system, the methods (1.2) and (1.3) may be considered as equally expensive.

The vectors Y_{n+1} and c will, respectively, be called the *stage vector* and the *block point vector*, and the points t_n and t_n+c_jh will, respectively, be called *step points* and *block points*. The minimal order achieved at the block points and step points are, respectively, the *stage order* and *step point order*.

If the method parameters are chosen in such a way that the stage order is as large as possible with c arbitrary, then (1.3) is equivalent to the IRK method derived from

Lagrange quadrature formulas and will be called a *Lagrange method*. If $c_j = j/k$, then Lagrange methods reduce to the *Newton-Cotes methods* studied in Watts and Shampine [23], and if the components of c equal the Lobatto quadrature points, then they reduce to the Lobatto IIIA methods. However, Newton-Cotes and Lobatto IIIA methods are only *weakly* A-stable (i.e., the method hardly damps the highly stiff components in the numerical error). It is our aim to construct Lagrange methods with better stability properties than Newton-Cotes and Lobatto IIIA methods, i.e., methods which damp both nonstiff and stiff components occurring in the numerical error (*strongly* A-stable methods).

An important family of IRK methods are the so-called *stiffly accurate methods* (cf. Alexander [1]). If the IRK method is of the form (1.3), then this family is obtained by setting

$$(1.4) \qquad b_0 = e_k^T a, \quad b^T = e_k^T A, \quad c_k = 1,$$

where e_k is the kth unit vector. Notice that, when represented by their Butcher array (1.3), the last row in (1.3) equals the preceding one. It was shown by Hairer et al. [11] that this property implies that for certain classes of stiff problems the method does not suffer the effect of order reduction. Examples of stiffly accurate IRK methods are the Lobatto IIIA, Radau IIA, and Newton-Cotes methods.

1.3. Diagonally implicit iteration of IRK methods

After a finite number of m iterations of the implicit relation for Y_{n+1} given in (1.3') by the aforementioned diagonally implicit iteration process (or briefly *diagonal iteration*) (see also Section 3), the resulting scheme actually is an $(mk+1)$-stage DIRK method. One of these stages is explicit and the other mk stages are of diagonally implicit form. However, a large number of these mk implicit stages can be computed in parallel, resulting in a process where only m stages have to be computed sequentially.

The iteration parameters of the method can be tuned in such a way that we get fast convergence to the stability characteristics of the corrector method, provided that the corrector is stiffly accurate (in Subsection 3.3.1, we will show that the diagonal iteration of the type employed in this paper is not suitable for iterating *nonstiffly accurate* correctors).

Second, it has been demonstrated that the iterated methods based on strongly A-stable correctors (such as the Radau IIA correctors and the Lagrange correctors derived in Section 4) are within a few iterations strongly A-stable themselves. It is highly unlikely that this nice property is shared by the methods based on (weakly) A-stable IRK correctors because the stability function of the iterated methods should converge to a (weakly) A-acceptable function. In fact, for a number of Newton-Cotes and

Lobatto IIIA correctors it was checked that the stability function becomes A-acceptable only after an infinite number of iterations.

Finally, numerical experiments reveal that the drop in accuracy, exhibited in many stiff problems by the conventionally constructed DIRK methods, is not shown by the DIRK methods constructed by the diagonal iteration process of this paper. In a forthcoming paper [4] it is intended to present a theoretical analysis of this phenomenon using the error analysis proposed in Burrage [3].

2. ACCURACY AND STABILITY OF THE CORRECTOR

In the the following two subsections, we discuss the stage order, step point order, and stability of the corrector equation (1.3').

2.1. Stage order

Let $Y(t_{n+1})$ denote the vector with components $y(t_n+c_ih)$ where y is the locally exact solution of (1.1) satisfying $y(t_n)=y_n$, then, following Butcher [7], (1.3') is said to have stage order r if the residual left upon substitution of $Y(t_{n+1})$ into the formula for Y_{n+1} is of order $r+1$ in h, i.e.,

$$(2.1) \qquad Y(t_{n+1}) - hAf(et_n+ch, Y(t_{n+1})) - ey_n - haf(t_n, y_n) = O(h^{r+1}).$$

The stage-order conditions for (1.3') are straightforwardly derived (cf. [22]) and are given by

$$(2.2) \qquad C_j = 0, \ j = 1, \ ..., \ r; \quad C_1 := a + Ae - c; \quad C_j := jAc^{j-1} - c^j, \quad j = 2, 3, \ ... \ ,$$

where c^j denotes the vector with components $(c_i)^j$. Thus, to achieve stage order r for a given block point vector c, we have to solve rk linear equations in k^2+k unknowns, so that the maximal stage order equals $k+1$. The corresponding methods will be called *Lagrange methods*.

2.2. Step point order

Consider the formula for y_{n+1} given in (1.3'):

$$(2.3) \qquad y_{n+1} = y_n + h b_0 f(t_n, y_n) + h b^T f(et_n+ch, Y_{n+1}).$$

Since Y_{n+1} approximates $Y(t_{n+1})$ with (local) order $r+1$, r being the stage order (cf. (2.1)), we can derive that y_{n+1} has (at least) order $p = \min\{r+1, q\}$ if the conditions

$$(2.4) \qquad D_j = 0, \ j = 1, \ ..., q; \quad D_1 := b_0 + b^T e - 1; \quad D_j := jb^T c^{j-1} - 1, \ j = 2, 3, \ ...$$

are satisfied. We remark that p may be larger than $\min\{r+1, q\}$ if the methods possess the property of so-called 'superconvergence' which for example is the case in Gauss, Radau, and Lobatto methods. The error constant of (2.3) is given by

$$(2.5) \qquad E_{q+1} := \frac{D_{q+1}}{(q+1)!} = \frac{(q+1)b^T c^q - 1}{(q+1)!}.$$

Assuming that c is given, the conditions (2.4) present a linear system of q equations in $k+1$ unknowns, so that by setting $q = k+1$ we achieve at least step point order $p = \min\{r+1, k+1\}$ for any block point vector c.

As already observed in the introduction, the usual approach in exploiting the vector c is the maximization of the step point order (to obtain 'superconvergence'). Alternatively, one may use c for improving the stability of the method or for the minimization of error constants. In this paper, we shall use c for achieving strong A-stability.

In the special case of stiffly accurate methods satisfying condition (1.4), y_{n+1} equals the last component of Y_{n+1} so that the step point order p is also at least the stage order r, but is sometimes higher. For instance, the Newton-Cotes methods have stage order $k+1$ and, if k is even, step point order $k+2$.

2.3. Stability

By applying (1.3') to the test equation $y'=\lambda y$, we are led to recursions of the form

$$(2.6) \qquad Y_{n+1} = [I - zA]^{-1}[e + za]y_n, \quad y_{n+1} = (1 + b_0 z)y_n + zb^T Y_{n+1}, \quad z := \lambda h.$$

Hence,

$$(2.7) \qquad y_{n+1} = R(z)y_n, \quad R(z) := 1 + b_0 z + zb^T[I - zA]^{-1}[e + za].$$

$R(z)$ is called the stability function of the one-step method. In the special case of stiffly accurate methods where (1.4) is satisfied, (2.7) reduces to

$$(2.8) \qquad y_{n+1} = R(z)y_n, \quad R(z) := e_k^T[I - zA]^{-1}[e + za].$$

The stability region of the method is defined by the region where R is bounded by 1. In the case of the Newton-Cotes methods where the components of c are equally spaced, it was shown in Watts and Shampine [23] that they are A-stable for $k \leq 8$ (but they are not for $k=9$ and $k=10$).

We conclude this section by summarizing in Table 2.1 the characteristics of a number of correctors available in the literature. In this table, it is assumed that the

IRK method is presented in the form (1.3'), so that for all methods listed the dimension of the implicit relation to be solved equals kd, d being the dimension of the system of ODEs.

Table 2.1. Summary of characteristics of IRK methods.

Method	Stages	Order p	Stage order r	Stability	Stiffly accurate	Reference
Gauss-Legendre	k	$2k$	k	A-stable for all k	no	[7]
Lobatto IIIA	$k+1$	$2k$	$k+1$	A-stable for all k	yes	[9]
Radau IIA	k	$2k-1$	k	L-stable for all k	yes	[7]
Newton-Cotes	$k+1$	$2\lfloor (k+2)/2 \rfloor$	$k+1$	A-stable for $k \leq 8$	yes	[23]
Lagrange	$k+1$	$k+1$	$k+1$	Strongly A-stable	yes	§ 4($k \leq 4$)

3. DIAGONAL ITERATION

We shall use a diagonal iteration method to solve the stage vector Y_{n+1} from the fully·implicit (corrector) equation defined in (1.3'). For scalar differential equations, the iteration method reads

$$Y^{(1)} - hDf(et_n + ch, Y^{(1)}) = y_n e + haf(t_n, y_n) + h[A-D]f(t^{(0)}, Y^{(0)}),$$

(3.1a)

$$Y^{(j)} - hDf(et_n + ch, Y^{(j)}) = y_n e + haf(t_n, y_n) + h[A-D]f(et_n + ch, Y^{(j-1)}),$$
$$j = 2, 3, \dots ,$$

where $(t^{(0)}, Y^{(0)})$ is an initial approximation to $(et_n + ch, Y_{n+1})$ and D is an arbitrary diagonal matrix. If m iterations are performed, then y_{n+1} is defined by

(3.1b) $y_{n+1} = y_n + hb_0 f(t_n, y_n) + hb^T f(et_n + ch, Y^{(m)})$ or $y_{n+1} = e_k^T Y^{(m)},$

respectively, for nonstiffly and stiffly accurate correctors (cf. (1.4)).

By virtue of the *diagonal* structure of D, the iterated method (3.1) is suitable for use on parallel processors because in each iteration the components of $Y^{(j)}$ can be computed in parallel.

There are many possibilities for choosing the matrix D which we summarize below:

(i) $D = O$: this is the most simple choice and yields an *explicit* iteration method (fixed point or functional iteration). This approach was followed in Nørsett and Simonsen [20], Lie [18], van der Houwen and Sommeijer [12], and Burrage [3].

These papers deal with the iteration of implicit methods for solving *nonstiff* ODEs. In the case of *stiff* ODEs, one should use matrices $D \neq O$.

(ii) D is such that for a *prescribed* number of iterations the method has favourable stability characteristics like A-stability or L-stability. This approach was followed in van der Houwen et al. [13], where the corrector only serves for providing its order of accuracy. In fact, it was shown that one may even use *explicit* correctors and still can obtain A- and L-stability after the particular number of iterations and a suitable choice of the matrix D.

(iii) $D = \operatorname{diag}(A\boldsymbol{e})$ or $D = \operatorname{diag}(A)$: this choice leads to nonlinear Jacobi-type iteration. The few experiments we performed revealed that the convergence is rather poor, so that we dropped this option.

(iv) D is such that the *nonstiff* components in the iteration error are strongly damped. This type of diagonal iteration will be called *nonstiff iteration*. Nonstiff iteration can be achieved by minimizing the spectral radius of the matrix $A - D$ (see Subsection 3.2). A large number of experiments showed that this is not the way to proceed, at least not in the case of the one-step initial approximations to Y_{n+1} used in this paper.

(v) D is such that the stability function $R_m(z)$ of the iterated method rapidly converges to the stability function $R_{\text{corr}}(z)$ of the corrector. Hence, the corrector not only serves for providing its order of accuracy as in [13], but the iterated method also reflects the (assumed) nice stability properties of the corrector. Within this 'stability function approach' there are various approaches:

$D^{-1}\boldsymbol{c} = A^{-1}\boldsymbol{c}$: this relation uniquely defines D provided that A is nonsingular. As observed by Hundsdorfer [15], such matrices D imply that the stability functions of the corrector and of the iterated method are identical at infinity. Although a few first experiments did not yet show satisfactory results, this option should be investigated more closely (see [4]).

Minimization of the spectral radius of the matrix $I - D^{-1}A$. This choice implies that R_m fastly converges to R_{corr} at infinity, but, at the same time, it also strongly damps the stiff components of the iteration error. This type of diagonal iteration will be called *stiff iteration*. It is the approach adopted in the present paper (see Subsection 3.3). Our experiments in Section 5 reveal that stiff iteration is suited for suppressing the phenomenon of order reduction within a few iterations, and in this respect, the methods of this paper perform much better than the methods proposed in [13].

Other options as suggested by one of the referees, where some norm of $I - D^{-1}A$ is minimized rather than the spectral radius, or where $R_m - R_{\text{corr}}$ is minimized along the negative z-axis (or larger portions of the left halfplane), has not yet been tested and may turn out to be still more effective.

(vi) D is such that the lower order error terms in the truncation error are minimized. Since after a finite number of iterations the iterated method (3.1) formally is still a DIRK method and therefore suffers from order reduction, such an approach directly attacks the source for order reduction. This topic will also be considered in [4].

The approach of stiff iteration followed in this paper seems to be rather effective. However, by no means we do claim that this is the best way to proceed. In [4] we shall present more firm theoretical and experimental evidence of the merits of the various approaches for choosing the matrix D.

3.1. Computational costs

Each step of the (outer) iteration method (3.1a) requires the solution of a diagonally implicit relation. In order to solve this relation, we apply Newton iteration (inner iteration). There are various possibilities for starting the iteration method (3.1a) and the Newton iteration method, and for choosing the Jacobian matrix $J := \partial f/\partial y$ needed in the Newton iteration process. Obvious choices are listed in Table 3.1.

Table 3.1. Starting the inner and outer iteration processes.

Order of approximation	0	1
Jacobian matrix	diag $[J(et_n, e y_n)]$	diag $[J(et_n + ch, y_n e + hcf(t_n, y_n))]$
Initial iterate in (3.1a)	$Y^{(0)} = y_n e,\ t^{(0)} = et_n$	$Y^{(0)} = y_n e + hcf(t_n, y_n),\ t^{(0)} = et_n + ch$
Initial Newton iterate	$Y^{(j-1)}$	$y_n e + haf(t_n, y_n) + hAf(et_n + ch, Y^{(j-1)})$

All possible combinations are equally expensive because the values of $f(t_n, y_n)$, $f(et_n + ch, Y^{(j-1)})$ and diag(J) are anyhow needed. The first-order approximations will reduce the magnitude of the smooth error components (low frequencies) more than the zero-order approximations do, but, unlike the zero-order approximations, they will also introduce stiff error components in the case of stiff differential equations. This particularly applies to the Jacobian matrix and the initial inner iterate because these approximations are needed in each outer iteration. Therefore, we shall only consider zero-order approximations to the Jacobian matrix and to the initial inner iterate (notice that in the case of systems of equations, the matrix J becomes a block-diagonal matrix). Furthermore, our experiments revealed that using zero-order approximations for the initial outer iterate is more robust than the above first-order approximations, and yields comparable accuracies. However, it should be observed that the topic of choosing suitable initial approximations to the stage vector (including multistep approximations in order to reduce the number of iterations), is extremely important and needs further research. Burrage [3] discussed this topic in the case of a general class of *explicit* predictor-corrector methods for nonstiff problems. His approach may be used to study initial approximations in the case of diagonally implicit predictor-corrector methods for stiff problems.

By performing m iterations, the method (3.1) may be considered as a DIRK method with $mk+1$ stages, of which one stage is explicit and the other mk stages are diagonally implicit. In fact, we may represent the method by the Butcher array

$$
\begin{array}{c|ccccccccc}
j=0 & 0 \\
j=1 & c-De & D \\
j=2 & a & A-D & D \\
j=3 & a & O & A-D & D \\
\cdot & \cdot & \cdot & \cdot & \cdot & \cdot \\
\cdot & \cdot & \cdot & \cdot & \cdot & \cdot & \cdot \\
\cdot & \cdot & \cdot & \cdot & \cdot & \cdot & \cdot & \cdot \\
j=m & a & O & & \cdots & & O & A-D & D \\
\hline
& b_0 & 0^T & & \cdots & & 0^T & 0^T & b^T \\
& & & & & & & \text{(nonstiffly accurate correctors)} \\
& e_k^T a & 0^T & & \cdots & & 0^T & e_k^T(A-D) & e_k^T D \\
& & & & & & & \text{(stiffly accurate correctors)}
\end{array}
$$

(3.1')

Since each iteration step in (3.1a) essentially requires the 'wall clock time' involved in evaluating one component of $f(et_n+ch, Y^{(j-1)})$ and solving one system of dimension d, we conclude that, effectively, the work involved in performing one step by the DIRK method (3.1') consists of

(evaluation of f and J) + (LU-decomposition of $I - d_j h J$) +

(3.2) m[evaluation of f + N (forward/backward substitution + evaluation of f)].

In this expression N is defined by

(3.3) $N := \dfrac{N_1 + N_2 + \ldots + N_m}{m},$

with N_j denoting the number of Newton iterations for computing that component of $Y^{(j)}$ which requires the largest number of Newton iterations. Usually, the m iterations are the most expensive part of the total effort per step, and therefore we shall say that a DIRK method has m *effective* or *sequential* stages if there are m diagonally implicit systems to be solved.

3.1.1. Comparison with conventional DIRK methods. In the experiments reported in this paper, we used the stopping criterion that the Newton correction should be about the machine precision which is for our computer 10^{-14}. It turned out that N_j rapidly decreases with j which can be explained by observing that the initial iterate for starting the next inner iteration becomes more accurate when j increases. This is an advantage when compared with conventionally constructed DIRK methods already available in the literature (such DIRK methods will be indicated by 'conventional' DIRK methods), because, for conventional DIRK methods, the number of Newton iterations for solving the implicit relations in the successive stages do, in general, not decrease.

In order to appreciate the computational costs of DIRK methods of type (3.1'), we should compare m with the number of sequential stages of conventional DIRK methods. In Table 3.2, the characteristics of such DIRK methods are listed together with the PARK and PDIRK methods derived in [16] and [13].

Table 3.2. Summary of characteristics of DIRK, PARK and PDIRK methods of order $p \geq 3$.

Order	Stage order	Seq. stages	Processors	Stability	Reference
$p=3$	1	$p-1$	1	A-stable	[19]
$p=3$	2	$p-1$	1	Strongly A-stable	[8]
$p=4$	1	$p-1$	1	A-stable	[8], [1]
$p=4$	1	$p-2$	2	L-stable	[16]
$p=3,4,5$	1	$p-1$	$\lfloor (p+1)/2 \rfloor$	Strongly A-stable	[13]
$p=6,7$	1	$p-1$	$\lfloor (p+1)/2 \rfloor$	Strongly A(α)-stable	[13]
$p\leq 6, p=8$	1	p	$\lfloor (p+1)/2 \rfloor$	L-stable	[13]
$p=7,8,10$	1	$p+1$	$\lfloor (p+1)/2 \rfloor$	L-stable	[13]

3.2. Order of accuracy

In order to analyse the order of accuracy of the iterated method (3.1), let $Y(t_{n+1})$ denote the vector with components $y(t_n+c_ih)$, where y is the locally exact solution of (1.1). Then, in first approximation, we obtain

$$Y(t_{n+1}) - Y^{(j)} = [Y(t_{n+1}) - Y_{n+1}] + [Y_{n+1} - Y^{(j)}]$$

(3.4a)
$$= [Y(t_{n+1}) - Y_{n+1}] + Z[Y_{n+1} - Y^{(j-1)}]$$

$$= [Y(t_{n+1}) - Y_{n+1}] + Z^j[Y_{n+1} - Y^{(0)}], \quad j = 1, 2, \dots,$$

where Z is the iteration matrix defined by

(3.4b) $Z = Z(hDJ) := [I - hDJ]^{-1} [AD^{-1} - I] hDJ,$

with J again denoting the Jacobian matrix of f.

Let r be the stage order of the corrector (1.3), then (cf. (2.1))

$$Y(t_{n+1}) - Y_{n+1} = O(h^{r+1}).$$

Since $Z = O(h)$ and $Y_{n+1} - Y^{(0)} = O(h)$, the local errors of the stage vectors satisfy the order relation

(3.5) $Y(t_{n+1}) - Y^{(j)} = O(h^{r+1}) + O(h^{j+1}),$

so that, after m iterations, (3.1) defines a method in which $Y^{(m)}$ approximates $Y(t_{n+1})$ with order $r^* = \min\{r, m\}$. We shall say that (3.1) has *stage order* r^* (although formally, when (3.1) is considered as a DIRK method, its stage order is only 1). Thus, the optimal stage-order methods, that is the methods based on the Lagrange methods as defined above, have stage order $r^* = k+1$ provided that at least $m = k+1$ iterations are performed.

In order to get more insight into the rate of convergence of the iteration process (3.1), we consider the test equation

(3.6) $\dfrac{dy(t)}{dt} = \lambda y(t),$

where λ runs through the spectrum $\Lambda(J)$ of J. The matrix Z assumes the form

(3.7) $Z = zD [I - zD]^{-1} [D^{-1}A - I] = z [I - zD]^{-1} [A - D], \quad z := \lambda h.$

Suppose that J has a complete eigensystem, and let us call the eigenvectors of hJ corresponding to the eigenvalues of large and small modulus, respectively, *stiff* and *nonstiff* components. From (3.7) we see that for the nonstiff components (i.e., corresponding to small values of $|z|$) the matrix Z behaves approximately as $z[A - D]$. Hence, these components in the iteration error are strongly damped if the matrix $A - D$ has eigenvalues of small magnitude. Thus, rapid convergence of the nonstiff components is obtained by minimizing the spectral radius of $A - D$. However, as already remarked above, such a *nonstiff* iteration process gives a poor overall convergence. Alternatively, for the stiff components (i.e., corresponding to large values of $|z|$), the matrix Z behaves as $-D^{-1}[A - D]$. Hence, a strong damping of these components requires the minimization of the spectral radius of $I - D^{-1}A$, leading to *stiff* iteration. In the following subsection, we shall see that this condition also plays a role in the stability of the iterated method.

3.3. Stability

One may argue that there is no reason to continue the iteration process after $m = r$ iterations, because the stage errors of the corrector and of the iterated method have become of the same order in h and may therefore be expected to be of comparable magnitude. However, there is no guarantee that after $m = r$ iterations the *stability properties* of (1.3') are also comparable with those of the corrector. This brings us to consider the stability of the DIRK method (3.1'). In order to see how the stability depends on the number of iterations m, we apply the method to the test equation (3.6), so that (3.1a) reduces to

$$Y^{(m)} = \left(Z^m e + [I - Z]^{-1}[I - Z^m][I - zD]^{-1}(e + za) \right) y_n.$$

We shall discuss the stability of iterating a nonstiffly accurate and a stiffly accurate corrector separately.

3.3.1. Nonstiffly accurate correctors. If y_{n+1} is computed by means of the formula

$$y_{n+1} = [1 + zb_0]y_n + zb^T Y^{(m)},$$

then it can be expressed as

(3.8) $\quad y_{n+1} = \left(1 + zb_0 + zb^T\left(Z^m e + [I - Z]^{-1}[I - Z^m][I - zD]^{-1}(e + za) \right) \right) y_n,$

so that the stability function is given by

(3.9) $\quad R_m(z) := 1 + zb_0 + zb^T\left(Z^m e + [I - Z]^{-1}[I - Z^m][I - zD]^{-1}(e + za) \right).$

It is easily verified that this function can be written in the form

$$R_m(z) := 1 + zb_0 + zb^T[I - zA]^{-1}(e + za) - z^2 b^T Z^m [I - zA]^{-1}(Ae + a).$$

Assuming that the stage order of the corrector is at least one, we may set $Ae + a = c$ (see (2.2)), so that

(3.10) $\quad R_m(z) := R_{corr}(z) - z^2 b^T [Z(z)]^m [I - zA]^{-1} c,$

where R_{corr} denotes the stability function of the corrector given by (2.7). Finally, on substitution of (3.7) into (3.10) we obtain

(3.11) $\qquad R_m(z) = R_{corr}(z) - z^{m+2} b^T \left([I - zD]^{-1} [A - D] \right)^m [I - zA]^{-1} c.$

From this expression we can derive the convergence behaviour of R_m to R_{corr} for large values of $|z|$:

$$R_m(z) = R_{corr}(z) + z b^T [I - D^{-1}A]^m A^{-1} c \quad \text{as } |z| \to \infty,$$

showing that for any fixed m the stability function becomes unbounded as $|z|$ tends to infinity, unless the matrix D is such that

$$b^T[I - D^{-1}A]^m A^{-1} c = 0.$$

Writing this equation as

$$b^T[I - D^{-1}A]^{m-1}[I - D^{-1}A]A^{-1}c = b^T[I - D^{-1}A]^{m-1}[A^{-1}c - D^{-1}c] = 0,$$

we see that it can be satisfied for all m if we choose D such that [15]

(3.12) $\qquad D^{-1}c = A^{-1}c.$

Unfortunately, a few first experiments showed that the performance of the corresponding method (3.1') is not satisfactory (see Subsection 5.3). Therefore, we conclude that diagonal iteration as defined by (3.1') is in general not suitable for iterating nonstiffly accurate correctors and excludes the Gauss-Legendre formulas as suitable corrector methods. However, it should be remarked that by defining the initial iterate $Y^{(0)}$ implicitly, rather than just setting $Y^{(0)} = y_n e$, the above stability problem can be avoided (cf. [13]), so that the matrix D remains available for improving the performance of the iteration process. As observed in Subsection 3.1, the topic of finding suitable initial approximations to the stage vector in diagonally iterated RK methods deserves further research, but will not be an issue in this paper.

3.3.2. Stiffly accurate correctors. In the stiffly accurate case where y_{n+1} is computed by means of the formula

$$y_{n+1} = e_k^T Y^{(m)},$$

we arrive at the stability function

(3.13) $R_m(z) = R_{corr}(z) - z e_k^T [Z(zD)]^m [I - zA]^{-1} c,$

where R_{corr} is defined by (2.8). We may express this function in the form

(3.13') $R_m(z) = R_{corr}(z) - [\sigma_m(z)]^m,$

where

$$\sigma_m(z) := \left[z e_k^T [Z(zD)]^m [I - zA]^{-1} c \right]^{1/m}$$

$$= \left[z^{m+1} e_k^T \left([I - zD]^{-1} [A - D] \right)^m [I - zA]^{-1} c \right]^{1/m}.$$

For fixed values of m and assuming that D has positive diagonal elements, the function $\sigma_m(z)$ is bounded for all z in the closed left halfplane. This suggests to characterize the rate of convergence of R_m to R_{corr} by means of $\sigma_m(z)$. We shall call $\sigma_m(z)$ the *convergence factor associated with z*. For example, we have

$$\sigma_m(0) = 0, \quad \sigma_m(\infty) := \left[-e_k^T [Z(-\infty)]^m A^{-1} c \right]^{1/m}$$
(3.14)
$$= \left[-e_k^T [I - D^{-1}A]^m A^{-1} c \right]^{1/m}.$$

Ideally, in order to get fast convergence of the stability function $R_m(z)$ to that of the corrector, we should try to minimize $\sigma_m(z)$ in the closed left halfplane. However, since in actual computation m is determined by some error criterion, we do not know m in advance, so that such an approach may be unattractive, particularly for larger values of k where more values of m have to be considered. Nevertheless, in a future paper [4], this possibility will be studied more closely in order to get further insight into how crucial the choice of D really is.

Another possibility is the minimization of $\sigma_m(z)$ for the highly stiff components (large values of $|z|$), because (3.14) shows that $\sigma_m(z)$ is already small for the nonstiff components. The most simple way to achieve this determines D according to (3.12), so that $\sigma_m(\infty)$ vanishes for all m [15]. In the experiments done so far, the convergence of the corresponding iteration process (3.1) is not satisfactory.

However, by choosing the matrix D, for a given corrector, such that the spectral radius of $Z(-\infty) = I - D^{-1}A$ is minimized over all possible diagonal matrices D with positive entries, we obtained a satisfactory convergence behaviour in a large number of experiments (see Section 5, and the Appendix to [14]). The better convergence may be explained by observing that in this way, not only the value of $\sigma_m(\infty)$ is expected to be small (cf. (3.14)), but as already shown in Subsection 3.2, at the same time the stiff components in the iteration error are strongly damped.

Together with the computation of the matrix D (cf. Section 4), we computed, as a posteriori test, for a few values of m the 'worst' convergence factor defined by

$$(3.15) \qquad \sigma_m := \underset{\operatorname{Re} z \leq 0}{\operatorname{Max}} |\sigma_m(z)|.$$

Because $\sigma_m(z)$ is an analytic function in the closed left halfplane, its maximum is assumed on the boundary, i.e., on the imaginary axis.

In calculating σ_m it turned out that this quantity is larger than 1 for small values of m but rather quickly decreases to a moderate size as m increases. The values of σ_m show by what factor the (maximal) difference between the two stability functions is reduced in each iteration if we continue to iterate when the stage order of the corrector has been reached. Due to the fact that $\sigma_m > 1$ for small m, it is likely that the corresponding iterated method is not A-stable. On the other hand, assuming that the iteration process (3.1) is convergent, we know that $[\sigma_m(z)]^m \to 0$ for $m \to \infty$, i.e., $R_m(z)$ converges to the A-acceptable stability function $R_{corr}(z)$. Therefore, it is of interest to know the minimal value of m such that $R_m(z)$ is A-acceptable for all m equal to or larger than this minimal value. This for the iteration process critical number of iterations will be denoted by m_{crit}. Evidently, the value of m_{crit} is expected to be large if the corrector is not strongly A-stable. In order to illustrate this, we considered the methods using weakly A-stable Newton-Cotes and Lobatto IIIA correctors (cf. Table 2.1) with minimized spectral radius of $I - D^{-1}A$. We verified that (for z in the closed left halfplane) the value of $\max |R_m(z)| \downarrow 1$ as $m \to \infty$, so that A-stability is only obtained in the limit. Hence, the Lobatto IIIA and the Newton-Cotes formulas seem to be less suitable as corrector methods. For the strongly A-stable Lagrange correctors and the L-stable Radau IIA correctors however, we found modest values of m_{crit}, so that after a few iterations the resulting method is already A-stable (see Section 4).

4. CONSTRUCTION OF METHODS

In this section, we consider a number of stiffly accurate correctors and we will construct the corresponding matrices D for use on two-, three- or four-processor computers (i.e., methods of dimension $k = 2, 3, 4$).

For $k = 2$, we shall give a rather detailed derivation, because in this case, it is still possible to construct suitable matrices D analytically. We derive matrices D for correctors of Newton-Cotes, Lobatto IIIA, strongly A-stable Lagrange, Radau IIA, and Gauss-Legendre type. The Gauss-Legendre method is not stiffly accurate, and therefore not suitable for diagonal iteration of type (3.1'), but it is included to demonstrate its unstable performance. For $k > 2$, we resort to numerical search methods for finding suitable matrices D. Here, we refrained from looking for D matrices for the Gauss-Legendre method because of the rather poor two-processor results. In Subsection 4.4 a summary of the main properties of the various methods is given.

It may be of interest to note that in our numerical search for strongly A-stable correctors we encountered strong numerical evidence for the following conjecture:

Conjecture. A necessary condition for a stiffly accurate Lagrange method as defined in Subsection 1.2 to be strongly A-stable is

$$\sum_{j=1}^{k} c_j > \frac{k+1}{2}.\ []$$

In order to save space, the correctors are presented by means of the matrix A and the vectors a and c, and the iterated versions by only giving the matrix D, because, together with the corrector, D completely defines the iterated method. In the following, we only consider *stiff* iteration, that is, the construction of D will always be based on the minimization of the spectral radius $\rho(I - D^{-1}A)$ of the matrix $I - D^{-1}A$. If the entries of D are not exact (i.e., for $k \geq 3$), then they are approximated by rational expressions. In addition to D, we present the values of $\rho(I - D^{-1}A)$, the range for σ_m with $r \leq m \leq 10$, the corresponding interval I_σ on the imaginary axis where the maxima are assumed, and the value of m_{crit} are given (cf. Subsection 3.3.2). Finally, the stage and step point orders of the methods are denoted by r and p, respectively.

4.1. Two-processor methods

4.1.1. Lagrange methods. Let us first consider two-dimensional Lagrange methods $(k = 2)$ satisfying the condition (1.4). The stage-order conditions (2.2) can be solved for $r = 3$ and yield the stiffly accurate Lagrange method

$$(4.1a) \quad A = \frac{1}{6(1-c)} \begin{pmatrix} c(3-2c) & -c^3 \\ c^{-1} & 2-3c \end{pmatrix}, \quad a = \frac{1}{6(1-c)} \begin{pmatrix} 3c - 4c^2 + c^3 \\ -c^{-1} + 4 - 3c \end{pmatrix}, \quad c = \begin{pmatrix} c \\ 1 \end{pmatrix}$$

with $p = r = 3$, and c a free parameter (recall that $p = 4$ if $c = 1/2$). An elementary calculation shows that the stability function of (4.1a) is given by

$$(4.2) \quad R(z) = \frac{6 + 2(2-c)z + (1-c)z^2}{6 - 2(c+1)z + cz^2}.$$

This function is A-acceptable for $c \geq 1/2$ and strongly A-acceptable for $c > 1/2$.

Next, we determine the matrix D in (3.1). It is convenient to write

$$D = \frac{1}{6(1-c)} \begin{pmatrix} 1/\delta_1 & 0 \\ 0 & 1/\delta_2 \end{pmatrix},$$

so that

$$I - D^{-1}A = \begin{pmatrix} 1 - c(3-2c)\delta_1 & c^3\delta_2 \\ -c^{-1}\delta_1 & 1 - (2-3c)\delta_2 \end{pmatrix}.$$

The eigenvalues of $I - D^{-1}A$ satisfy the equation

$$\mu^2 - S\mu + P = 0,$$

$$S := 2 - c(3-2c)\delta_1 - (2-3c)\delta_2, \quad P := [1 - c(3-2c)\delta_1][1-(2-3c)\delta_2] + c^2\delta_1\delta_2.$$

By setting $S = P = 0$ we achieve that $\rho(I - D^{-1}A)$ vanishes. The parameters δ_1 and δ_2 then satisfy the equations

$$c(3-2c)\delta_1 + (2-3c)\delta_2 = 2, \quad [1 - c(3-2c)\delta_1]^2 - c^2\delta_1\delta_2 = 0,$$

leading to

$$\delta_1 = \frac{1+Q}{c(3-2c)}, \quad \delta_2 = \frac{1-Q}{2-3c}, \quad Q := \frac{\pm\sqrt{6c}}{6(1-c)},$$

so that the matrix D is given by

(4.1b) $\quad D = \dfrac{1}{6(1-c)} \begin{pmatrix} \dfrac{c(3-2c)}{1+Q} & 0 \\ 0 & \dfrac{2-3c}{1-Q} \end{pmatrix}, \quad \rho(I - D^{-1}A) = 0.$

The iterated Lagrange method with zero convergence factor at infinity is completely determined by the corrector (4.1a) and the matrix (4.1b).

For $c = 1/2$ we derive from (4.1a) the Newton-Cotes corrector (with $p=4$ and $r=3$)

(4.3a) $\qquad A = \dfrac{1}{24}\begin{pmatrix} 8 & -1 \\ 16 & 4 \end{pmatrix}, \quad a = \dfrac{1}{24}\begin{pmatrix} 5 \\ 4 \end{pmatrix}, \quad c = \begin{pmatrix} 1/2 \\ 1 \end{pmatrix}.$

We observe that this corrector coincides with the three-stage Lobatto IIIA method. The stability function R of (4.3a) reduces to the (2,2)-Padé approximation to the exponential function. Recall that R is A-acceptable but not *strongly* A-acceptable. From (4.1b) we obtain the matrix

$$(4.3b) \quad D = \begin{pmatrix} \dfrac{1}{3+\sqrt{3}} & 0 \\ 0 & \dfrac{1}{2(3-\sqrt{3})} \end{pmatrix}, \quad \rho(I - D^{-1}A) = 0, \quad \sigma_m \in [0.21, 0.36],$$

$$I_\sigma = [3.9i, 5.1i], \quad m_{crit} = \infty.$$

A natural question now is, whether it is possible to choose c such that the stability is improved. Unfortunately, (4.1a) shows that it is not possible to achieve L-stability (which would require $c = 1$), but strong A-stability is obtained for $c > 1/2$. For example, by choosing $c = 3/4$ we have $R(\infty) = 1/3$. The corresponding Lagrange method is defined by

$$(4.4a) \quad A = \frac{1}{288} \begin{pmatrix} 216 & -81 \\ 256 & -48 \end{pmatrix}, \quad a = \frac{1}{288} \begin{pmatrix} 81 \\ 80 \end{pmatrix}, \quad c = \begin{pmatrix} 3/4 \\ 1 \end{pmatrix}$$

for which $p = r = 3$. The iterated version is defined by

$$(4.4b) \quad D = \begin{pmatrix} \dfrac{3}{4(\sqrt{2}+1)} & 0 \\ 0 & \dfrac{1}{6(\sqrt{2}-1)} \end{pmatrix}, \quad \rho(I - D^{-1}A) = 0, \quad \sigma_m \in [0.21, 0.33],$$

$$I_\sigma = [3.2i, 4.1i], \quad m_{crit} = 2.$$

4.1.2. Gauss and Radau methods. As reference methods for our numerical experiments, we take the conventional two-stage Gauss-Legendre and Radau IIA methods. The Gauss-Legendre corrector, and its iterated version is defined by

$$(4.5a) \quad A = \frac{1}{12} \begin{pmatrix} 3 & 3-2\sqrt{3} \\ 3+2\sqrt{3} & 3 \end{pmatrix}, \quad a = 0, \quad b_0 = 0, \quad b = \frac{1}{2}e, \quad c = \frac{1}{12} \begin{pmatrix} 6-2\sqrt{3} \\ 6+2\sqrt{3} \end{pmatrix},$$

$$p = 4, \quad r = 2,$$

$$(4.5b) \quad D = \frac{1}{6} \begin{pmatrix} 1 & 0 \\ 0 & 3 \end{pmatrix}, \quad \rho(I - D^{-1}A) = 0.$$

The Radau IIA-based method is given by:

$$(4.6a) \quad A = \frac{1}{12}\begin{pmatrix} 5 & -1 \\ 9 & 3 \end{pmatrix}, \quad a = 0, \quad b_0 = 0, \quad b^T = e_2^T A, \quad c = \begin{pmatrix} 1/3 \\ 1 \end{pmatrix},$$

$$p = 3, \quad r = 2,$$

$$(4.6b) \quad D = \frac{1}{30}\begin{pmatrix} 20-5\sqrt{6} & 0 \\ 0 & 12+3\sqrt{6} \end{pmatrix}, \quad \rho(I - D^{-1}A) = 0, \quad \sigma_m \in [0.27, 0.35],$$

$$I_\sigma = [2.6i, 3.7i], \quad m_{crit} = 1.$$

4.2. Three-processor methods

4.2.1. Newton-Cotes method.
For $k = 3$ and equidistant abscissas the corrector is given by

$$(4.7a) \quad A = \frac{1}{72}\begin{pmatrix} 19 & -5 & 1 \\ 32 & 8 & 0 \\ 27 & 27 & 9 \end{pmatrix}, \quad a = \frac{1}{72}\begin{pmatrix} 9 \\ 8 \\ 9 \end{pmatrix}, \quad b_0 = e_3^T a, \quad b^T = e_3^T A, \quad c = \frac{1}{3}\begin{pmatrix} 1 \\ 2 \\ 3 \end{pmatrix}$$

with $p = r = 4$, and with A-acceptable stability function (see Watts and Shampine [23]). By a numerical search we found the matrix

$$(4.7b) \quad D = \begin{pmatrix} \dfrac{897}{7303} & 0 & 0 \\ 0 & \dfrac{2485}{10968} & 0 \\ 0 & 0 & \dfrac{8980}{27627} \end{pmatrix}, \quad \rho(I - D^{-1}A) \approx 0.01, \quad \sigma_m \in [0.49, 0.77],$$

$$I_\sigma = [7.1i, 8.4i], \quad m_{crit} = \infty.$$

4.2.2. Lobatto IIIA method.
For $k = 3$ and Lobatto abscissas the corrector is given by

$$(4.8a) \quad A = \frac{1}{120}\begin{pmatrix} 25-\sqrt{5} & 25-13\sqrt{5} & -1+\sqrt{5} \\ 25+13\sqrt{5} & 25+\sqrt{5} & -1-\sqrt{5} \\ 50 & 50 & 10 \end{pmatrix}, \quad a = \frac{1}{120}\begin{pmatrix} 11+\sqrt{5} \\ 11-\sqrt{5} \\ 10 \end{pmatrix}, \quad b_0 = e_3^T a,$$

$$b^T = e_3^T A, \quad c = \frac{1}{10}\begin{pmatrix} 5-\sqrt{5} \\ 5+\sqrt{5} \\ 10 \end{pmatrix},$$

with $p = 6$ and $r = 4$, and with A-acceptable stability function (see Dekker and Verwer [9]). The iterated version is generated by

$$(4.8b) \quad D = \begin{pmatrix} \dfrac{2661}{5542} & 0 & 0 \\ 0 & \dfrac{754}{6891} & 0 \\ 0 & 0 & \dfrac{1567}{9771} \end{pmatrix}, \quad \rho(I - D^{-1}A) \approx 0.0043, \quad \sigma_m \in [0.52, 0.88],$$

$$I_\sigma = [8.9i, 10i], \quad m_{crit} = \infty.$$

4.2.3. Lagrange method. By keeping c_1 and c_2 free, we can construct *strongly A-stable* methods with stage order four. It can be shown that the stability function is A-acceptable for $c_1 + c_2 = 1$ and strongly A-acceptable for $c_1 + c_2 > 1$. A numerical search produced the block point vector $c = (7/12, 5/6, 1)^T$ for which parameter values of acceptable magnitude and a damping factor $|R(\infty)| \approx 0.143$ are obtained. The corresponding corrector reads

$$(4.9a) \quad A = \frac{1}{120960} \begin{pmatrix} 98392 & -81634 & 31213 \\ 112000 & -61600 & 28000 \\ 110592 & -48384 & 36288 \end{pmatrix}, \quad a = \frac{1}{120960} \begin{pmatrix} 22589 \\ 22400 \\ 22464 \end{pmatrix},$$

$$b_0 = e_3^T a, \quad b^T = e_3^T A, \quad c = \frac{1}{12} \begin{pmatrix} 7 \\ 10 \\ 12 \end{pmatrix}$$

with $p = r = 4$. The iterated method is generated by

$$(4.9b) \quad D = \begin{pmatrix} \dfrac{2246}{10669} & 0 & 0 \\ 0 & \dfrac{2537}{8794} & 0 \\ 0 & 0 & \dfrac{3026}{8923} \end{pmatrix}, \quad \rho(I - D^{-1}A) \approx 0.011, \quad \sigma_m \in [0.49, 0.69],$$

$$I_\sigma = [5.1i, 6.2i], \quad m_{crit} = 3.$$

4.2.4. Radau method. The 3-stage Radau IIA corrector is defined by [7]

$$(4.10a) \quad A = \begin{pmatrix} \dfrac{88 - 7\sqrt{6}}{360} & \dfrac{296 - 169\sqrt{6}}{1800} & \dfrac{-2 + 3\sqrt{6}}{225} \\ \dfrac{296 + 169\sqrt{6}}{1800} & \dfrac{88 + 7\sqrt{6}}{360} & \dfrac{-2 - 3\sqrt{6}}{225} \\ \dfrac{16 - \sqrt{6}}{36} & \dfrac{16 + \sqrt{6}}{36} & \dfrac{1}{9} \end{pmatrix}, \quad a = 0, \quad b_0 = 0,$$

$$b^T = e_3^T A, \quad c = Ae$$

with $p = 5$, $r = 3$, and L-acceptable stability function. The matrix D is given by

$$(4.10b) \quad D = \begin{pmatrix} \frac{4365}{13624} & 0 & 0 \\ 0 & \frac{1032}{7373} & 0 \\ 0 & 0 & \frac{1887}{5077} \end{pmatrix}, \quad \rho(I - D^{-1}A) \approx 0.0047, \quad \sigma_m \in [0.52, 1.0],$$

$$I_\sigma = [6.6i, 9.3i], \quad m_{crit} = 5.$$

4.3. Four-processor methods

4.3.1. Newton-Cotes method. For $k = 4$ and equidistant abscissas the corrector is given by

$$(4.11a) \quad A = \frac{1}{2880} \begin{pmatrix} 646 & -264 & 106 & -19 \\ 992 & 192 & 32 & -8 \\ 918 & 648 & 378 & -27 \\ 1024 & 384 & 1024 & 224 \end{pmatrix}, \quad a = \frac{1}{2880} \begin{pmatrix} 251 \\ 232 \\ 243 \\ 224 \end{pmatrix}, \quad b_0 = e_4^T a,$$

$$b^T = e_4^T A, \quad c = \frac{1}{4} \begin{pmatrix} 1 \\ 2 \\ 3 \\ 4 \end{pmatrix}$$

with $p = 6$, $r = 5$, and with A-acceptable stability function. A numerical search did not produce a better matrix D than

$$(4.11b) \quad D = \begin{pmatrix} \frac{992}{10759} & 0 & 0 & 0 \\ 0 & \frac{1365}{8107} & 0 & 0 \\ 0 & 0 & \frac{2709}{11281} & 0 \\ 0 & 0 & 0 & \frac{1717}{5549} \end{pmatrix}, \quad \rho(I - D^{-1}A) \approx 0.1, \quad \sigma_m \in [0.76, 1.04],$$

$$I_\sigma = [8.7i, 11.8i], \quad m_{crit} = \infty.$$

4.3.2. Lobatto IIIA method. For $k = 4$ and Lobatto abscissas the corrector is given by

$$A = \begin{pmatrix} \dfrac{343-9\sqrt{21}}{2520} & \dfrac{392-96\sqrt{21}}{2205} & \dfrac{343-69\sqrt{21}}{2520} & \dfrac{-21+3\sqrt{21}}{1960} \\[2mm] \dfrac{392+105\sqrt{21}}{2880} & \dfrac{8}{45} & \dfrac{392-105\sqrt{21}}{2880} & \dfrac{3}{320} \\[2mm] \dfrac{343+69\sqrt{21}}{2520} & \dfrac{392+96\sqrt{21}}{2205} & \dfrac{343+9\sqrt{21}}{2520} & \dfrac{-21-3\sqrt{21}}{1960} \\[2mm] \dfrac{49}{180} & \dfrac{16}{45} & \dfrac{49}{180} & \dfrac{1}{20} \end{pmatrix},$$

(4.12a)

$$a = \begin{pmatrix} \dfrac{119+3\sqrt{21}}{1960} \\[2mm] \dfrac{13}{320} \\[2mm] \dfrac{119-3\sqrt{21}}{1960} \\[2mm] \dfrac{1}{20} \end{pmatrix}, \quad b_0 = e_4^{\mathrm{T}} a, \quad b^{\mathrm{T}} = e_4^{\mathrm{T}} A, \quad c = \begin{pmatrix} \dfrac{7-\sqrt{21}}{14} \\[2mm] \dfrac{1}{2} \\[2mm] \dfrac{7+\sqrt{21}}{14} \\[2mm] 1 \end{pmatrix}$$

with $p = 8$, $r = 5$, and with A-acceptable stability function. A numerical search produced the matrix

(4.12b) $\quad D = \begin{pmatrix} \dfrac{2964}{9943} & 0 & 0 & 0 \\[2mm] 0 & \dfrac{1875}{10334} & 0 & 0 \\[2mm] 0 & 0 & \dfrac{608}{9403} & 0 \\[2mm] 0 & 0 & 0 & \dfrac{3799}{23419} \end{pmatrix}, \quad \rho(I - D^{-1}A) \approx 0.021, \; \sigma_m \in [0.87, 1.32],$

$$I_\sigma = [15.4i, 19i], \quad m_{\mathrm{crit}} = \infty.$$

4.3.3. Lagrange method. Numerically, we found that the stability function is A-acceptable for $c_1+c_2+c_3 = 3/2$ and strongly A-acceptable for $c_1+c_2+c_3 > 3/2$. For $c = (1/6, 7/12, 11/12, 1)^{\mathrm{T}}$ we obtained parameter values of acceptable magnitude and a damping factor $|R(\infty)| \approx 0.325$. The corresponding corrector with $p = r = 5$ reads

$$A = \frac{1}{49896000} \begin{pmatrix} 5452832 & -872784 & 926800 & -556248 \\ 17484082 & 13296591 & -6182575 & 3486252 \\ 16192946 & 22005423 & 7263025 & -1229844 \\ 16232832 & 21897216 & 9676800 & 598752 \end{pmatrix},$$

(4.13a)

$$a = \frac{1}{332640} \begin{pmatrix} 22436 \\ 6811 \\ 10043 \\ 9936 \end{pmatrix}, \quad b_0 = e_4^T a, \quad b^T = e_4^T A, \quad c = \frac{1}{12} \begin{pmatrix} 2 \\ 7 \\ 11 \\ 12 \end{pmatrix}.$$

The iterated method is generated by

(4.13b) $\quad D = \begin{pmatrix} \dfrac{5147}{38467} & 0 & 0 & 0 \\ 0 & \dfrac{1983}{17459} & 0 & 0 \\ 0 & 0 & \dfrac{3197}{14090} & 0 \\ 0 & 0 & 0 & \dfrac{3086}{12339} \end{pmatrix}, \quad \rho(I - D^{-1}A) \approx 0.045, \quad \sigma_m \in [0.59, 0.93],$

$$I_\sigma = [8.2i, 11.8i], \quad m_{crit} = 6.$$

4.3.4. Radau method. The four-stage Radau IIA corrector reads

$$A = \begin{pmatrix} .11299947932316 & -.04030922072352 & .02580237742034 & -.0099046765073 \\ .23438399574740 & .20689257393536 & -.04785712804854 & .01604742280652 \\ .21668178462325 & .40612326386737 & .18903651817006 & -.02418210489983 \\ .22046221117677 & .38819346884317 & .32884431998006 & 1/16 \end{pmatrix}$$

(4.14a)

$$a = 0, \quad b_0 = 0, \quad b^T = e_4^T A, \quad c = Ae$$

with $p = 7$, $r = 4$, and with L-acceptable stability function. The iterated method is generated by

(4.14b) $\quad D = \begin{pmatrix} \dfrac{3055}{9532} & 0 & 0 & 0 \\ 0 & \dfrac{531}{5956} & 0 & 0 \\ 0 & 0 & \dfrac{1471}{8094} & 0 \\ 0 & 0 & 0 & \dfrac{1848}{7919} \end{pmatrix}, \quad \rho(I - D^{-1}A) \approx 0.024, \quad \sigma_m \in [0.74, 1.31],$

$$I_\sigma = [10.0i, 17.2i], \quad m_{crit} = 7.$$

4.4. Survey of methods

In Table 4.1, we have summarized a few characteristics of the methods derived in the preceding subsections.

Table 4.1. Main characteristics of diagonally iterated IRK methods.

Method	p	r	k	$\rho(I-D^{-1}A)$	σ_m-range $(r \leq m \leq 10)$	m_{crit}
Newton-Cotes (4.3)	4	3	2	0	[0.21, 0.36]	∞
Lagrange (4.4)	3	3	2	0	[0.21, 0.33]	2
Radau IIA (4.6)	3	2	2	0	[0.27, 0.35]	1
Gauss (4.5)	4	2	2	0	∞	∞
Newton-Cotes (4.7)	4	4	3	0.008	[0.49, 0.77]	∞
Lobatto IIIA (4.8)	6	4	3	0.0043	[0.52, 0.88]	∞
Lagrange (4.9)	4	4	3	0.01	[0.49, 0.69]	3
Radau IIA (4.10)	5	3	3	0.0047	[0.52, 1.0]	5
Newton-Cotes (4.11)	6	5	4	0.1	[0.76, 1.04]	∞
Lobatto IIIA (4.12)	8	5	4	0.021	[0.87, 1.32]	∞
Lagrange (4.13)	5	5	4	0.045	[0.59, 0.93]	6
Radau IIA (4.14)	7	4	4	0.024	[0.74, 1.31]	7

In this table, the value of the step point order p corresponds to values of m equal to or greater than p, and the value of the stage order r corresponds to that of the corrector. From a computational point of view, the Lagrange and Radau IIA methods are the most attractive ones, because m_{crit} is relatively small. Thus, if these methods are implemented with some local error strategy for automatically estimating the number of iterations m and the stepsize h needed to meet the local error tolerance, then the value of the 'computational efficiency' quantity mL/h for integrating an interval of length L will not be unnecessarily large because of the development of instabilities. This observation is confirmed by the numerical experiments in Subsection 5.4.

5. NUMERICAL EXPERIMENTS

In this section, the (stiff) diagonal iteration method developed above will be tested by integrating a number of stiff test problems. Subsection 5.1 presents these test problems. Subsection 5.2 compares the effective orders of Gauss-Legendre, Newton-Cotes, Lobatto IIIA, Radau IIA, and Lagrange correctors, and in Subsection 5.3, the performance of the diagonal iteration process with respect to the number of

154

iterations is tested for a few two-processor correctors. Finally, in Subsection 5.4, we compare the efficiency of the iterated methods with a few DIRK methods from the literature.

We recall that we only used the zero-order approximations to the Jacobian matrix and to the initial inner and outer iterates. In the tables of results, the accuracy of the results is given by means of the number of correct digits Δ of the numerical solution at the endpoint T (i.e., we write the maximum norm of the error at $t = T$ in the form $10^{-\Delta}$). The computational costs are proportional to mL/h, where h is the fixed step length, $L := T - t_0$ is the length of the integration interval, and m is the fixed number of outer iterations per step. In actual applications of these methods, some strategy is needed to select h and m. However, since our test problems are such that the exact solution is equally smooth in the whole integration interval, it is reasonable to use fixed h and m.

5.1. Test problems

We briefly discuss a few test problems partly taken from the literature and partly constructed in order to test some special aspect of the methods. All problems are defined on the interval $[t_0,T]$.

Our first problem is the stability test problem of Prothero and Robinson [21]

$$(5.1a) \qquad \frac{dy}{dt} = -\varepsilon^{-1}(y - g(t)) + g'(t), \quad y(t_0) = g(t_0), \qquad t_0 = 0, T = 1,$$

where the exact solution equals $g(t)$ and ε is a small parameter. Prothero and Robinson used this problem to show the order reduction of RK methods when ε is small. In our experiments we set

$$(5.1b) \qquad g(t) = \cos(t), \quad \varepsilon = 10^{-3}.$$

The second test problem is the nonlinearization of problem (5.1):

$$(5.2a) \qquad \frac{dy}{dt} = -\varepsilon^{-1}(y^3 - g(t)^3) + g'(t), \quad y(t_0) = g(t_0), \qquad t_0 = 0, T = 1,$$

with exact solution $y(t) = g(t)$ for all values of the parameter ε. As in the preceding problem we set

$$(5.2b) \qquad g(t) = \cos(t), \quad \varepsilon = 10^{-3}.$$

The third test problem is that of Kaps [17]:

$$\frac{dy_1}{dt} = -(2 + \varepsilon^{-1})y_1 + \varepsilon^{-1}(y_2)^2, \qquad \frac{dy_2}{dt} = y_1 - y_2(1 + y_2),$$

(5.3)

$$y_1(t_0) = y_2(t_0) = 1, \qquad t_0 = 0, \ T = 1,$$

with the smooth exact solution $y_1 = \exp(-2t)$ and $y_2 = \exp(-t)$ for all values of the parameter ε. This problem belongs to the class of problems for which stiffly accurate RK methods do not suffer order reduction whatever small ε is (cf. Hairer et al. [11]).

The test set of Enright et al. [10] contains the following system of ODEs describing a chemical reaction:

(5.4a)
$$\frac{dy}{dt} = - \begin{pmatrix} .013 + 1000y_3 & 0 & 0 \\ 0 & 2500y_3 & 0 \\ .013 & 0 & 1000y_1 + 2500y_2 \end{pmatrix} y,$$

with $y(0) = (1, 1, 0)^T$. Since we use fixed step sizes in our experiments, we avoided the initial phase by choosing the starting point at $t_0 = 1$ and we used the corresponding initial values

(5.4b)
$$y(1) \approx \begin{pmatrix} 0.990731920827 \\ 1.009264413846 \\ -.366532612659 \ 10^{-5} \end{pmatrix}.$$

At $t = T = 51$ we found the approximate solution

$$y(51) \approx \begin{pmatrix} 0.591045966680 \\ 1.408952165382 \\ -.186793736719 \ 10^{-5} \end{pmatrix}.$$

In order to show the performance of the methods on PDEs we included the convection-diffusion problem

(5.5)
$$\frac{\partial u}{\partial t} = u \frac{\partial^2 u}{\partial x^2} - x \cos(t) \frac{\partial u}{\partial x} - x^2 \sin(t), \qquad 0 \leq x \leq 1, \qquad t_0 = 0, \ T = 1,$$

with Dirichlet boundary conditions and with exact solution $u(x,t) = x^2\cos(t)$. Standard finite difference discretization of the spatial derivatives on a uniform grid with mesh size $1/40$ leads to a system of 39 ODEs whose exact solution is given by $(j/40)^2 \cos(t), j = 1,...,39$.

5.2. Effective orders of the correctors

First of all, we want to show that in many stiff problems the property of superconvergence does not pay because of the phenomenon of order reduction, and that strong stability properties may improve the accuracy considerably.

The Tables 5.1a, 5.1b, and 5.1c present Δ-values for the various test problems obtained for $L/h = 1, 2, 4, 8, 16$ by iterating the corrector to convergence.

Table 5.1a. Problems (5.1) and (5.2). Values of Δ for $L/h = 1, 2, 4, 8, 16$.

Corrector	p	r	k			(5.1)					(5.2)		
(4.3a)	4	3	2	4.7	5.4	6.0	6.7	7.7	4.7	5.3	5.9	6.6	7.5
(4.4a)	3	3	2	5.1	5.9	6.8	7.8	8.8	5.0	5.8	6.7	7.7	8.7
(4.5a)	4	2	2	1.9	2.5	3.1	3.8	4.7	1.9	2.5	3.1	3.8	4.6
(4.6a)	3	2	2	4.2	4.7	5.3	5.9	6.5	4.2	4.7	5.2	5.8	6.4
(4.7a)	4	4	3	6.1	7.3	8.5	9.7	–	6.0	7.3	8.5	9.7	–
(4.8a)	6	4	3	6.1	7.3	8.6	9.8	–	6.1	7.3	8.5	9.7	–
(4.9a)	4	4	3	6.5	7.6	8.8	10.1	–	6.5	7.6	8.8	10.0	–
(4.10a)	5	3	3	5.0	6.0	6.9	7.9	–	4.9	5.9	6.9	7.8	–
(4.11a)	6	5	4	7.0	8.2	9.5	–	–	6.9	8.1	9.4	–	–
(4.12a)	8	5	4	7.1	8.4	9.6	–	–	7.0	8.3	9.5	–	–
(4.13a)	5	5	4	7.5	8.9	10.5	–	–	7.4	8.9	10.4	–	–
(4.14a)	7	4	4	6.3	7.4	8.6	–	–	6.3	7.3	8.5	–	–

Table 5.1b. Problem (5.3) with $\varepsilon = 10^{-3}$ and 10^{-8}. Values of Δ for $L/h = 1, 2, 4, 8, 16$.

Corrector	p	r	k		(5.3) with $\varepsilon = 10^{-3}$					(5.3) with $\varepsilon = 10^{-8}$			
(4.3a)	4	3	2	3.3	4.3	5.1	5.9	7.0	3.3	4.5	5.7	6.9	8.1
(4.4a)	3	3	2	2.7	3.6	4.4	5.3	6.2	2.7	3.6	4.4	5.3	6.2
(4.5a)	4	2	2	1.2	1.8	2.4	3.2	4.3	1.2	1.8	2.4	3.0	3.6
(4.6a)	3	2	2	2.4	3.2	4.1	5.0	5.9	2.4	3.2	4.1	5.0	5.9
(4.7a)	4	4	3	4.2	5.4	6.6	7.8	–	4.2	5.4	6.7	7.9	–
(4.8a)	6	4	3	4.7	6.0	7.3	9.3	–	5.4	7.2	9.0	10.8	–
(4.9a)	4	4	3	3.8	5.0	6.1	7.3	–	3.9	5.0	6.2	7.3	–
(4.10a)	5	3	3	4.0	5.3	6.3	7.3	–	4.4	5.8	7.3	8.8	–
(4.11a)	6	5	4	5.4	6.7	8.0	–	–	5.9	7.7	9.6	–	–
(4.12a)	8	5	4	5.6	6.8	8.2	–	–	7.8	10.2	12.6	–	–
(4.13a)	5	5	4	5.8	7.2	8.8	–	–	6.0	7.4	8.8	–	–
(4.14a)	7	4	4	5.0	6.4	7.8	–	–	6.6	8.7	10.8	–	–

Table 5.1c. Problems (5.4) and (5.5). Values of Δ for $L/h = 1, 2, 4, 8, 16$.

Corrector	p	r	k	(5.4)					(5.5)				
(4.3a)	4	3	2	4.5	5.7	6.9	8.2	9.4	3.2	4.2	5.4	6.5	7.7
(4.4a)	3	3	2	3.1	4.0	4.9	5.8	6.7	3.1	4.0	4.8	5.7	6.6
(4.5a)	4	2	2	5.0	6.1	7.3	8.5	9.7	1.9	2.6	3.2	3.9	4.8
(4.6a)	3	2	2	3.4	4.3	5.2	6.1	7.0	2.5	3.2	4.0	4.8	5.7
(4.7a)	4	4	3	4.7	5.9	7.1	8.3	–	4.6	5.9	7.2	8.4	–
(4.8a)	6	4	3	6.4	8.3	10.1	11.8	–	4.8	6.2	7.7	9.1	–
(4.9a)	4	4	3	4.2	5.4	6.6	7.8	–	4.5	5.6	6.8	7.9	–
(4.10a)	5	3	3	5.3	6.8	8.3	9.8	–	3.6	4.8	6.1	7.3	–
(4.11a)	6	5	4	6.7	8.5	10.3	–	–	5.7	7.4	9.2	–	–
(4.12a)	8	5	4	8.6	11.0	–	–	–	6.0	7.7	9.5	–	–
(4.13a)	5	5	4	6.9	8.2	9.7	–	–	6.4	7.8	9.3	–	–
(4.14a)	7	4	4	7.9	9.8	11.8	–	–	5.2	6.5	8.0	–	–

From these results we can derive for each test problem the effective orders by computing $(\Delta(h) - \Delta(2h))/0.3$. For h we chose the smallest value for which results are available. The resulting effective orders are listed in Table 5.2. For each problem, the result of the most accurate corrector is indicated in bold face.

The results for the first three problems clearly demonstrate that the various methods often do not show their step point order, so that the property of superconvergence is of limited value in the case of stiff problems.

Table 5.2. Effective orders shown by the correctors for Problems (5.1) - (5.5).

Corrector	p	r	k	(5.1)	(5.2)	(5.3) $\varepsilon=10^{-3}$	(5.3) $\varepsilon=10^{-8}$	(5.4)	(5.5)
Newton-C. (4.3a)	4	3	2	3.3	3.0	**3.7**	**4.0**	4.0	**4.0**
Lagrange (4.4a)	3	3	2	**3.3**	**3.3**	3.0	3.0	3.0	3.0
Gauss (4.5a)	4	2	2	3.0	2.7	3.7	2.0	**4.0**	3.0
Radau IIA (4.6a)	3	2	2	2.0	2.0	3.0	3.0	3.0	3.0
Newton-C. (4.7a)	4	4	3	4.0	4.0	4.0	4.0	4.0	4.0
Lobatto IIIA (4.8a)	6	4	3	4.0	4.0	**6.7**	**6.0**	**5.7**	**4.7**
Lagrange (4.9a)	4	4	3	**4.3**	**4.0**	4.0	3.7	4.0	3.7
Radau IIA (4.10a)	5	3	3	3.3	3.0	3.3	5.0	5.0	4.0
Newton-C. (4.11a)	6	5	4	4.3	4.3	4.3	6.3	6.0	6.0
Lobatto IIIA (4.12a)	8	5	4	4.0	4.0	4.7	**8.0**	**8.0**	**6.0**
Lagrange (4.13a)	5	5	4	**5.3**	**5.0**	**5.3**	4.7	5.0	5.0
Radau IIA (4.14a)	7	4	4	4.0	4.0	4.7	7.0	6.7	5.0

5.3. Performance of the iteration process for two-processor correctors.

In this subsection, we consider the performance of the iteration method for solving the two-processor corrector equations. Since the rate of convergence of a particular iteration method turned out to be comparable for the Newton-Cotes corrector and the Lagrange corrector, we only present results for the most accurate one. In the case of the Gauss and Radau corrector, the iteration methods behaved quite differently so that we include results for both correctors. Moreover, the Gauss corrector was also iterated with a matrix D defined by the relation (3.12). Since for the two-processor Gauss corrector (4.5a) we have $Ae = c$, i.e., $A^{-1}c = e$, it follows that $D^{-1}c = e$, so that

$$D = \text{diag}(c) = \frac{1}{12}\begin{pmatrix} 6 - 2\sqrt{3} & 0 \\ 0 & 6 + 2\sqrt{3} \end{pmatrix}, \quad \rho(I - D^{-1}A) = \frac{1}{2}.$$

In the Tables 5.3 and 5.4 we only present results for the problems (5.2) and (5.4) for which most methods, respectively, show their stage order and their step point order (additional results for the other test problems may be found in the Appendix to [14]). Divergence of the inner iteration is indicated by $*$, and values in bold face indicate that the accuracy of the corrector is reached (and that Δ does not change anymore). For several values of L/h the accuracies corresponding to the correctors of Lagrange type (first column), of Gauss-Legendre with D defined by (4.5b) (second column), of Gauss-Legendre with D defined above (third column), and of Radau IIA (fourth column) are listed. These results confirm that, in general, the Gauss corrector is not suited to be iterated by diagonal iteration methods when started with an explicit predictor.

Table 5.3. Values of Δ for Problem (5.2) obtained by iterating the Lagrange corrector (4.4a), Gauss corrector (4.5a), and Radau IIA corrector (4.6a).

m	$L/h=2$				$L/h=4$				$L/h=8$				$L/h=16$			
1	4.1	−2.2	−2.2	5.3	4.0	*	*	4.8	3.6	*	*	5.0	2.7	*	*	5.3
2	**5.8**	−1.1	1.1	**4.7**	6.5	*	1.1	**5.2**	6.7	*	0.6	5.9	6.7	*	*	6.7
3		2.4	2.2		**6.7**	2.9	2.6		7.7	3.9	3.2	**5.8**	8.4	1.9	3.8	**6.4**
4		**2.5**	1.9			**3.1**	2.5			**3.8**	3.1		**8.7**	4.6	3.8	
5			2.1				2.6				3.2				3.9	
⋮		⋮				⋮				⋮				⋮		
10			2.6				3.2				4.1				5.3	
20			**2.5**				**3.1**				**3.8**				**4.6**	

Table 5.4. Values of Δ for Problem (5.4) obtained by iterating the Lagrange corrector (4.4a), Gauss corrector (4.5a), and Radau IIA corrector (4.6a).

m	$L/h=2$				$L/h=4$				$L/h=8$				$L/h=16$			
1	2.3	1.5	1.5	2.1	2.6	*	*	2.4	2.8	*	*	2.7	3.1	*	*	3.0
2	3.9	2.9	2.8	3.5	4.5	*	3.4	4.1	5.2	*	4.0	4.7	5.8	*	4.5	5.3
3	5.4	4.8	3.8	4.5	6.4	5.7	4.7	5.4	7.4	6.6	5.6	6.3	8.3	6.9	6.5	7.2
4	**5.7**	5.9	4.9	**4.3**	**6.9**	7.1	6.1	**5.2**	8.1	8.3	7.2	**6.1**	9.3	9.5	8.4	**7.0**
5		**6.1**	5.7			**7.3**	7.1			**8.2**	**8.5**	8.3		9.4	**9.7**	9.5	
6			**6.1**				**7.3**				**8.5**				9.5	
7																**9.7**

5.4. Efficiency of diagonally iterated IRK correctors

In this final subsection, we compare the efficiency of the diagonally iterated IRK correctors with three fourth-order DIRK methods from the literature, viz. the three-stage method generated by the Butcher array

$$(5.6)\quad
\begin{array}{c|ccc}
\frac{1}{2}(1+\xi) & \frac{1}{2}(1+\xi) & & \\
\frac{1}{2} & -\frac{1}{2}\xi & \frac{1}{2}(1+\xi) & \\
\frac{1}{2}(1-\xi) & (1+\xi) & -(1+2\xi) & \frac{1}{2}(1+\xi) \\
\hline
 & \frac{1}{6\xi^2} & 1-\frac{1}{3\xi^2} & \frac{1}{6\xi^2}
\end{array}
\ ,\quad \xi=\frac{2}{3}\sqrt{3}\,\cos\!\left(\frac{\pi}{18}\right),$$

(cf. Crouzeix [8] and Alexander [1]), and the four-stage, parallel DIRK methods of Iserles and Nørsett [16]:

$$(5.7)\quad
\begin{array}{c|cccc}
\frac{1}{2} & \frac{1}{2} & & & \\
1 & 0 & 1 & & \\
\frac{1}{2} & \frac{3}{2} & -\frac{3}{2} & \frac{1}{2} & \\
0 & -3 & 2 & 0 & 1 \\
\hline
 & \frac{1}{3} & \frac{1}{6} & \frac{1}{3} & \frac{1}{6}
\end{array}\ ,$$

$$(5.8) \qquad
\begin{array}{c|ccccc}
\frac{1}{2} & \frac{1}{2} & & & & \\[4pt]
\frac{2}{3} & 0 & \frac{2}{3} & & & \\[4pt]
\frac{1}{2} & -\frac{5}{2} & \frac{5}{2} & \frac{1}{2} & & \\[4pt]
\frac{1}{3} & -\frac{5}{3} & \frac{4}{3} & 0 & \frac{2}{3} & \\[4pt]
\hline
 & -1 & \frac{3}{2} & -1 & \frac{3}{2} &
\end{array} \; ,$$

The method (5.6) is A-stable and requires three sequential stages per step. The methods (5.7) and (5.8) are A-stable and L-stable, respectively, and require only two sequential stages per step (when run on a two-processor computer).

We restrict our considerations to the above three DIRK methods and to the Newton-Cotes, Lobatto IIIA, Lagrange, and Radau IIA correctors where each method uses a fixed number of m iterations per step. Recalling that iterating an IRK corrector by means of m diagonal iterations in each step yields a method that is in fact a DIRK method with m sequential stages, we conclude that all methods have in common that they belong to the class of DIRK methods. However, in the case of the 'genuine' DIRK methods (5.6), (5.7), and (5.8), the number of sequential stages per step is known in advance, whereas in the case of the DIRK methods based on iteration the number of sequential stages m that yields acceptable accuracies, is not known in advance and, in actual computation, it should be determined on the basis of some local error strategy. On the other hand, as we shall see, the accuracy of the iterated methods is less sensitive to the phenomenon of order reduction.

In the Tables 5.5 and 5.6, m always denotes the number of sequential stages per step. Hence, all results in one column of these tables correspond to DIRK methods that use m sequential stages per step, so that all results corresponding to the same value of mL/h required roughly the same computational effort. In the tables, the highest value of Δ corresponding to the same mL/h value, that is, the 'most efficient' integration result, is indicated in bold face. As in the preceding subsection, we only present results for the problems (5.2) and (5.4). Results for the additional test problems may be found in the Appendix to [14].

In the case of the nonlinear Prothero-Robinson problem, Table 5.5a shows that the number of iterations needed by the iterated methods to 'reach' the accuracy of the corrector solution increases with k, that is, the higher-order methods need more iterations to solve the corrector; moreover, they have a 'slow start': after 2 iterations the accuracy is still rather modest, whereas the lower-order methods have already converged, showing full corrector-precision. This can be explained by observing that we used a zero-order predictor for $Y^{(0)}$ for all k, so that the 'distance' between predictor and corrector solution increases with k. Thus, for this problem, the lower-order methods are more efficient than the higher-order ones, unless very high accuracies are requested. Furthermore, when we compare the various types of iterated methods (Newton-Cotes, Lobatto, Lagrange, or Radau), then the Lobatto IIIA methods perform not as well whereas the strongly A-stable Lagrange methods are slightly superior to the others. In the case of the 'genuine' DIRK methods (5.6), (5.7) and (5.8), the Iserles-Nørsett methods are more accurate than the Crouzeix-Alexander method, which is presumably due to the L-stability property of the Iserles-Nørsett method.

It is of particular interest to see how the iterated methods compare with the 'genuine' DIRK methods. For example, Table 5.5a shows that the Newton-Cotes, Lobatto IIIA, Lagrange, and Radau IIA based methods, respectively, produce 5, 0, 21 and 4 'most efficient' results, whereas the 'genuine' DIRK methods none. A further indication of the superiority of the iterated methods is given by Table 5.5b where we list results for the iterated methods with $m = 4$ and for the parallel DIRK methods (5.7) and (5.8). All these methods have step point order $p = 4$, but the accuracies obtained for the same computational-costs value of mL/h differ largely, which is caused by the order reduction exhibited by the 'genuine' DIRK methods.

For the more innocent chemical reaction problem (5.4) the order reduction is not shown. Table 5.6a shows that the high-order iterated methods again require more iterations to obtain the corrector precision than the lower-order methods, however, here for low values of m, all iterated methods are roughly equally efficient. Furthermore, the scores of 'most efficient' results for the Newton-Cotes, Lobatto IIIA, Lagrange, and Radau IIA based methods are respectively 8, 5, 6 and 7, and among the DIRK methods only (5.7) scores twice. The analogue of Table 5.5b is given by Table 5.6b. It reveals that the iterated methods are usually much more efficient than the parallel DIRK methods and in any case at least competitive.

Table 5.5a. Problem (5.2): Results for diagonally iterated correctors and for the methods (5.6), (5.7), and (5.8).

Method	k	L/h	$m=1$	$m=2$	$m=3$	$m=4$	$m=5$	$m=6$	$m=7$	$m=8$	$m=9$	$m=10$	⋯	$m=\infty$
Crouzeix-Alex. (5.6)	1	1	–	–	1.0									–
Iserles-Nørsett (5.7)	2		–	1.5										–
Iserles-Nørsett (5.8)			–	2.1										–
Newton-C. (4.3)			3.4	4.7										4.7
Lagrange (4.4)			3.5	**5.0**										5.0
Radau IIA (4.6)			**3.8**	4.2										4.2
Newton-C. (4.7)	3		3.2	3.7	**5.6**	6.1	6.0							6.0
Lobatto IIIA (4.8)			3.0	2.7	4.7	6.0	6.0	6.1						6.1
Lagrange (4.9)			3.2	3.9	5.5	**6.7**	6.5							6.5
Radau IIA (4.10)			3.4	3.1	5.0	4.9								4.9
Newton-C. (4.11)	4		3.1	3.6	4.9	4.7	5.2	6.0	**7.2**	7.0	6.9			6.9
Lobatto IIIA (4.12)			2.7	2.2	2.3	3.9	4.6	5.4	6.8	6.9	7.0			7.0
Lagrange (4.13)			3.0	2.8	3.1	3.9	5.0	6.4	7.1	**7.3**	**7.4**			**7.4**
Radau IIA (4.14)			2.9	2.8	3.0	4.7	5.6	**6.8**	6.3					6.3
Crouzeix-Alex. (5.6)	1	2	–	–	2.5									–
Iserles-Nørsett (5.7)	2		–	2.4										–
Iserles-Nørsett (5.8)			–	2.7										–
Newton-C. (4.3)			4.0	5.3										5.3
Lagrange (4.4)			4.1	**5.8**										5.8
Radau IIA (4.6)			**5.3**	4.7										4.7
Newton-C. (4.7)	3		3.4	3.5	**6.4**	**8.1**	7.2	7.3						7.3
Lobatto IIIA (4.8)			3.0	2.2	5.3	6.0	7.3							7.3
Lagrange (4.9)			3.5	3.8	5.9	7.5	**7.6**							7.6
Radau IIA (4.10)			3.8	2.8	5.9	5.7	5.9							5.9
Newton-C. (4.11)	4		3.3	3.3	5.2	5.2	5.3	5.9	6.7	7.8	8.3	8.1		8.1
Lobatto IIIA (4.12)			2.3	1.1	1.4	4.0	4.5	5.5	6.9	7.3	8.4	8.3		8.3
Lagrange (4.13)			2.9	2.3	2.7	4.9	5.2	6.5	**8.3**	**8.9**				**8.9**
Radau IIA (4.14)			2.8	2.2	2.6	5.0	6.0	7.0	7.5	7.3				7.3
Crouzeix-Alex. (5.6)	1	4	–	–	2.8									–
Iserles-Nørsett (5.7)	2		–	3.0										–
Iserles-Nørsett (5.8)			–	3.2										–
Newton-C. (4.3)			3.9	5.8	5.9									5.9
Lagrange (4.4)			4.0	**6.5**	6.7									6.7
Radau IIA (4.6)			**4.8**	5.2										5.2
Newton-C. (4.7)	3		3.1	3.0	6.6	**7.7**	8.4	8.5						8.5
Lobatto IIIA (4.8)			2.3	0.7	5.5	6.2	7.7	8.1	8.5					8.5
Lagrange (4.9)			3.2	3.5	6.2	**7.7**	**9.9**	8.8						8.8
Radau IIA (4.10)			3.6	2.0	5.6	6.2	6.8	6.9						6.9
Newton-C. (4.11)	4		2.9	2.5	5.0	5.5	5.5	6.0	6.8	7.7	8.7	9.8		9.4
Lobatto IIIA (4.12)			1.1	*	*	5.0	4.3	5.6	6.4	7.2	8.3	9.0		9.5
Lagrange (4.13)			2.3	0.8	1.5	5.1	5.6	6.8	7.9	**8.8**	9.7	10.8		**10.4**
Radau IIA (4.14)			2.1	0.6	1.2	5.2	6.3	7.9	8.4	8.5				8.5

Table 5.6a. Problem (5.4): Results for diagonally iterated correctors and for the methods (5.6), (5.7), and (5.8).

Method	k	L/h	m=1	m=2	m=3	m=4	m=5	m=6	m=7	m=8	⋯ m=∞
Crouzeix-Alex. (5.6)	1	1	–	–	3.4						–
Iserles-Nørsett (5.7)	2		–	3.4							–
Iserles-Nørsett (5.8)			–	3.3							–
Newton-C. (4.3)			**2.1**	3.4	4.3	4.5					4.5
Lagrange (4.4)			**2.1**	3.5	3.1						3.1
Radau IIA (4.6)			1.7	2.9	3.6	3.4					3.4
Newton-C. (4.7)	3		1.8	3.5	5.1	4.7					4.7
Lobatto IIIA (4.8)			1.6	3.1	4.3	5.6	6.3	6.4			6.4
Lagrange (4.9)			1.8	3.5	4.3	4.2					4.2
Radau IIA (4.10)			2.0	3.2	4.3	5.9	5.3				5.3
Newton-C. (4.11)	4		1.7	**3.6**	5.2	6.5	6.7				6.7
Lobatto IIIA (4.12)			1.4	2.7	4.6	6.0	7.1	**8.3**	**8.6**		**8.6**
Lagrange (4.13)			1.6	3.1	**5.8**	6.6	7.0	6.9			6.9
Radau IIA (4.14)			1.5	3.2	4.8	**7.4**	**7.8**	7.9			7.9
Crouzeix-Alex. (5.6)	1	2	–	–	4.4						–
Iserles-Nørsett (5.7)	2		–	**4.5**							–
Iserles-Nørsett (5.8)			–	4.4							–
Newton-C. (4.3)			**2.3**	3.9	5.4	5.7					5.7
Lagrange (4.4)			**2.3**	**4.5**	4.0						4.0
Radau IIA (4.6)			2.1	3.5	4.5	4.3					4.3
Newton-C. (4.7)	3		2.0	4.2	6.2	5.9					5.9
Lobatto IIIA (4.8)			1.9	3.8	5.1	6.8	8.1	8.3			8.3
Lagrange (4.9)			2.1	4.1	5.5	5.4					5.4
Radau IIA (4.10)			2.2	3.8	5.1	6.9	6.8				6.8
Newton-C. (4.11)	4		2.0	**4.5**	**6.7**	7.9	8.5				8.5
Lobatto IIIA (4.12)			1.7	3.3	5.4	7.2	8.5	10.0	**10.9**	**11.0**	**11.0**
Lagrange (4.13)			1.9	3.7	6.3	7.5	8.3	8.2			8.2
Radau IIA (4.14)			1.8	3.7	5.6	**8.0**	**8.8**	**10.1**	9.8		9.8
Crouzeix-Alex. (5.6)	1	4	–	–	5.5						–
Iserles-Nørsett (5.7)	2		–	**5.7**							–
Iserles-Nørsett (5.8)			–	5.6							–
Newton-C. (4.3)			**2.6**	4.5	6.4	6.9					6.9
Lagrange (4.4)			**2.6**	4.7	4.9						4.9
Radau IIA (4.6)			2.4	4.1	5.4	5.2					5.2
Newton-C. (4.7)	3		2.3	5.0	**7.2**	7.1					7.1
Lobatto IIIA (4.8)			2.2	4.4	6.0	7.9	9.7	10.1			10.1
Lagrange (4.9)			2.4	4.8	6.8	6.6					6.6
Radau IIA (4.10)			2.5	4.5	6.0	7.9	8.3				8.3
Newton-C. (4.11)	4		2.3	5.4	7.1	8.9	**10.6**	10.3			10.3
Lobatto IIIA (4.12)			2.0	4.0	6.1	8.4	10.1	11.9	**12.3**		**12.3**
Lagrange (4.13)			2.2	4.2	**7.2**	8.7	9.9	9.7			9.7
Radau IIA (4.14)			2.1	4.3	6.6	**9.1**	10.2	**12.2**	11.8		11.8

164

Table 5.5b. Problem (5.2): Efficiency test of fourth-order methods.

Method	p	m	k	$mL/h=4$	$mL/h=8$	$mL/h=16$
Iserles-Nørsett (5.7)	4	2	2	2.4	3.0	3.6
Iserles-Nørsett (5.8)	4	2	2	2.7	3.2	3.8
Newton-C. (4.3)	4	4	2	4.7	5.3	5.9
Newton-C. (4.7)	4	4	3	6.1	**8.1**	**7.7**
Lobatto IIIA (4.8)	4	4	3	6.0	6.0	6.2
Lagrange (4.9)	4	4	3	**6.7**	7.5	**7.7**
Radau IIA (4.10)	4	4	3	4.9	5.7	6.2
Newton-C. (4.11)	4	4	4	4.7	5.2	5.5
Lobatto IIIA (4.12)	4	4	4	3.9	4.0	5.0
Lagrange (4.13)	4	4	4	3.9	4.9	5.1
Radau IIA (4.14)	4	4	4	4.7	5.0	5.2

Table 5.6b. Problem (5.4): Efficiency test of fourth-order methods.

Method	p	m	k	$mL/h=4$	$mL/h=8$	$mL/h=16$
Iserles-Nørsett (5.7)	4	2	2	4.5	5.7	6.9
Iserles-Nørsett (5.8)	4	2	2	4.4	5.6	6.7
Newton-C. (4.3)	4	4	2	4.5	5.7	6.9
Newton-C. (4.7)	4	4	3	4.7	5.9	7.1
Lobatto IIIA (4.8)	4	4	3	5.6	6.8	7.9
Lagrange (4.9)	4	4	3	4.2	5.4	6.6
Radau IIA (4.10)	4	4	3	5.9	6.9	7.9
Newton-C. (4.11)	4	4	4	6.5	7.9	8.9
Lobatto IIIA (4.12)	4	4	4	6.0	7.2	8.4
Lagrange (4.13)	4	4	4	6.6	7.5	8.7
Radau IIA (4.14)	4	4	4	**7.4**	**8.0**	**9.1**

6. CONCLUDING REMARKS

In this paper we have derived a diagonally implicit iteration scheme to solve a fully implicit Runge-Kutta method. The structure of this iteration process is such that a parallel computer can be fully exploited. Starting with an implicit RK method with k implicit stages (the corrector), each iteration requires the solution of k systems of equations of dimension equal to the number of ODEs. Since these systems can be solved completely independently, the *effective* computational work per iteration equals the solution of one such system, provided that k processors are available.

The free parameters in the iteration scheme are chosen in such a way that the corresponding stability functions converge as quickly as possible to the stability function of the corrector, which is chosen to be (at least) A-acceptable. Although we have numerical evidence that this is not a bad choice, we do not claim that it is the best possible. In a forthcoming paper it is intended to give theoretical support for this choice.

A second aspect considered in this paper, is the choice of the particular corrector method. The well-known implicit RK methods of high classical order, such as the Gauss-Legendre, Radau, and Lobatto methods, seem to be suitable candidates. However, since it is the *stage order* which usually determines the order behaviour in integrating stiff differential equations, these methods are not necessarily optimal correctors. Because the stage order is significantly smaller than the classical order for these methods, we will encounter the phenomenon of order reduction. Therefore, we also considered Newton-Cotes and Lagrange correctors, which have − for the same number of implicit relations per iteration − a stage order which is one higher than for Gauss-Legendre and Radau methods and is equal to the stage order of Lobatto methods.

Apart from these order considerations, it turned out that the stability behaviour of the iterated scheme largely depends on the choice of the corrector. For example, it is shown that the Gauss-Legendre corrector is not suitable in this context, since it is not stiffly accurate. Consequently, only for very 'innocent' stiff problems, where we have no order reduction, the Gauss-Legendre corrector is useful, but as a method for general stiff problems it is disadvantageous.

The other four types of correctors are all stiffly accurate, which has the effect that certain classes of stiff problems can be integrated without order reduction. For such problems the classical order should be a decisive factor, viz. in these cases the Lobatto IIIA corrector is superior and also the Newton-Cotes corrector is a good choice. However, these correctors are only A-stable and it is shown that the stability function of the iterated method is not A-acceptable unless the corrector is really solved. This means that the iteration process based on these correctors easily encounters stability problems. Hence, a corrector possessing better stability characteristics, such as the Radau IIA method (L-stable) and the Lagrange method (strongly A-stable), will be much more robust. We showed that after a few iterations the stability function of the iterated methods based on these correctors is A-acceptable.

Since the stage order of the Lagrange corrector is one larger than that of the Radau IIA corrector, we think that it is a good choice for integrating general stiff equations; it combines adequate stability characteristics with a relatively high stage order. Our numerical experiments confirm this advice.

Furthermore, we have compared our methods with sequential and parallel DIRK methods from the literature. This comparison is rather obvious since the effective computational work per iteration equals the work per stage in a DIRK method. It turned out that the diagonally iterated RK methods are much more efficient than the 'conventional' DIRKs. The reason is that only low order 'conventional' DIRKs with good stability properties are available in the literature and, more importantly, these DIRKs have a stage order equal to 1. This property gives these methods a very poor performance in case of general stiff problems.

Finally, we remark that the construction of diagonally iterated methods of arbitrarily high order is straightforward, and we observed in our experiments that, especially the high order methods, showed remarkably high accuracies.

ACKNOWLEDGMENT

The authors are grateful to Dr. W. H. Hundsdorfer for carefully reading the manuscript and for many valuable suggestions during the investigations reported in this paper.

REFERENCES

[1] **Alexander, R.** (1977): *Diagonally implicit Runge-Kutta methods for stiff ODEs*, SIAM J. Numer. Anal. **14**, 1006-1021.

[2] **Burrage, K.** (1978): *A special family of Runge-Kutta methods for solving stiff differential equations*, BIT **18**, 22-41.

[3] **Burrage, K.** (1991): *The error behaviour of a general class of predictor-corrector methods*, Appl. Numer. Math. **8**, 201-216.

[4] **Burrage, K., Houwen, P.J. van der, Hundsdorfer, W.H. & Sommeijer, B.P.** (1991): *Diagonal iteration of Runge-Kutta methods* (in preparation).

[5] **Butcher, J.C.** (1976): *On the implementation of implicit Runge-Kutta methods*, BIT **16**, 237-240.

[6] **Butcher, J.C.** (1979): *A transformed implicit Runge-Kutta method*, J. Assoc. Comput. Mach. **26**, 731-738.

[7] **Butcher, J.C.** (1987): *The numerical analysis of ordinary differential equations, Runge-Kutta and general linear methods*, Wiley, New York.

[8] **Crouzeix, M.** (1975): *Sur l'approximation des équations différentielles opérationnelles linéaires par des méthodes de Runge-Kutta*, Ph. D. Thesis, Université de Paris.

[9] **Dekker, K. & Verwer, J.G.** (1984): *Stability of Runge-Kutta methods for stiff nonlinear differential equations,* CWI Monograph 2, North-Holland, Amsterdam.

[10] **Enright, W.H., Hull, T.E. & Lindberg, B.** (1975): *Comparing numerical methods for stiff systems of ODEs*, BIT **15**, 10-48.

[11] Hairer, E., Lubich, Ch. & Roche, M. (1988): *Error of Runge-Kutta methods for stiff problems studied via differential algebraic equations*, BIT **28**, 678-700.

[12] Houwen, P.J. van der & Sommeijer, B.P. (1990): *Parallel iteration of high-order Runge-Kutta methods with stepsize control*, J. Comp. Appl. Math. **29**, 111-127.

[13] Houwen, P.J. van der, Sommeijer, B.P. & Couzy, W. (1992): *Embedded diagonally implicit Runge-Kutta algorithms on parallel computers*, Math. Comp. **58**, 135-159.

[14] Houwen, P.J. van der & Sommeijer, B.P. (1990): *Iterated Runge-Kutta methods on parallel computers*, Report NM-R9001, Centre for Mathematics and Computer Science, Amsterdam.

[15] Hundsdorfer, W.H. (1990): Private communication.

[16] Iserles, A. & Nørsett, S.P. (1990): *On the theory of parallel Runge-Kutta methods*, IMA J. Numer. Anal. **10**, 463-488.

[17] Kaps, P. (1981): *Rosenbrock-type methods, in: Numerical methods for stiff initial value problems*, G. Dahlquist and R. Jeltsch (eds.), Bericht nr. 9, Inst. für Geometrie und Praktische Mathematik der RWTH Aachen.

[18] Lie, I. (1987): *Some aspects of parallel Runge-Kutta methods*, Report No. 3/87, Division Numerical Mathematics, University of Trondheim.

[19] Nørsett, S.P. (1974): *Semi-explicit Runge-Kutta methods*, Report Mathematics and Computation No.6/74, Depart. of Mathematics, University of Trondheim.

[20] Nørsett, S.P. & Simonsen, H.H. (1989): *Aspects of parallel Runge-Kutta methods*, in: Numerical methods for ordinary differential equations, A. Bellen, C.W. Gear & E. Russo (eds.), Proceedings L'Aquila 1987, Lecture Notes in Mathematics **1386**, Springer-Verlag, Berlin.

[21] Prothero, A. & Robinson, A. (1974): *On the stability and accuracy of one-step methods for solving stiff systems of ordinary differential equations*, Math. Comp. **28**, 145-162.

[22] Sommeijer, B.P., Couzy, W. & van der Houwen, P.J. (1992): *A-stable parallel block methods for ordinary and integro-differential equations*, Appl. Numer. Math. **9**, 267-281.

[23] Watts, H.A. & Shampine, L.F. (1972): *A-stable block implicit one-step methods*, BIT **12**, 252-266.

CHAPTER VI

Analysis of parallel diagonally implicit iteration
of Runge-Kutta methods

Reprinted from

Appl. Numer. Math. **11** (1993), 169-188

with granted permission from ELSEVIER SCIENCE PUBLISHERS B.V.

Analysis of parallel diagonally implicit iteration of Runge-Kutta methods

P.J. van der Houwen and B.P. Sommeijer

Centre for Mathematics and Computer Science
P.O. Box 94079, 1090 GB Amsterdam, The Netherlands

Abstract. In this paper, we analyse parallel, diagonally implicit iteration of Runge-Kutta methods (PDIRK methods) for solving large systems of stiff equations on parallel computers. Like Newton-iterated backward differentiation formulas (BDFs), these PDIRK methods are such that in each step the (sequential) costs consist of solving a number of linear systems with the same matrix of coefficients and with the same dimension as the system of differential equations. Although for PDIRK methods the number of linear systems is usually higher than for Newton iteration of BDFs, the more computational intensive work of computing the matrix of coefficients and its LU-decomposition is identical. The advantage of PDIRK methods over Newton-iterated BDFs is their unconditional stability (A-stability for Gauss-based methods and L-stability for Radau-based methods) for any order of accuracy.

Special characteristics of the PDIRK methods will be studied, such as the rate of convergence, the influence of particular predictors on the resulting stability properties, and the stiff error constants in the global error.

1991 Mathematics Subject Classification: 65L06, 65L20

1991 C.R. Classification: G.1.7

Key Words: Diagonally implicit Runge-Kutta methods, parallelism.

1. INTRODUCTION

Consider the initial value problem for systems of ordinary differential equations (ODEs) of dimension d

$$(1.1) \quad y'(t) = f(t,y(t)), \quad y(t_0) = y_0, \quad y : \mathbb{R} \to \mathbb{R}^d, \quad f : \mathbb{R} \times \mathbb{R}^d \to \mathbb{R}^d, \quad t_0 \le t \le t_{end}.$$

In this paper, we analyze integration methods based on iteration of implicit Runge-Kutta (RK) methods of collocation type. Such RK methods possess both a large step-point order and a large stage order. Furthermore, by a suitable choice of the collocation parameters, these RK methods are unconditionally stable for any order of accuracy.

We shall employ the *diagonally implicit* iteration-type methods proposed in [7, 8]. These methods are designed in such a way that a large number of the implicit systems to be solved can be processed in parallel, so that the number of systems that have to be solved *sequentially* is substantially reduced when implemented on multi-processor computers. As a reference method, we take the method based on the backward differentiation formulas (BDFs), which is considered as one of the best methods for sequential computers. The sequential computations (i.e., the computations that cannot be performed in parallel on a multi-processor system) of the parallel diagonal-implicitly iterated RK (PDIRK) methods are of the same nature as those of Newton-iterated BDFs, that is, in each step, both types of methods require the sequential solution of a number of linear systems with the same matrix of coefficients and with the same dimension as the system of differential equations. Although, this number of linear systems is usually higher for PDIRK methods than for Newton iteration of BDFs, the effort required for computing the Jacobian and the *LU*-decomposition of the matrix of coefficients is identical. For large systems of equations, these computations are the more computational intensive work, so that the overall computation time is primarily determined by the number of Jacobian updates and *LU*-decompositions. The advantage of PDIRK methods over Newton-iterated BDFs is their *A*-stability (Gauss correctors [2]), strong *A*-stability (Lagrange correctors derived in [7]) or even *L*-stability (e.g. Radau IIA correctors) for high orders of accuracy. The property that unconditional stability can be combined with high orders reduces the number of integration steps (and therefore the number of Jacobian updates and *LU*-decompositions) considerably.

In Section 2, we define the PDIRK iteration scheme and discuss some favourable properties of the underlying implicit RK method (the corrector). We analyze the influence of the initial iterate (the predictor) with respect to the stability of the final result. Both implicit and explicit predictors of one-step and multistep type are discussed. Furthermore, several options for the iteration parameters are considered. Section 3 describes the convergence and stability for several predictor-corrector (PC) combinations. An expression for the global error for the linear inhomogeneous test equation $y'(t)=\lambda y(t)+g(t)$ will be derived in Section 4. For various PC combinations and several one-step predictors, the principal stiff error constants in the global error expansion are calculated for several iteration strategies. Finally, in Section 5 the results are compared and some recommendations are formulated.

2. PDIRK METHODS

In this section we define PDIRK methods by specifying the RK corrector, the iteration scheme for solving the stage vector equation, the predictor formula, and the formula for the step-point values. The various families of PDIRK methods are determined by special choices of the iteration parameters occurring in the iteration scheme. In order to simplify the notations, the formulas are given for *scalar* ODEs. The extension to *systems* of ODEs is straightforward.

2.1. The corrector

We consider RK methods of the form

(2.1)
$$Y - hAf(et_n + ch,Y) = ey_n + h a\ f(t_n,y_n),$$
$$y_{n+1} = y_n + h\ b_0 f(t_n,y_n) + h\ b^{\mathrm{T}} f(et_n + ch,Y), \qquad c := a + Ae,$$

where b_0 is a scalar parameter, e is the vector with unit entries, $a = (a_i)$, $b = (b_i)$ and $c = (c_i)$ are k-dimensional vectors, and $A = (a_{ij})$ is a k-by-k matrix. In (2.1) we used the convention that for any given vectors $v = (v_j)$ and $t = (t_j)$, $f(t,v)$ denotes the vector with entries $f(t_j,v_j)$. We always assume that the matrix A is nonsingular. If the vector a or the parameter b_0 does not vanish, then (2.1) presents an $(s = k+1)$-stage RK method requiring k *implicit* stages and one explicit stage. If $a = 0$ and $b_0 = 0$, then (2.1) reduces to the general $(s = k)$-stage RK method with s implicit stages. For a discussion of the order of accuracy and the stage order of RK methods, we refer to e.g. [4] and [3]. In the sequel, the method (2.1) will be called the *corrector*.

2.2. The iteration scheme

The stage vector equation in (2.1) is solved by applying the diagonal iteration method studied in [8] and [7]. Let $Y^{(\mu)}$ denote the successive iterates, then we may define the (highly parallel) iteration process

(2.2)
$$Y^{(1)} - hDf(et_n + ch,Y^{(1)}) =$$
$$ey_n + a\ hf(t_n,y_n) + hAf(et_n + c^*h,Y^{(0)}) - hDf(et_n + c^*h,Y^{(0)}),$$
$$Y^{(\mu)} - hDf(et_n + ch,Y^{(\mu)}) =$$
$$ey_n + a\ hf(t_n,y_n) + hAf(et_n + ch,Y^{(\mu-1)}) - hDf(et_n + ch,Y^{(\mu-1)}),$$

where $\mu = 2, ..., m$, and D is a diagonal matrix whose diagonal elements δ_i $(i = 1,...,k)$ are the iteration parameters which are assumed to be positive. The parameter vector c^* depends on the predictor formula used for computing $Y^{(0)}$ and serves to make the arguments of f consistent in the first iteration (see Section 2.4). The step-point formula defining y_{n+1} and the predictor formula will be discussed in the Sections 2.3 and 2.4, respectively. Together, the predictor formula, the iteration scheme (2.2), and the step-point formula determine the PDIRK method.

Each iteration in (2.2) requires the solution of k nonlinear systems which can be obtained by applying modified Newton iteration. We shall call this last iteration the

172

inner iteration method and the iteration (2.2) the *outer* iteration method. Notice that in each outer iteration the k nonlinear systems can be solved in parallel, provided that k processors are available. Thus, the *sequential* costs per step consist of computing $Y^{(0)}$ and of solving m nonlinear systems of ODE dimension.

For particular choices of the predictor formula (e.g., explicit RK formulas) and for step-point formulas as defined in Section 2.3, the PDIRK method as described above can be interpreted as a diagonally implicit RK (DIRK) method using mk diagonally implicit stages. Since the k stages in each outer iteration can be computed in parallel, we arrive at a DIRK method with m *sequential* diagonally implicit stages. These methods form a subclass of the much wider class of the PaRK methods investigated by Jackson and Nørsett [9, 10].

In [7] and [8] the performance of PDIRK methods was studied in the case where in each of the m outer iterations the inner iteration method was continued until convergence before starting the next outer iteration (this iteration strategy is also used in conventional DIRK methods). However, this strategy may be rather expensive if many iterations are needed to get the inner iteration converged. Moreover, it does not take into account the special structure of the method. The essential difference with conventional DIRK methods lies in the fact that the ith component of each stage vector $Y^{(\mu)}$ is an approximation to the exact solution at the point $t_n + c_i h$. This implies that $Y^{(\mu-1)}$ furnishes an excellent initial approximation to the solution $Y^{(\mu)}$ to be obtained in the inner iteration process. As a consequence, each outer iteration needs only a few inner iterations. Furthermore, in first approximation, the convergence of the inner-outer iteration scheme and the stability of the PDIRK method do not depend on the number of inner iterations. This motivates our strategy to perform only one inner iteration per outer iteration, leading to the iteration process

$$[I - hDJ]\left(Y^{(0)} - Y^{(1)}\right) = Y^{(0)} - hDf(et_n + ch, Y^{(0)})$$
$$- \left[ey_n + a\,hf(t_n,y_n) + hAf(et_n + c^*h, Y^{(0)}) - hDf(et_n + c^*h, Y^{(0)})\right],$$

(2.3a)

$$[I - hDJ]\left(Y^{(\mu-1)} - Y^{(\mu)}\right) = Y^{(\mu-1)}$$
$$- \left[ey_n + a\,hf(t_n,y_n) + hAf(et_n + ch, Y^{(\mu-1)})\right], \quad \mu = 2,\ldots,m.$$

Here, J denotes an approximation to the derivative of f at the point (t_n, y_n). Evidently, if (2.3a) converges, then $Y^{(\mu)}$ converges to Y. In fact, one may interpret (2.3a) as a modified Newton iteration scheme for solving Y from the stage vector equation in (2.1) employing a *diagonal approximation* to the Jacobian matrix of $Y - hAf(et_n + ch, Y)$.

It may be useful to consider (2.3a) in the case of *systems* of ODEs. Then, the k components $Y_i^{(\mu)}$ of the stage vector iterate $Y^{(\mu)}$ have to satisfy the equations

$$[I - h\delta_i J]\,(Y_i^{(0)} - Y_i^{(1)}) = Y_i^{(0)} - h\,\delta_i f(t_n + c_i h, Y_i^{(0)})$$
$$-\left[y_n + a_i\, hf(t_n, y_n) + h\sum_{j=1}^{k} a_{ij} f(t_n + c_j{}^*h, Y_j^{(0)}) - h\,\delta_i f(t_n + c_i{}^*h, Y_i^{(0)})\right],$$

$$[I - h\delta_i J]\,(Y_i^{(\mu-1)} - Y_i^{(\mu)}) = Y_i^{(\mu-1)}$$
$$-\left[y_n + a_i\, hf(t_n, y_n) + h\sum_{j=1}^{k} a_{ij} f(t_n + c_j h, Y_j^{(\mu-1)})\right], \qquad \mu = 2, \dots, m,$$

where $i = 1, \dots, k$ and where now J denotes an approximation to the Jacobian matrix of f at the point (t_n, y_n). Notice that this iteration scheme can be viewed as a modified Newton method for solving the stage vector equation employing a *block-diagonal approximation* to the Jacobian. Clearly, the k linear systems that are to be solved in each outer iteration step can be solved in parallel. Since each system has dimension equal to that of the system of ODEs, the computational complexity per step and per processor essentially consists of the computation of $Y_i^{(0)}$, the evaluation and *LU*-decomposition of the matrix $I - h\,\delta_i J$ (or its updating), $m+2$ evaluations of f, and m forward-backward substitutions. Of these costs, the evaluation and *LU*-decomposition of $I - h\,\delta_i J$ are the most time consuming, while the evaluations of f and the forward-backward substitutions are relatively cheap (notice that the iteration parameters δ_i are independent of μ in order to avoid repeated *LU*-decompositions of $I - h\,\delta_i J$ in the successive iterations). Thus, when basing a code on PDIRK methods, first of all the number of stepsize changes (which automatically requires new *LU*-decompositions) and the number of Jacobian updates should be minimized.

It is of interest to compare the sequential costs of PDIRK methods with the sequential costs of the celebrated BDF-based methods. If the BDFs are solved by using m modified Newton iterations, then the sequential costs in each step of the PDIRK methods and the Newton-iterated BDFs are almost identical. We expect that PDIRK methods need more iterations but, because of their higher order, less steps to produce some given accuracy. As explained above, evaluations of f and the forward-backward substitutions are relatively cheap, so that for modest values of m, the sequential costs per step of PDIRK methods are expected to be not much higher than those of the BDFs. The reduced number of steps required by the PDIRKs should make them superior to the BDFs.

2.3. The step-point values

Suppose that we adopt $Y^{(m)}$ as a sufficiently accurate approximation to the exact stage vector solution Y of the corrector (2.1). Then, the most natural way to approximate the step-point value y_{n+1} in (2.1) defines this value according to the formula

$$(2.4) \qquad y_{n+1} = y_n + h\, b_0 f(t_n, y_n) + h\, b^{\mathrm{T}} f(e t_n + ch, Y^{(m)}).$$

However, the presence of the right-hand side evaluations in this formula may give rise to loss of accuracy in the case of stiff problems (cf. [12]). This difficulty can be overcome by applying a similar approach as proposed in [6] for the implementation of implicit RK methods. Observing that the corrector (2.1) can be written in the form

$$y_{n+1} = y_n + b_0\, h f(t_n, y_n) + b^{\mathrm{T}} A^{-1} [Y - e y_n - a\, h f(t_n, y_n)],$$

provided that A is nonsingular, we can approximate the corrector solution y_{n+1} by the formula

$$(2.3b) \qquad y_{n+1} = y_n + b_0\, h f(t_n, y_n) + b^{\mathrm{T}} A^{-1} [Y^{(m)} - e y_n - a\, h f(t_n, y_n)],$$

where $Y^{(m)}$ denotes the last computed approximation to Y. In many cases the corrector satisfies the relations of stiff accuracy, i.e., $c_k = 1$, $b_0 = a_k$ and $b^{\mathrm{T}} A^{-1} = e_k^{\mathrm{T}}$, so that (2.3b) reduces to $y_{n+1} = e_k^{\mathrm{T}} Y^{(m)}$. In order to avoid confusion, we shall from now on denote the corrector solution and stage vector values obtained from y_n by u_{n+1} and U, respectively.

2.4. The predictor

In [8] we considered one-step predictors of the form

$$(2.5) \qquad Y^{(0)} := e y_n + h\, E f(e t_n, e y_n) + h\, B f(e t_n + c^* h, Y^{(0)}),$$

where B and E are k-by-k matrices. Of particular interest are the cases where E vanishes and where B is either the zero matrix yielding *last step-value predictors* (LSP) or $B = D$ yielding *implicit Euler predictors* (IEP).

However, by using information from the preceding step, that is the values of y_n and the stage vector $Y^{(m)}$ computed in the last step, we can construct more accurate predictors. In order to indicate to which step a particular stage vector corresponds, we define $Y_n := Y^{(m)}$ if $Y^{(m)}$ corresponds to the step $[t_{n-1}, t_n]$. Consider the two-step predictor

$$(2.6) \qquad Y^{(0)} = V Y_n + v\, y_n + h\, B f(e t_n + c^* h, Y^{(0)}),$$

where either $B = O$ or $B = D$, and where the matrix V and the vector v satisfy the usual consistency conditions (we shall assume that the vector v vanishes in the case of stiffly accurate correctors). The cases $B = O$ and $B = D$ will be referred to as the *extrapolation predictor* (EXP) and the *backward differentiation predictor* (BDP).

If $B = D$, then both (2.5) and (2.6) require the solution of k implicit relations. Similar to the strategy followed in solving the implicit relations in (2.2), we shall perform just one Newton iteration (notice that the right-hand side derivatives required in the Newton iteration method are identical to those occurring in (2.3a)). In order to perform this Newton iteration we need an initial guess $Y^{(-1)}$ for $Y^{(0)}$. For the cases (2.5) and (2.6) we shall, respectively, use

$$Y^{(-1)} = e y_n, \quad c^* = (E + B)e; \qquad Y^{(-1)} = W Y_n + w y_n, \quad c^* = c,$$

where W and w are to be determined (we shall assume that w vanishes in the case of stiffly accurate correctors, and that $W = V$, $w = v$ in the case where $B = O$). If the corrector is based on collocation, then the matrix W and the vector w can be computed by extrapolating the collocation polynomial defined in $[t_{n-1}, t_n]$ to the interval $[t_n, t_{n+1}]$ and can be expressed in terms of the Lagrange interpolation polynomials.

2.5. The iteration parameters

There are various options for choosing the number of iterations m, and the iteration parameters δ_i. In this paper, we consider three cases:

Option 1: *fixed-number-of-iterations option*
— the number of iterations is fixed and such that the orders of the PDIRK and corrector are equal
— the iteration parameters are chosen such that the stability region in the left halfplane is optimized.

Option 2: *minimal-spectral-radius option*
— the number of iterations is sufficiently large to closely approximate the corrector solution
— the iteration parameters are such that the spectral radius of the matrix $D^{-1}A - I$ is minimized.

Option 3: *minimal-stiff-error-constant option*
— the number of iterations is sufficiently large to closely approximate the corrector solution
— the iteration parameters are such that the principal stiff error constant of the PDIRK method is minimized.

Several families of methods constructed according to the fixed-number-of-iterations option were already considered in [8]. An interesting family considered in that paper possesses the stability functions investigated by Wolfbrandt [13] and uses constant iteration parameters δ_i determined by these stability functions. However, because of the fixed number of iterations, these methods are in fact DIRK methods and consequently, they have the disadvantage of possessing stage order $q = 1$. In many stiff problems, such a low stage order may lead to reduced accuracies. In order to get insight into the extent of this accuracy reduction, we shall consider the magnitude of the stiff error constants for the 'fixed-number-of-iterations PDIRK methods' (see Section 4.2, Table 4.1).

For the explicit one-step predictor, [7] presents a number of PDIRK methods constructed according to the minimal-spectral-radius option. The effect of minimizing the spectral radius of the matrix $D^{-1}A - I$ is a strong damping of the stiff iteration error components. On the one hand, the number of iterations m should be sufficiently large to solve more or less the RK corrector, on the other hand, m should be sufficiently small to achieve that the (sequential) costs per step are not excessive when compared with those of the BDFs. In this paper, we shall investigate a few characteristics of the 'minimal-spectral-radius PDIRK methods' as a function of m. In particular, in Section 3 we consider the rate of convergence (Table 3.1) and the effect on the stability of the various predictors (Tables 3.2a and 3.2b), and in Section 4 we consider the magnitude of the principal stiff error constants (Tables 4.2 and 4.3).

Option 3 offers an alternative to option 2 and directly addresses the truncation error of PDIRK methods when applied to stiff systems. In this paper, we present preliminary results for the simple inhomogeneous test equation $y'(t) = \lambda y(t) + g(t)$.

3. CONVERGENCE AND STABILITY

We shall investigate convergence and stability by means of the scalar test equation $y' = \lambda y$. Note that for this simple test equation the particular strategy used in the inner iterations is not relevant. For a rigorous convergence analysis of parallel RK methods containing the PDIRK methods of this paper we refer to Jackson and Nørsett [9, 10].

3.1. Rate of convergence

From (2.2) it can be deduced that the iteration error satisfies the recursion

$$(3.1) \qquad U - Y_{n+1} = Z(z)\left(U - Y^{(m-1)}\right) = \cdots = Z^m(z)\left(U - Y^{(0)}\right),$$
$$Z(z) := zD[I - zD]^{-1}[D^{-1}A - I], \qquad z := \lambda h.$$

The region in the complex z-plane where $Z^m(z) \to 0$ for $m \to \infty$ will be called the *region of convergence*. We define the *iteration function C* of the PDIRK method by the spectral radius of $Z(z)$, i.e.,

$$(3.2) \qquad C(z) := \rho(Z(z)) = \rho\big(zD[I - zD]^{-1} [D^{-1}A - I]\big).$$

Evidently, the region of convergence is determined by the set of points where $C(z) < 1$. The rate of convergence is larger as the norm of $C(z)$ is smaller in the region of relevant values of z. Thus, adopting the maximum norm, we are led to the minimization of $C(z)$ in this region. In this connection we introduce the following definition:

Definition 3.1. A PDIRK method is said to be *strongly A-convergent* if its iteration function $C(z) \leq \eta < 1$ in the whole left halfplane Re $z < 0$. If, in addition, $C(-\infty) = 0$, then the PDIRK method is called *L-convergent*.   []

First we consider the constant-δ_i-case which is of interest in the case of fixed-number-of-iterations methods.

Theorem 3.1. If D has constant, positive diagonal elements, then minimization of $\rho(D^{-1}A - I)$ implies that the norm of $C(z)$ is minimized whenever z is in the left halfplane.

Proof. If $D = \delta \cdot I$, then we may write $C(z) = |\delta z| \rho(\delta^{-1} A - I) / |1 - \delta z|$. In the left halfplane, the maximum of the function $|\delta z / (1 - \delta z)|$ does not depend on δ, provided that $\delta > 0$. Hence, the norm of $C(z)$ is minimized if $\rho(D^{-1}A - I)$ is minimized.   []

In the case where D does not have constant diagonal entries, we cannot derive such a simple expression for $C(z)$, and a numerical search is needed to find the matrix D that minimizes the norm of $C(z)$ in the left halfplane. However, our numerical experiments revealed that also in the nonconstant-δ_i-case the minimization of $\rho(D^{-1}A - I)$ yields fast converging PDIRK methods and that $\|C\| := \max\{C(z): \text{Re } z \leq 0\}$ is considerably smaller than in the constant-δ_i-case.

Example 3.1. We consider an example of the fixed-number-of-iterations methods studied in [8] which is based on the third-order Radau IIA corrector. For

$$m = 3, \qquad A = \frac{1}{12}\begin{pmatrix} 5 & -1 \\ 9 & 3 \end{pmatrix}, \qquad D = \delta \cdot I, \qquad \delta = 0.43586650$$

this leads to a third-order, L-stable PDIRK method. The convergence function associated with this method is given by $C(z) = |\delta z|\, \rho(\delta^{-1} A - I)/|1 - \delta z|$, where $\rho(\delta^{-1} A - I) = \delta^{-1}\sqrt{1/6 - 2\delta/3 + \delta^2}$. Setting $\delta = 0.43586650$ we find that $C(z) < 0.59$ in the whole left halfplane. Among the methods with $D = \delta I$ this method is almost optimal (the minimizing value is given by $\delta = 1/2$ leading to $C(z) < \sqrt{1/3} \approx 0.577$).

Next, we consider the case where D minimizes $\rho(D^{-1}A - I)$. In [7] it was shown that the method can be made L-convergent (i.e., it has vanishing $\rho(D^{-1}A - I)$) for $\delta_1 = (4 - \sqrt{6})/6$ and $\delta_2 = (4 + \sqrt{6})/10$. The corresponding matrix $Z(z)$ is easily computed, yielding $\|C\| \approx 0.262$. []

Table 3.1 lists the $\|C\|$-values for a number of minimal-spectral-radius PDIRK methods. These methods are based on Radau IIA correctors and on the so-called Lagrange correctors derived in [7]. The Lagrange methods are strongly A-stable, stiffly accurate collocation methods which are completely determined by the collocation vector c (see Table 3.1). Their stage order is one higher than that of the Radau IIA methods which was achieved by using one explicit and k implicit stages. However, they do not possess the superconvergence property of the Radau methods, so that the computation of the *nonstiff* solution components is considerably less accurate.

For the Radau IIA and Lagrange correctors with k implicit stages, the iteration parameters are contained in the matrices D_{kR} and D_{kL} ($k = 2, 3, 4$):

$$(3.3a) \quad D_{2R} = \frac{1}{30}\begin{pmatrix} 20-5\sqrt{6} & 0 \\ 0 & 12+3\sqrt{6} \end{pmatrix}, \quad D_{2L} = \begin{pmatrix} \dfrac{3}{4(\sqrt{2}+1)} & 0 \\ 0 & \dfrac{1}{6(\sqrt{2}-1)} \end{pmatrix},$$

$$(3.3b) \quad D_{3R} = \begin{pmatrix} \dfrac{4365}{13624} & 0 & 0 \\ 0 & \dfrac{1032}{7373} & 0 \\ 0 & 0 & \dfrac{1887}{5077} \end{pmatrix}, \quad D_{3L} = \begin{pmatrix} \dfrac{2246}{10669} & 0 & 0 \\ 0 & \dfrac{2537}{8794} & 0 \\ 0 & 0 & \dfrac{3026}{8923} \end{pmatrix},$$

$$(3.3c) \quad D_{4R} = \begin{pmatrix} \dfrac{3055}{9532} & 0 & 0 & 0 \\ 0 & \dfrac{531}{5956} & 0 & 0 \\ 0 & 0 & \dfrac{1471}{8094} & 0 \\ 0 & 0 & 0 & \dfrac{1848}{7919} \end{pmatrix}, \quad D_{4L} = \begin{pmatrix} \dfrac{5147}{38467} & 0 & 0 & 0 \\ 0 & \dfrac{1983}{17459} & 0 & 0 \\ 0 & 0 & \dfrac{3197}{14090} & 0 \\ 0 & 0 & 0 & \dfrac{3086}{12339} \end{pmatrix}.$$

Table 3.1 shows that these methods can all be made strongly A-convergent, and that only the methods based on a *two*-stage corrector are L-convergent (see also [7]). Furthermore, we observe that the rates of convergence of the Lagrange-based methods are slightly better. Hence, together with their increased stage order, the Lagrange correctors seem to be attractive alternatives to the Radau correctors in problems where the order of accuracy is determined by the stage order. However, in problems where, apart from the stage order, the nonstiff (or, classical) order is important, the superconvergent Radau correctors are to be preferred. As to the ‖C‖-values given in Table 3.1, it should be remarked that these are 'worst case' values, that is, in actual computation, where the relevant values of z are located in a restricted region of the left halfplane, the corresponding bound on $C(z)$ may be much smaller.

Table 3.1. ‖C‖-values for minimal-spectral-radius PDIRK methods based on Radau IIA and Lagrange correctors.

Corrector	k		‖C‖	strongly A-convergent	L-convergent
Radau IIA	2		0.262	yes	yes
	3		0.401	yes	no
	4		0.527	yes	no
Lagrange	2	$c = (3/4,1)^T$	0.182	yes	yes
	3	$c = (7/12,5/6,1)^T$	0.403	yes	no
	4	$c = (1/6,7/12,11/12,1)^T$	0.404	yes	no

3.2. Region of stability

In order to investigate the stability properties of PDIRK methods we have to specify the predictor formula. The stability of PDIRK methods using the one-step predictor (2.5) was extensively discussed in [8] for the case where y_{n+1} is defined by (2.4). For the case (2.3b) considered in this paper, we have the following theorems:

Theorem 3.2. For the equation $y' = \lambda y$ the PDIRK solution generated by {(2.3a), (2.3b), (2.5)} satisfies the recursion

$$y_{n+1} = R_m(z)y_n, \qquad R_m(z) := R(z) - E_m(z),$$

$$R(z) := 1 + zb_0 + zb^T[I - zA]^{-1}[e + za],$$
$$E_m(z) := b^TA^{-1}Z^m(z)\big([I - zA]^{-1}[e + za] - [I - zB]^{-1}[I + zE]\,e\big).$$

Here, $R(z)$ is the stability function of the corrector reducing to

$$R(z) = e_k^T[I - zA]^{-1}[e + za]$$

in the stiffly accurate case.

180

Proof. From the relations

(3.4) $Y^{(0)} = [I - zB]^{-1} [I + zE] ey_n,$ $U = [I - zA]^{-1} [e + za] y_n,$

it follows that

(3.5) $U - Y_{n+1} = Z^m(z)(U - Y^{(0)}) = Z^m(z)([I-zA]^{-1} [e+za] - [I-zB]^{-1} [I+zE] e)y_n.$

Hence, from the step-point formula (2.3b) we obtain

(3.6) $u_{n+1} - y_{n+1} = b^T A^{-1}(U - Y_{n+1})$
$$= b^T A^{-1} Z^m(z)([I - zA]^{-1} [e + za] - [I - zB]^{-1} [I + zE] e)y_n.$$

Furthermore, introducing the stability function $R(z)$ of the corrector, we may write

(3.7) $u_{n+1} = R(z)y_n,$

where $R(z)$ is defined in the theorem. From (3.6) and (3.7) the assertion of the theorem is immediate.   []

Theorem 3.3. For the equation $y' = \lambda y$ the PDIRK solution generated by {(2.3), (2.6)} satisfies the recursion

$$\begin{pmatrix} Y_{n+1} \\ y_{n+1} \end{pmatrix} = M_m(z) \begin{pmatrix} Y_n \\ y_n \end{pmatrix},$$

where $M_m(z)$ is the amplification matrix

$$M_m(z) := \begin{pmatrix} I & 0 \\ -b^T A^{-1} & 1 \end{pmatrix}^{-1} \cdot$$
$$\begin{pmatrix} Z^m(z) [I-zB]^{-1} V & [I-Z^m(z)][I-zA]^{-1}[e+za] + Z^m(z) [I-zB]^{-1} v \\ 0^T & 1 + b_0 z - b^T A^{-1}[e+za] \end{pmatrix}.$$

Proof. By means of the equation for U given in (3.4), relation (3.5) and

(3.8) $Y^{(0)} = [I - zB]^{-1}[V Y_n + v y_n]$

we derive that

(3.9) $Y_{n+1} = Z^m(z) [I - zB]^{-1} V Y_n +$
$$([I - Z^m(z)][I - zA]^{-1}[e + za] + Z^m(z) [I - zB]^{-1} v)y_n.$$

Together with the step-point formula (2.3b) the one-step recursion of the theorem is easily obtained.   []

With the amplification matrix $M_m(z)$ we associate the *stability function*

(3.10) $R_m(z) := \rho(M_m(z))$,

where $\rho(M_m)$ denotes the spectral radius of the matrix M_m. The region in the complex z-plane where $R_m(z) < 1$ will be called the *region of stability associated with m*. Furthermore, we define m_{crit} as the minimal value of m for which this region contains the whole left halfplane for all $m \geq m_{crit}$.

For future reference, we have computed the value of m_{crit} for a number of predictor-corrector (PC) pairs. For the correctors we again chose the Radau IIA methods and the Lagrange methods of Section 3.1. The predictors are those defined in Section 2.4 and the matrices D are defined according to the minimal-spectral-radius option (see (3.3a), (3.3b), and (3.3c)). Table 3.2a shows that m_{crit} increases if the number of stages of the corrector increases. However, in actual computation, the minimal number of iterations may be much smaller because many stiff problems require only $A(\alpha)$-stability. This means that automatic codes based on PDIRK methods are likely to choose the number of iterations not larger than necessary to ensure a stable performance. Table 3.2b presents the corresponding angles α as a function of m (lack of $A(0)$-stability is indicated by $*$). The results illustrate the favourable $A(\alpha)$-stability characteristics of minimal-spectral-radius PDIRK methods after only a few iterations. In general, the implicit predictors IEP and BDP possess (of course) larger stability angles α than the explicit predictors LSP and EXP, even if we take into account that the implicit predictors require extra computational effort roughly comparable with an additional iteration. Furthermore, if we compare IEP and BDP, then IEP has the best stability characteristics (in particular for Radau-based methods). However, the overall efficiency will be reduced because of its low-order of accuracy. Therefore, we drop the low-order predictors LSP and IEP and recommend either the EXP or BDP predictor.

Table 3.2a. Values of m_{crit} of minimal-spectral-radius PDIRK methods for various PC pairs

Corrector		LSP	EXP	IEP	BDP
Radau IIA	$k = 2$	1	1	1	1
	$k = 3$	5	5	2	4
	$k = 4$	7	7	4	7
Lagrange	$k = 2$	2	2	2	2
	$k = 3$	3	3	3	3
	$k = 4$	6	7	5	6

Table 3.2b. Values of $\alpha = \alpha(m)$ (in degrees) of minimal-spectral-radius PDIRK methods for various PC pairs

Predictor	Corrector	k	m = 1	m = 2	m = 3	m = 4	m = 5	m = 6	m = 7
LSP	Radau IIA	2	90						
EXP			90						
IEP			90						
BDP			90						
LSP		3	*	*	81.9	89.94	90		
EXP			*	*	64.7	88.7	90		
IEP			87.5	90					
BDP			65.0	81.8	88.4	90			
LSP		4	*	*	*	40.3	80.5	88.5	90
EXP			*	*	*	*	70.3	84.2	90
IEP			60.2	75.9	86.1	90			
BDP			43.0	14.6	67.1	78.2	84.6	88.6	90
LSP	Lagrange	2	*	90					
EXP			*	90					
IEP			86.5	90					
BDP			89.82	90					
LSP		3	*	*	90				
EXP			*	*	90				
IEP			77.2	*	90				
BDP			83.4	*	90				
LSP		4	*	*	*	60.8	86.7	90	
EXP			*	*	*	*	73.0	88.0	90
IEP			51.6	*	*	86.5	90		
BDP			48.8	*	*	79.9	87.6	90	

4. THE ERROR FUNCTIONS FOR THE LINEAR INHOMOGENEOUS TEST EQUATION

The following theorem presents a result for general RK methods derived in [1]:

Theorem 4.1. For RK methods the global error e_n when applied to the test equation $y'(t) = \lambda y(t) + g(t)$ satisfies

$$e_{n+1} = R(z)\, e_n + \sum_{j=q+1} Q_j(z)\, h^j\, y_{ex}^{(j)}(t_n),$$
$$Q_j(z) := \frac{1}{j!}\,[1 - j\,b^{\mathrm{T}} c^{j-1}] + \frac{1}{j!} z\, b^{\mathrm{T}} [I - zA]^{-1}\,[c^j - j A\, c^{j-1}],$$

where $y_{ex}(t)$ denotes the exact solution of the test equation, $R(z)$ is the stability function of the RK method, and q is its stage order (i.e., the largest integer such that $1 - j\,b^{\mathrm{T}} c^{j-1} = c^j - j A c^{j-1} = 0$ for $j = 1, \dots , q$).   []

We shall prove a similar theorem for PDIRK methods employing one-step predictors. As before, the simplicity of the test equation $y'(t) = \lambda y(t) + g(t)$ implies that the particular strategy used in the inner iteration process is not relevant.

In the following, $y(t)$ denotes the locally exact solution at t_n, i.e., $y_n = y(t_n)$. It is straightforwardly verified that for the linear inhomogeneous equation the recursion (3.5) changes to

$$(4.1) \qquad U - Y_{n+1} = Z^m(z)\Big(U - Y^{(0)} + h\,z^{-1}\,[g(t_n e + hc) - g(t_n e + hc^*)]\Big).$$

Assuming that g is sufficiently differentiable, we may write for any fixed vector v

$$(4.2) \qquad g(t_n e + hv) = \sum_{j=0} \frac{1}{j!}\,(h\,v)^j\,g^{(j)}(t_n) \;=\; \frac{1}{h}\sum_{j=0}\frac{1}{j!}\,h^j\,y^{(j)}(t_n)\,[jv^{j-1} - zv^j].$$

Hence,

$$h\,[g(t_n e + hc) - g(t_n e + hc^*)] = \sum_{j=1}\frac{1}{j!}\,\gamma_j(z)\,h^j\,y^{(j)}(t_n),$$

$$\gamma_j(z) := jc^{j-1} - zc^j - j(c^*)^{j-1} + z(c^*)^j.$$

Furthermore, it follows from (2.1) that

$$U = [I - zA]^{-1}\,[y(t_n)e + h\,y'(t_n)a + h\,A\,g(t_n e + hc)],$$

so that

$$(4.3a) \qquad U = y_n e + \sum_{j=1}\frac{1}{j!}\,c_j(z)\,h^j\,y^{(j)}(t_n),$$

$$c_1(z) := c, \qquad c_j(z) := [I - zA]^{-1}A\,[jc^{j-1} - zc^j], \quad j \geq 2.$$

4.1. One-step predictors

Let us assume that $Y^{(0)}$ is provided by a one-step formula, then it can also be expanded in terms of a similar Taylor series with coefficients $c_j^*(z)$:

$$(4.3b) \qquad Y^{(0)} = y_n e + \sum_{j=1}\frac{1}{j!}\,c_j^*(z)\,h^j\,y^{(j)}(t_n).$$

Thus,

$$(4.4) \qquad U - Y_{n+1} = Z^m(z)\sum_{j=1}q_j(z)\,h^j\,y^{(j)}(t_n),$$

$$q_1(z) := c^* - c_1^*(z), \qquad q_j(z) := \frac{1}{j!}\,[c_j(z) - c_j^*(z) + z^{-1}\gamma_j(z)], \quad j \geq 2.$$

Assuming that $c_1{}^*(z)$ does not depend on z, we may choose in (2.3) $c^* = c_1{}^*$ so that $q_1(z)$ vanishes. Using the relation

$$y^{(j)}(t_n) = y_{ex}^{(j)}(t_n) + \lambda^j \left[y(t_n) - y_{ex}(t_n) \right] = y_{ex}^{(j)}(t_n) + \lambda^j \left[y_n - y_{ex}(t_n) \right],$$

the iteration error (4.4) can be expanded in terms of derivatives of the exact solution. We obtain

(4.4') $$U - Y_{n+1} = Z^m(z) \sum_{j=2} q_j(z) \left(z^j \left[y_n - y_{ex}(t_n) \right] + h^j y_{ex}^{(j)}(t_n) \right).$$

Since

(4.5) $$u_{n+1} - y_{n+1} = b^T A^{-1} \left[U - Y_{n+1} \right],$$

we find

(4.6a) $$u_{n+1} - y_{n+1} = S_m(z) [y_n - y_{ex}(t_n)] + \sum_{j=2} Q_{mj}(z) \, h^j \, y_{ex}^{(j)}(t_n),$$

(4.6b) $$S_m(z) := b^T A^{-1} Z^m(z) \sum_{j=2} q_j(z) \, z^j, \qquad Q_{mj}(z) := b^T A^{-1} Z^m(z) q_j(z).$$

Applying Theorem 4.1 to the corrector at the point t_n with $e_n = y_n - y_{ex}(t_n)$ and assuming that $j b^T c^{j-1} = 1, j = 0, 1, \ldots, q)$ yields

(4.7) $$u_{n+1} - y_{ex}(t_{n+1}) = R(z) [y_n - y_{ex}(t_n)]$$
$$+ \frac{1}{(q+1)!} z b^T [I - zA]^{-1} [c^{q+1} - (q+1) A \, c^q] h^{q+1} y_{ex}^{(q+1)}(t_n)$$
$$+ O(h^{q+2});$$

hence,

$$y_{n+1} - y_{ex}(t_{n+1}) = y_{n+1} - u_{n+1} + u_{n+1} - y_{ex}(t_{n+1})$$
$$= y_{n+1} - u_{n+1} + R(z) \left[y_n - y_{ex}(t_n) \right] + O(h^{q+1}).$$

Thus, using (4.6a) we obtain

(4.8) $$y_{n+1} - y_{ex}(t_{n+1}) = (R(z) - S_m(z)) \left[y_n - y_{ex}(t_n) \right]$$
$$- \sum_{j=2} Q_{mj}(z) \, h^j \, y_{ex}^{(j)}(t_n) + O(h^{q+1}).$$

The functions $Q_{mj}(z)$ will be called the *error functions* of the PDIRK method.

Finally, we show that the function $R(z) - S_m(z)$ is identical with the stability function R_m of the PDIRK method. For that purpose, we consider the particular case where the inhomogeneous term g vanishes. It is easily verified that we then may write

(4.9) $y_{n+1} - y_{ex}(t_{n+1}) = R_m(z) [y_n - y_{ex}(t_n)] + (R_m(z) - e^z) y_{ex}(t_n), \quad g = 0.$

Now, suppose that the initial value y_0 tends to zero. Then, $y_{ex}(t)$ also tends to zero. Since (4.8) holds for vanishing g too, it follows that $R_m(z) = R(z) - S_m(z)$. Notice that in the case of the predictor (2.5) the functions $S_m(z)$ and $E_m(z)$ as defined in Theorem 3.2 are apparently identical. Thus, we have proved the following PDIRK analogue of Theorem 4.1:

Theorem 4.2. For one-step predictors possessing the expansion (4.3b) with $c^* = c_1^*$ the global error of PDIRK methods when applied to the test equation $y'(t) = \lambda y(t) + g(t)$ satisfies the recursion

$$y_{n+1} - y_{ex}(t_{n+1}) = R_m(z) [y_n - y_{ex}(t_n)] - \sum_{j=2} Q_{mj}(z) \, h^j \, y_{ex}^{(j)}(t_n) + O(h^{q+1}),$$

$$R_m(z) = R(z) - S_m(z),$$

$$S_m(z) := b^T A^{-1} Z^m(z) \sum_{j=2} q_j(z) z^j, \quad Q_{mj}(z) := b^T A^{-1} Z^m(z) q_j(z),$$

where q is the stage order of the corrector, and $R(z)$ and $R_m(z)$ are the stability functions of the corrector and the PDIRK method, respectively.   []

This theorem shows that the stage order of PDIRK methods is only one, unless the error function $Q_{m2}(z)$ is identically zero for the m-value used (this is not surprising because formally PDIRK methods are just DIRK methods which are known to have stage order one). However, as all error functions $Q_{mj}(z)$ contain the factor $Z^m(z)$, their maximal values $|Q_{mj}|$ are expected to decrease rapidly with m in any region of the left halfplane, so that effectively the stage order shown in actual computation is much higher.

The following corollary presents an explicit expression of Q_{mj} for the predictor (2.5).

Corollary 4.1. For the predictor (2.5) the error functions are given by

$$Q_{mj}(z) := \frac{1}{j!} b^T A^{-1} Z^m(z) z^{-1} \left(j c^{j-1} - [I - zB]^{-1} [j(c^*)^{j-1} - z(c^*)^j] \right),$$

for $j = 2, \ldots, q$, where $c^* := (B + E)e$.

Proof. In the case (2.5) the expansion (4.3b) becomes

$$Y^{(0)} = [I - zB]^{-1} \left([I + zE]\, y(t_n)e + h\, E\, g(t_n)e + h\, B\, g(t_n e + hc^*) \right)$$

$$= y(t_n)e + [I - zB]^{-1} \left(E\, h\, y'(t_n)e + B \sum_{j=1} \frac{1}{j!} h^j\, y^{(j)}(t_n)\, [j(c^*)^{j-1} - z(c^*)^j] \right),$$

so that

$$c_1^*(z) = [I - zB]^{-1}\, (Ee + Be - zBc^*) = c^* = (B + E)e,$$

$$c_j^*(z) = [I - zB]^{-1}\, z\, B\, [jz^{-1}(c^*)^{j-1} - (c^*)^j], \quad j \geq 2.$$

By virtue of Theorem 4.2 we may write

$$Q_{mj}(z) = b^T A^{-1}\, Z^m(z) q_j(z) = \frac{1}{j!}\, b^T A^{-1}\, Z^m(z)\, [c_j(z) - c_j^*(z) + z^{-1} \gamma_j(z)]$$

$$= \frac{1}{j!} b^T A^{-1}\, Z^m(z) z^{-1} \left([I - zA]^{-1} [jc^{j-1} - zc^j] - [I - zB]^{-1} [j(c^*)^{j-1} - z(c^*)^j] \right).$$

By means of the simplifying condition $C(q)$ associated with (2.1) (cf. [3]), we obtain the relation $jAc^{j-1} = c^j$ for $j = 2, \ldots, q$ which leads to the result of the corollary. []

4.2. Last step-value predictor with constant iteration parameters

In the case of the predictor LSP (predictor (2.5) with $B = E = O$) with constant iteration parameters ($D = \delta I$), the error functions $Q_{mj}(z)$ can be factorized into factors that depend on z and factors that do not depend on z. This enables us to derive an explicit upper bound for $Q_{mj}(z)$.

Theorem 4.3. Let $D = \delta \cdot I$ and let the predictor be given by (2.5). Then the error function bound in a region $\mathbb{R}$ is given by

$$|Q_{mj}|_{\mathbb{R}} = \frac{1}{(j-1)!}\, d(m)\, |b^T A^{-1} D\, (D^{-1}A - I)^m\, c^{j-1}|, \quad j = 2, \ldots, q;$$

$$d(m) := \left| \frac{(\delta z)^{m-1}}{(1 - \delta z)^m} \right|_{\mathbb{R}}.$$

If $\mathbb{R}$ is the infinite wedge defined by $\mathbb{W} := \{ z: \pi/2 \leq \phi \leq \arg(z) \leq \pi, \ -\pi \leq \arg(z) \leq -\phi \}$, then

$$d(m) = \frac{x_m^{m-1}}{\left(m(1 - x_m \cos(\phi)) \right)^{m/2}},$$

where x_m is the positive root of the equation $x^2 - (2 - m)\, x\, \cos(\phi) - m + 1 = 0$.

Proof. The expression for the error bound $|Q_{mj}|_{\mathbb{R}}$ immediately follows from Corollary 4.1. In order to derive an expression for the function $d(m)$ we first observe that

$$\left|\frac{z}{1-z}\right| = \frac{|z|}{\sqrt{1 - 2|z|\cos(\arg(z)) + |z|^2}}$$

where $\pi/2 \le \arg(z) \le \pi$ or $-\pi \le \arg(z) \le -\pi/2$. Hence,

$$\left|\frac{z^{m-1}}{(1-z)^m}\right| = \frac{|z|^{m-1}}{[1 - 2|z|\cos(\arg(z)) + |z|^2]^{m/2}} .$$

Since the function $z^{m-1}(1-z)^{-m}$ is analytic, its maximum value in $\mathbb{W}$ is assumed at a point on the line $\arg(z) = \phi$. An elementary calculation reveals that the modulus of this point is given by the positive root x_m of the quadratic equation $x^2 - (2 - m)\cos(\phi)x - m + 1 = 0$. This leads us to the bound $d(m)$ given in the theorem. []

This theorem shows that in the case where the relevant z-values are in an infinite wedge $\mathbb{W}$, the optimal choice of the matrix $D = \delta \cdot I$ does not depend on $\mathbb{W}$. Furthermore, the function $d(m)$ is slowly varying with m. This can be concluded from the extreme cases where $\mathbb{R}$ is either only the negative axis or the whole left halfplane. We then have, respectively, $x_m = m - 1$ and $x_m = \sqrt{m-1}$, which yields

$$d(m) = \frac{1}{m-1}\left(1 - \frac{1}{m}\right)^m \quad \text{and} \quad d(m) = \frac{1}{\sqrt{m-1}}\left(1 - \frac{1}{m}\right)^{m/2} .$$

Thus, within a few iterations the function $d(m)$ slowly converges to zero.

It is of interest to compare the error functions $Q_j(z)$ of conventional DIRK methods (cf. Theorem 4.1) with the error functions $Q_{mj}(z)$ of PDIRK methods. Table 4.1 presents a comparison for two conventional Nørsett-DIRK methods [11] and a few L-stable, fixed-number-of-iterations PDIRK methods constructed according to option 1 [8]. In this table, k denotes the number of processors needed, $p*$ is the order of the method, and m denotes the number of sequential stages per step (both for the Nørsett-DIRK and PDIRK methods). Clearly, the PDIRK methods possess considerably smaller error bounds.

Table 4.1. Values of $|Q_j|_\mathbb{R}$ and $|Q_{mj}|_\mathbb{R}$ with $\mathbb{R} = \{z: \mathrm{Re}\, z \leq 0\}$ for the Nørsett-DIRK methods and fixed-number-of-iterations PDIRK methods.

Method / PC pair	k	δ_i	m	p^*	$j=2$	$j=3$	$j=4$	$j=5$
Nørsett-DIRK	1		2	3	0.144	0.076	0.024	0.0055
{LSP, Radau IIA}	2	0.43586650	3	3	0.024	0.015	0.005	0.0012
{LSP, Lagrange}	2	0.43586650	3	3	0.038	0.015	0.005	0.0012
Nørsett-DIRK	1		3	4	0.112	0.054	0.015	0.0040
{LSP, Radau IIA}	3	0.278053841	5	5	0.019	0.006	0.0014	0.0003
{LSP, Lagrange}	3	0.572816063	4	4	0.046	0.013	0.0001	0.0012
{LSP, Lagrange}	4	0.278053841	5	5	0.025	0.005	0.0001	0.0001

4.3. Minimal-spectral-radius PDIRK methods

Table 4.2 lists values of $|Q_{mj}|_\mathbb{R}$ with $\mathbb{R} = \{z: \mathrm{Re}\, z \leq 0\}$ for minimal-spectral-radius PDIRK methods (option 2), based on {LSP, Radau IIA} pairs and using the iteration parameters given in (3.3). It turns out that for $m > p^*$ the error constants decrease by an almost constant reduction factor r as m increases by 1 and that they are substantially smaller than those of the fixed-number-of-iterations PDIRK methods of Table 4.1 (notice that r is almost independent of j).

Table 4.2. Values of the error constants for minimal-spectral-radius PDIRK methods.

PC pair	k	m	p^*	$j=2$	$j=3$	$j=4$	$j=5$
{LSP, Radau IIA}	2	2	2	0.0249	0.0263	0.0102	0.0027
		3	3	0.0060	0.0062	0.0024	0.0006
		...	3	$r \approx .25$	$r \approx .25$	$r \approx .25$	$r \approx .25$
{LSP, Radau IIA}	3	3	3	0.0360	0.0086	0.0027	0.00076
		4	4	0.0138	0.0031	0.0009	0.00025
		5	5	0.0052	0.0012	0.0003	0.00009
		...	5	$r \approx .40$	$r \approx .38$	$r \approx .39$	$r \approx .38$
{LSP, Radau IIA}	4	5	5	0.0153	0.00098	0.000031	0.00004
		6	6	0.0079	0.00051	0.000016	0.00002
		7	7	0.0041	0.00027	0.000008	0.00001
		...	7	$r \approx .50$	$r \approx .52$	$r \approx .50$	$r \approx .52$

For future reference, we give a survey of the *principal stiff error constants* $|Q_{m2}|_\mathbb{R}$ with $\mathbb{R} = \{z: \mathrm{Re}\, z \leq 0\}$ for a number of PC pairs. In Table 4.3, p denotes the order of the corrector and the order of the iterated method is in all cases given by $p^* = \min\{p, m\}$. From these results we conclude that the explicit predictor LSP leads to slightly smaller principal error constants than the implicit predictor IEP, provided that we count the application of IEP as an additional iteration. Furthermore, the Lagrange-based methods show considerably smaller error constants. However, we should bear in mind that the *nonstiff* error constants of the Radau-based methods decrease much faster than those of the Lagrange-based methods because of the high (nonstiff) orders of the Radau correctors. Finally, note that the reduction factors are very close to the $\|C\|$-values listed in Table 3.1.

Table 4.3. Values of the principal error constant for minimal-spectral-radius PDIRK methods.

Method	k	p	$m = k$	$m = k+1$	$m = k+2$	r
{LSP, Radau IIA}	2	3	0.025	0.0060	0.0015	0.25
{IEP, Radau IIA}	2	3	0.024	0.0059	0.0015	0.25
{LSP, Lagrange}	2	3	0.013	0.0023	0.0004	0.18
{IEP, Lagrange}	2	3	0.006	0.0011	0.0002	0.18
{LSP, Radau IIA}	3	5	0.036	0.0138	0.0052	0.40
{IEP, Radau IIA}	3	5	0.014	0.0053	0.0020	0.41
{LSP, Lagrange}	3	4	0.008	0.0034	0.0014	0.40
{IEP, Lagrange}	3	4	0.004	0.0018	0.0007	0.40
{LSP, Radau IIA}	4	7	0.027	0.0153	0.0079	0.50
{IEP, Radau IIA}	4	7	0.017	0.0088	0.0044	0.50
{LSP, Lagrange}	4	5	0.022	0.0092	0.0037	0.40
{IEP, Lagrange}	4	5	0.013	0.0054	0.0021	0.40

5. CONCLUDING REMARKS

In this paper, we have studied special characteristics, such as the rate of convergence, the (linear) stability, and the stiff error constants of PDIRK methods based on Radau IIA and Lagrange correctors using various types of iteration parameters and predictors. The minimal-spectral-radius methods turn out to be either comparable or superior to fixed-number-of-iterations methods. Confining our considerations to minimal-spectral-radius methods, the following conclusions can be drawn from our analysis:

Rate of convergence: Lagrange correctors are superior to Radau corrector for $k = 2$ or $k = 4$. For $k = 3$, these correctors are comparable.

Linear stability:	Lagrange correctors are slightly superior to Radau correctors.
	The implicit predictors IEP and BDP are superior to explicit predictors EXP and LSP.
Order reduction:	Lagrange correctors are superior to Radau correctors (both with respect to the stage order and the magnitude of the error constants).
	The explicit predictor LSP is slightly superior to the implicit predictor IEP.
Nonstiff error constants:	The two-stage Radau corrector is comparable with the two-stage Lagrange corrector. Radau correctors are by far superior to Lagrange correctors for $k > 2$.
	The predictors EXP and BDP are by far superior to the predictors LSP and IEP.

By these conclusions, we are led to recommend PDIRK methods using an {EXP, Radau} PC pair and the minimal-spectral-radius iteration strategy as the most efficient in the class of PDIRK methods.

REFERENCES

[1] **Burrage, K., Hundsdorfer, W.H. & Verwer, J.G.** (1986): *A study of B-convergence of Runge-Kutta methods*, Computing **36**, 17-34.

[2] **Butcher, J.C.** (1964): *Implicit Runge-Kutta processes*, Math. Comp. **18**, 50-64.

[3] **Butcher, J.C.** (1987): *The numerical analysis of ordinary differential equations, Runge-Kutta and general linear methods*, Wiley, New York.

[4] **Dekker, K. & Verwer, J.G.** (1984): *Stability of Runge-Kutta methods for stiff nonlinear differential equations*, North-Holland, Amsterdam.

[5] **Hairer, E., Nørsett, S.P. & Wanner, G.** (1987): *Solving ordinary differential equations, I. Nonstiff problems*, Springer Series in Comp. Math., Vol. **8**, Springer-Verlag, Berlin.

[6] **Hairer, E. & Wanner, G.** (1991): *Solving ordinary differential equations, II. Stiff and differential-algebraic problems*, Springer Series in Comp. Math., Vol. **14**, Springer-Verlag, Berlin.

[7] **Houwen, P.J. van der & Sommeijer, B.P.** (1991): *Iterated Runge-Kutta methods on parallel computers*, SIAM J. Sci. Stat. Comput. **12**, 1000-1028.

[8] **Houwen, P.J. van der, Sommeijer, B.P. & Couzy, W.** (1992): *Embedded diagonally implicit Runge-Kutta algorithms on parallel computers*, Math. Comp. **58**, 135-159.

[9] **Jackson, K.R.** & **Nørsett, S.P.** (1990): *The potential for parallelism in Runge-Kutta methods, Part I: RK formulas in standard form*, Technical Report No. 239/90, Department of Computer Science, University of Toronto.

[10] **Jackson, K.R.** & **Nørsett, S.P.**: *The potential for parallelism in Runge-Kutta methods, Part II: RK predictor-corrector formulas*, in preparation.

[11] **Nørsett, S.P.** (1974): *Semi-explicit Runge-Kutta methods*, Report Mathematics and Computation No.6/74, Depart. of Mathematics, University of Trondheim.

[12] **Shampine, L.F.** (1980): *Implementation of implicit formulas for the solution of ODEs*, SIAM J. Sci. Stat. Comput. **1**, 103-118.

[13] **Wolfbrandt, A.** (1977): *A study of Rosenbrock processes with respect to order conditions and stiff stability*, Ph. D. Thesis, Chalmers University of Technology, Göteborg.

Index

A page number followed by the letter f indicates that relevant information can also be found on the pages directly following the mentioned page. Major references are in **bold face**.

CWI TRACTS

1 D.H.J. Epema. *Surfaces with canonical hyperplane sections.* 1984.

2 J.J. Dijkstra. *Fake topological Hilbert spaces and characterizations of dimension in terms of negligibility.* 1984.

3 A.J. van der Schaft. *System theoretic descriptions of physical systems.* 1984.

4 J. Koene. *Minimal cost flow in processing networks, a primal approach.* 1984.

5 B. Hoogenboom. *Intertwining functions on compact Lie groups.* 1984.

6 A.P.W. Böhm. *Dataflow computation.* 1984.

7 A. Blokhuis. *Few-distance sets.* 1984.

8 M.H. van Hoorn. *Algorithms and approximations for queueing systems.* 1984.

9 C.P.J. Koymans. *Models of the lambda calculus.* 1984.

10 C.G. van der Laan, N.M. Temme. *Calculation of special functions: the gamma function, the exponential integrals and error-like functions.* 1984.

11 N.M. van Dijk. *Controlled Markov processes; time-discretization.* 1984.

12 W.H. Hundsdorfer. *The numerical solution of nonlinear stiff initial value problems: an analysis of one step methods.* 1985.

13 D. Grune. *On the design of ALEPH.* 1985.

14 J.G.F. Thiemann. *Analytic spaces and dynamic programming: a measure theoretic approach.* 1985.

15 F.J. van der Linden. *Euclidean rings with two infinite primes.* 1985.

16 R.J.P. Groothuizen. *Mixed elliptic-hyperbolic partial differential operators: a case-study in Fourier integral operators.* 1985.

17 H.M.M. ten Eikelder. *Symmetries for dynamical and Hamiltonian systems.* 1985.

18 A.D.M. Kester. *Some large deviation results in statistics.* 1985.

19 T.M.V. Janssen. *Foundations and applications of Montague grammar, part 1: Philosophy, framework, computer science.* 1986.

20 B.F. Schriever. *Order dependence.* 1986.

21 D.P. van der Vecht. *Inequalities for stopped Brownian motion.* 1986.

22 J.C.S.P. van der Woude. *Topological dynamix.* 1986.

23 A.F. Monna. *Methods, concepts and ideas in mathematics: aspects of an evolution.* 1986.

24 J.C.M. Baeten. *Filters and ultrafilters over definable subsets of admissible ordinals.* 1986.

25 A.W.J. Kolen. *Tree network and planar rectilinear location theory.* 1986.

26 A.H. Veen. *The misconstrued semicolon: Reconciling imperative languages and dataflow machines.* 1986.

27 A.J.M. van Engelen. *Homogeneous zero-dimensional absolute Borel sets.* 1986.

28 T.M.V. Janssen. *Foundations and applications of Montague grammar, part 2: Applications to natural language.* 1986.

29 H.L. Trentelman. *Almost invariant subspaces and high gain feedback.* 1986.

30 A.G. de Kok. *Production-inventory control models: approximations and algorithms.* 1987.

31 E.E.M. van Berkum. *Optimal paired comparison designs for factorial experiments.* 1987.

32 J.H.J. Einmahl. *Multivariate empirical processes.* 1987.

33 O.J. Vrieze. *Stochastic games with finite state and action spaces.* 1987.

34 P.H.M. Kersten. *Infinitesimal symmetries: a computational approach.* 1987.

35 M.L. Eaton. *Lectures on topics in probability inequalities.* 1987.

36 A.H.P. van der Burgh, R.M.M. Mattheij (eds.). *Proceedings of the first international conference on industrial and applied mathematics (ICIAM 87).* 1987.

37 L. Stougie. *Design and analysis of algorithms for stochastic integer programming.* 1987.

38 J.B.G. Frenk. *On Banach algebras, renewal measures and regenerative processes.* 1987.

39 H.J.M. Peters, O.J. Vrieze (eds.). *Surveys in game theory and related topics.* 1987.

40 J.L. Geluk, L. de Haan. *Regular variation, extensions and Tauberian theorems.* 1987.

41 Sape J. Mullender (ed.). *The Amoeba distributed operating system: Selected papers 1984-1987.* 1987.

42 P.R.J. Asveld, A. Nijholt (eds.). *Essays on concepts, formalisms, and tools.* 1987.

43 H.L. Bodlaender. *Distributed computing: structure and complexity.* 1987.

44 A.W. van der Vaart. *Statistical estimation in large parameter spaces.* 1988.

45 S.A. van de Geer. *Regression analysis and empirical processes.* 1988.

46 S.P. Spekreijse. *Multigrid solution of the steady Euler equations.* 1988.

47 J.B. Dijkstra. *Analysis of means in some non-standard situations.* 1988.

48 F.C. Drost. *Asymptotics for generalized chi-square goodness-of-fit tests.* 1988.

49 F.W. Wubs. *Numerical solution of the shallow-water equations.* 1988.

50 F. de Kerf. *Asymptotic analysis of a class of perturbed Korteweg-de Vries initial value problems.* 1988.

51 P.J.M. van Laarhoven. *Theoretical and computational aspects of simulated annealing.* 1988.

52 P.M. van Loon. *Continuous decoupling transformations for linear boundary value problems.* 1988.

53 K.C.P. Machielsen. *Numerical solution of optimal control problems with state constraints by sequential quadratic programming in function space.* 1988.

54 L.C.R.J. Willenborg. *Computational aspects of survey data processing.* 1988.

55 G.J. van der Steen. *A program generator for recognition, parsing and transduction with syntactic patterns.* 1988.

56 J.C. Ebergen. *Translating programs into delay-insensitive circuits.* 1989.

57 S.M. Verduyn Lunel. *Exponential type calculus for linear delay equations.* 1989.

58 M.C.M. de Gunst. *A random model for plant cell population growth.* 1989.

59 D. van Dulst. *Characterizations of Banach spaces not containing l^1.* 1989.

60 H.E. de Swart. *Vacillation and predictability properties of low-order atmospheric spectral models.* 1989.

61 P. de Jong. *Central limit theorems for generalized multilinear forms.* 1989.

62 V.J. de Jong. *A specification system for statistical software.* 1989.

63 B. Hanzon. *Identifiability, recursive identification and spaces of linear dynamical systems, part I.* 1989.

64 B. Hanzon. *Identifiability, recursive identification and spaces of linear dynamical systems, part II.* 1989.

65 B.M.M. de Weger. *Algorithms for diophantine equations.* 1989.

66 A. Jung. *Cartesian closed categories of domains.* 1989.

67 J.W. Polderman. *Adaptive control & identification: Conflict or conflux?.* 1989.

68 H.J. Woerdeman. *Matrix and operator extensions.* 1989.

69 B.G. Hansen. *Monotonicity properties of infinitely divisible distributions.* 1989.

70 J.K. Lenstra, H.C. Tijms, A. Volgenant (eds.). *Twenty-five years of operations research in the Netherlands: Papers dedicated to Gijs de Leve.* 1990.

71 P.J.C. Spreij. *Counting process systems. Identification and stochastic realization.* 1990.

72 J.F. Kaashoek. *Modeling one dimensional pattern formation by anti-diffusion.* 1990.

73 A.M.H. Gerards. *Graphs and polyhedra. Binary spaces and cutting planes.* 1990.

74 B. Koren. *Multigrid and defect correction for the steady Navier-Stokes equations. Application to aerodynamics.* 1991.

75 M.W.P. Savelsbergh. *Computer aided routing.* 1992.

76 O.E. Flippo. *Stability, duality and decomposition in general mathematical programming.* 1991.

77 A.J. van Es. *Aspects of nonparametric density estimation.* 1991.

78 G.A.P. Kindervater. *Exercises in parallel combinatorial computing.* 1992.

79 J.J. Lodder. *Towards a symmetrical theory of generalized functions.* 1991.

80 S.A. Smulders. *Control of freeway traffic flow.* 1993.

81 P.H.M. America, J.J.M.M. Rutten. *A parallel object-oriented language: design and semantic foundations.* 1992.

82 F. Thuijsman. *Optimality and equilibria in stochastic games.* 1992.

83 R.J. Kooman. *Convergence properties of recurrence sequences.* 1992.

84 A.M. Cohen (ed.). *Computational aspects of Lie group representations and related topics. Proceedings of the 1990 Computational Algebra Seminar at CWI, Amsterdam.* 1991.

85 V. de Valk. *One-dependent processes.* 1993.

86 J.A. Baars, J.A.M. de Groot. *On topological and linear equivalence of certain function spaces.* 1992.

87 A.F. Monna. *The way of mathematics and mathematicians.* 1992.

88 E.D. de Goede. *Numerical methods for the three-dimensional shallow water equations.* 1993.

89 M. Zwaan. *Moment problems in Hilbert space with applications to magnetic resonance imaging.* 1993.

90 C. Vuik. *The solution of a one-dimensional Stefan problem.* 1993.

91. E.R. Verheul. *Multimedians in metric and normed spaces.* 1993.

92. J.L.M. Maubach. *Iterative methods for non-linear partial differential equations.* 1993.

93. A.W. Ambergen. *Statistical uncertainties in posterior probabilities.* 1993.

94. P.A. Zegeling. *Moving-grid methods for time-dependent partial differential equations.* 1993.

95. M.J.C. van Pul. *Statistical analysis of software reliability models.* 1993.

96. J.K. Scholma. *A Lie algebraic study of some integrable systems associated with root systems.* 1993.

97. J.L. van den Berg. *Sojourn times in feedback and processor sharing queues.* 1993.

98. A.J. Koning. *Stochastic integrals and goodness-of-fit tests.* 1993.

99. B.P. Sommeijer. *Parallelism in the numerical integration of initial value problems.* 1993.

MATHEMATICAL CENTRE TRACTS

1 T. van der Walt. *Fixed and almost fixed points.* 1963.

2 A.R. Bloemena. *Sampling from a graph.* 1964.

3 G. de Leve. *Generalized Markovian decision processes, part I: model and method.* 1964.

4 G. de Leve. *Generalized Markovian decision processes, part II: probabilistic background.* 1964.

5 G. de Leve, H.C. Tijms, P.J. Weeda. *Generalized Markovian decision processes, applications.* 1970.

6 M.A. Maurice. *Compact ordered spaces.* 1964.

7 W.R. van Zwet. *Convex transformations of random variables.* 1964.

8 J.A. Zonneveld. *Automatic numerical integration.* 1964.

9 P.C. Baayen. *Universal morphisms.* 1964.

10 E.M. de Jager. *Applications of distributions in mathematical physics.* 1964.

11 A.B. Paalman-de Miranda. *Topological semigroups.* 1964.

12 J.A.Th.M. van Berckel, H. Brandt Corstius, R.J. Mokken, A. van Wijngaarden. *Formal properties of newspaper Dutch.* 1965.

13 H.A. Lauwerier. *Asymptotic expansions.* 1966, out of print; replaced by MCT 54.

14 H.A. Lauwerier. *Calculus of variations in mathematical physics.* 1966.

15 R. Doornbos. *Slippage tests.* 1966.

16 J.W. de Bakker. *Formal definition of programming languages with an application to the definition of ALGOL 60.* 1967.

17 R.P. van de Riet. *Formula manipulation in ALGOL 60, part 1.* 1968.

18 R.P. van de Riet. *Formula manipulation in ALGOL 60, part 2.* 1968.

19 J. van der Slot. *Some properties related to compactness.* 1968.

20 P.J. van der Houwen. *Finite difference methods for solving partial differential equations.* 1968.

21 E. Wattel. *The compactness operator in set theory and topology.* 1968.

22 T.J. Dekker. *ALGOL 60 procedures in numerical algebra, part 1.* 1968.

23 T.J. Dekker, W. Hoffmann. *ALGOL 60 procedures in numerical algebra, part 2.* 1968.

24 J.W. de Bakker. *Recursive procedures.* 1971.

25 E.R. Paërl. *Representations of the Lorentz group and projective geometry.* 1969.

26 European Meeting 1968. *Selected statistical papers, part I.* 1968.

27 European Meeting 1968. *Selected statistical papers, part II.* 1968.

28 J. Oosterhoff. *Combination of one-sided statistical tests.* 1969.

29 J. Verhoeff. *Error detecting decimal codes.* 1969.

30 H. Brandt Corstius. *Exercises in computational linguistics.* 1970.

31 W. Molenaar. *Approximations to the Poisson, binomial and hypergeometric distribution functions.* 1970.

32 L. de Haan. *On regular variation and its application to the weak convergence of sample extremes.* 1970.

33 F.W. Steutel. *Preservation of infinite divisibility under mixing and related topics.* 1970.

34 I. Juhász, A. Verbeek, N.S. Kroonenberg. *Cardinal functions in topology.* 1971.

35 M.H. van Emden. *An analysis of complexity.* 1971.

36 J. Grasman. *On the birth of boundary layers.* 1971.

37 J.W. de Bakker, G.A. Blaauw, A.J.W. Duijvestijn, E.W. Dijkstra, P.J. van der Houwen, G.A.M. Kamsteeg-Kemper, F.E.J. Kruseman Aretz, W.L. van der Poel, J.P. Schaap-Kruseman, M.V. Wilkes, G. Zoutendijk. *MC-25 Informatica Symposium.* 1971.

38 W.A. Verloren van Themaat. *Automatic analysis of Dutch compound words.* 1972.

39 H. Bavinck. *Jacobi series and approximation.* 1972.

40 H.C. Tijms. *Analysis of (s,S) inventory models.* 1972.

41 A. Verbeek. *Superextensions of topological spaces.* 1972.

42 W. Vervaat. *Success epochs in Bernoulli trials (with applications in number theory).* 1972.

43 F.H. Ruymgaart. *Asymptotic theory of rank tests for independence.* 1973.

44 H. Bart. *Meromorphic operator valued functions.* 1973.

45 A.A. Balkema. *Monotone transformations and limit laws.* 1973.

46 R.P. van de Riet. *ABC ALGOL, a portable language for formula manipulation systems, part 1: the language.* 1973.

47 R.P. van de Riet. *ABC ALGOL, a portable language for formula manipulation systems, part 2: the compiler.* 1973.

48 F.E.J. Kruseman Aretz, P.J.W. ten Hagen, H.L. Oudshoorn. *An ALGOL 60 compiler in ALGOL 60, text of the MC-compiler for the EL-X8.* 1973.

49 H. Kok. *Connected orderable spaces.* 1974.

50 A. van Wijngaarden, B.J. Mailloux, J.E.L. Peck, C.H.A. Koster, M. Sintzoff, C.H. Lindsey, L.G.L.T. Meertens, R.G. Fisker (eds.). *Revised report on the algorithmic language ALGOL 68.* 1976.

51 A. Hordijk. *Dynamic programming and Markov potential theory.* 1974.

52 P.C. Baayen (ed.). *Topological structures.* 1974.

53 M.J. Faber. *Metrizability in generalized ordered spaces.* 1974.

54 H.A. Lauwerier. *Asymptotic analysis, part 1.* 1974.

55 M. Hall, Jr., J.H. van Lint (eds.). *Combinatorics, part 1: theory of designs, finite geometry and coding theory.* 1974.

56 M. Hall, Jr., J.H. van Lint (eds.). *Combinatorics, part 2: graph theory, foundations, partitions and combinatorial geometry.* 1974.

57 M. Hall, Jr., J.H. van Lint (eds.). *Combinatorics, part 3: combinatorial group theory.* 1974.

58 W. Albers. *Asymptotic expansions and the deficiency concept in statistics.* 1975.

59 J.L. Mijnheer. *Sample path properties of stable processes.* 1975.

60 F. Göbel. *Queueing models involving buffers.* 1975.

63 J.W. de Bakker (ed.). *Foundations of computer science.* 1975.

64 W.J. de Schipper. *Symmetric closed categories.* 1975.

65 J. de Vries. *Topological transformation groups, 1: a categorical approach.* 1975.

66 H.G.J. Pijls. *Logically convex algebras in spectral theory and eigenfunction expansions.* 1976.

68 P.P.N. de Groen. *Singularly perturbed differential operators of second order.* 1976.

69 J.K. Lenstra. *Sequencing by enumerative methods.* 1977.

70 W.P. de Roever, Jr. *Recursive program schemes: semantics and proof theory.* 1976.

71 J.A.E.E. van Nunen. *Contracting Markov decision processes.* 1976.

72 J.K.M. Jansen. *Simple periodic and non-periodic Lamé functions and their applications in the theory of conical waveguides.* 1977.

73 D.M.R. Leivant. *Absoluteness of intuitionistic logic.* 1979.

74 H.J.J. te Riele. *A theoretical and computational study of generalized aliquot sequences.* 1976.

75 A.E. Brouwer. *Treelike spaces and related connected topological spaces.* 1977.

76 M. Rem. *Associons and the closure statement.* 1976.

77 W.C.M. Kallenberg. *Asymptotic optimality of likelihood ratio tests in exponential families.* 1978.

78 E. de Jonge, A.C.M. van Rooij. *Introduction to Riesz spaces.* 1977.

79 M.C.A. van Zuijlen. *Empirical distributions and rank statistics.* 1977.

80 P.W. Hemker. *A numerical study of stiff two-point boundary problems.* 1977.

81 K.R. Apt, J.W. de Bakker (eds.). *Foundations of computer science II, part 1.* 1976.

82 K.R. Apt, J.W. de Bakker (eds.). *Foundations of computer science II, part 2.* 1976.

83 L.S. van Benthem Jutting. *Checking Landau's "Grundlagen" in the AUTOMATH system.* 1979.

84 H.L.L. Busard. *The translation of the elements of Euclid from the Arabic into Latin by Hermann of Carinthia (?), books vii-xii.* 1977.

85 J. van Mill. *Supercompactness and Wallman spaces.* 1977.

86 S.G. van der Meulen, M. Veldhorst. *Torrix I, a programming system for operations on vectors and matrices over arbitrary fields and of variable size.* 1978.

88 A. Schrijver. *Matroids and linking systems.* 1977.

89 J.W. de Roever. *Complex Fourier transformation and analytic functionals with unbounded carriers.* 1978.

90 L.P.J. Groenewegen. *Characterization of optimal strategies in dynamic games.* 1981.

91 J.M. Geysel. *Transcendence in fields of positive characteristic.* 1979.

92 P.J. Weeda. *Finite generalized Markov programming.* 1979.

93 H.C. Tijms, J. Wessels (eds.). *Markov decision theory.* 1977.

94 A. Bijlsma. *Simultaneous approximations in transcendental number theory.* 1978.

95 K.M. van Hee. *Bayesian control of Markov chains.* 1978.

96 P.M.B. Vitányi. *Lindenmayer systems: structure, languages, and growth functions.* 1980.

97 A. Federgruen. *Markovian control problems; functional equations and algorithms.* 1984.

98 R. Geel. *Singular perturbations of hyperbolic type.* 1978.

99 J.K. Lenstra, A.H.G. Rinnooy Kan, P. van Emde Boas (eds.). *Interfaces between computer science and operations research.* 1978.

100 P.C. Baayen, D. van Dulst, J. Oosterhoff (eds.). *Proceedings bicentennial congress of the Wiskundig Genootschap, part 1.* 1979.

101 P.C. Baayen, D. van Dulst, J. Oosterhoff (eds.). *Proceedings bicentennial congress of the Wiskundig Genootschap, part 2.* 1979.

102 D. van Dulst. *Reflexive and superreflexive Banach spaces.* 1978.

103 K. van Harn. *Classifying infinitely divisible distributions by functional equations.* 1978.

104 J.M. van Wouwe. *Go-spaces and generalizations of metrizability.* 1979.

105 R. Helmers. *Edgeworth expansions for linear combinations of order statistics.* 1982.

106 A. Schrijver (ed.). *Packing and covering in combinatorics.* 1979.

107 C. den Heijer. *The numerical solution of nonlinear operator equations by imbedding methods.* 1979.

108 J.W. de Bakker, J. van Leeuwen (eds.). *Foundations of computer science III, part 1.* 1979.

109 J.W. de Bakker, J. van Leeuwen (eds.). *Foundations of computer science III, part 2.* 1979.

110 J.C. van Vliet. *ALGOL 68 transput, part I: historical review and discussion of the implementation model.* 1979.

111 J.C. van Vliet. *ALGOL 68 transput, part II: an implementation model.* 1979.

112 H.C.P. Berbee. *Random walks with stationary increments and renewal theory.* 1979.

113 T.A.B. Snijders. *Asymptotic optimality theory for testing problems with restricted alternatives.* 1979.

114 A.J.E.M. Janssen. *Application of the Wigner distribution to harmonic analysis of generalized stochastic processes.* 1979.

115 P.C. Baayen, J. van Mill (eds.). *Topological structures II, part 1.* 1979.

116 P.C. Baayen, J. van Mill (eds.). *Topological structures II, part 2.* 1979.

117 P.J.M. Kallenberg. *Branching processes with continuous state space.* 1979.

118 P. Groeneboom. *Large deviations and asymptotic efficiencies.* 1980.

119 F.J. Peters. *Sparse matrices and substructures, with a novel implementation of finite element algorithms.* 1980.

120 W.P.M. de Ruyter. *On the asymptotic analysis of large-scale ocean circulation.* 1980.

121 W.H. Haemers. *Eigenvalue techniques in design and graph theory.* 1980.

122 J.C.P. Bus. *Numerical solution of systems of nonlinear equations.* 1980.

123 I. Yuhász. *Cardinal functions in topology - ten years later.* 1980.

124 R.D. Gill. *Censoring and stochastic integrals.* 1980.

125 R. Eising. *2-D systems, an algebraic approach.* 1980.

126 G. van der Hoek. *Reduction methods in nonlinear programming.* 1980.

127 J.W. Klop. *Combinatory reduction systems.* 1980.

128 A.J.J. Talman. *Variable dimension fixed point algorithms and triangulations.* 1980.

129 G. van der Laan. *Simplicial fixed point algorithms.* 1980.

130 P.J.W. ten Hagen, T. Hagen, P. Klint, H. Noot, H.J. Sint, A.H. Veen. *ILP: intermediate language for pictures.* 1980.

131 R.J.R. Back. *Correctness preserving program refinements: proof theory and applications.* 1980.

132 H.M. Mulder. *The interval function of a graph.* 1980.

133 C.A.J. Klaassen. *Statistical performance of location estimators.* 1981.

134 J.C. van Vliet, H. Wupper (eds.). *Proceedings international conference on ALGOL 68.* 1981.

135 J.A.G. Groenendijk, T.M.V. Janssen, M.J.B. Stokhof (eds.). *Formal methods in the study of language, part I.* 1981.

136 J.A.G. Groenendijk, T.M.V. Janssen, M.J.B. Stokhof (eds.). *Formal methods in the study of language, part II.* 1981.

137 J. Telgen. *Redundancy and linear programs.* 1981.

138 H.A. Lauwerier. *Mathematical models of epidemics.* 1981.

139 J. van der Wal. *Stochastic dynamic programming, successive approximations and nearly optimal strategies for Markov decision processes and Markov games.* 1981.

140 J.H. van Geldrop. *A mathematical theory of pure exchange economies without the no-critical-point hypothesis.* 1981.

141 G.E. Welters. *Abel-Jacobi isogenies for certain types of Fano threefolds.* 1981.

142 H.R. Bennett, D.J. Lutzer (eds.). *Topology and order structures, part 1.* 1981.

143 J.M. Schumacher. *Dynamic feedback in finite- and infinite-dimensional linear systems.* 1981.

144 P. Eijgenraam. *The solution of initial value problems using interval arithmetic; formulation and analysis of an algorithm.* 1981.

145 A.J. Brentjes. *Multi-dimensional continued fraction algorithms.* 1981.

146 C.V.M. van der Mee. *Semigroup and factorization methods in transport theory.* 1981.

147 H.H. Tigelaar. *Identification and informative sample size.* 1982.

148 L.C.M. Kallenberg. *Linear programming and finite Markovian control problems.* 1983.

149 C.B. Huijsmans, M.A. Kaashoek, W.A.J. Luxemburg, W.K. Vietsch (eds.). *From A to Z, proceedings of a symposium in honour of A.C. Zaanen.* 1982.

150 M. Veldhorst. *An analysis of sparse matrix storage schemes.* 1982.

151 R.J.M.M. Does. *Higher order asymptotics for simple linear rank statistics.* 1982.

152 G.F. van der Hoeven. *Projections of lawless sequences.* 1982.

153 J.P.C. Blanc. *Application of the theory of boundary value problems in the analysis of a queueing model with paired services.* 1982.

154 H.W. Lenstra, Jr., R. Tijdeman (eds.). *Computational methods in number theory, part I.* 1982.

155 H.W. Lenstra, Jr., R. Tijdeman (eds.). *Computational methods in number theory, part II.* 1982.

156 P.M.G. Apers. *Query processing and data allocation in distributed database systems.* 1983.

157 H.A.W.M. Kneppers. *The covariant classification of two-dimensional smooth commutative formal groups over an algebraically closed field of positive characteristic.* 1983.

158 J.W. de Bakker, J. van Leeuwen (eds.). *Foundations of computer science IV, distributed systems, part 1.* 1983.

159 J.W. de Bakker, J. van Leeuwen (eds.). *Foundations of computer science IV, distributed systems, part 2.* 1983.

160 A. Rezus. *Abstract AUTOMATH.* 1983.

161 G.F. Helminck. *Eisenstein series on the metaplectic group, an algebraic approach.* 1983.

162 J.J. Dik. *Tests for preference.* 1983.

163 H. Schippers. *Multiple grid methods for equations of the second kind with applications in fluid mechanics.* 1983.

164 F.A. van der Duyn Schouten. *Markov decision processes with continuous time parameter.* 1983.

165 P.C.T. van der Hoeven. *On point processes.* 1983.

166 H.B.M. Jonkers. *Abstraction, specification and implementation techniques, with an application to garbage collection.* 1983.

167 W.H.M. Zijm. *Nonnegative matrices in dynamic programming.* 1983.

168 J.H. Evertse. *Upper bounds for the numbers of solutions of diophantine equations.* 1983.

169 H.R. Bennett, D.J. Lutzer (eds.). *Topology and order structures, part 2.* 1983.

90